The Brotherhood of the Magi

by the same author

•

Books

Non-Fiction

KINTUI; VISION OF THE INCA'S
The Shaman's Journey to Enlightenment

RECIPES FOR REJUVENATION
Nourishing the Body, Mind and Spirit
(forthcoming)

Fiction

THE LINEAGE OF THE CODES OF LIGHT

THE PRIESTESS AND THE MAGUS
(forthcoming in this series)

•

Audio

DEEP TRANCE SHAMANIC JOURNEY
Volume One: Pachamama's Child
(compact disc)

DEEP TRANCE SHAMANIC JOURNEY
Volume Two: Right Relationship
(compact disc - forthcoming in this series)

THE
BROTHERHOOD
OF THE
MAGI

Jessie E. Ayani
Ph.D.

HEART OF THE SUN
2002

Published by Heart of the Sun, P.O. Box 495, Mount Shasta, CA 96067
First Edition
First Printing 2002
Ayani, Jessie E.
The Brotherhood of the Magi / Jessie E. Ayani - 1st Heart of the Sun Edition
ISBN# 0-9648763-2-9
1. Myth & Magic 2. Spirituality 3. Enlightenment 4. Ascension
5. Shamanism

Cover Art:
"Expanded Sri Yantra" - Over Titicaca Lake, by Francene Hart
www.awakenvisions.com/hart hartart@haii.net

Cover Design:
Silverlining Designs, Leanne Krause, 210B Castle St., Mount Shasta, CA 96067
silverlining@snowcrest.net

Editing and typesetting:
Heart of the Sun

This book is printed on partially recycled paper

Published by
Heart of the Sun
P.O. Box 495, Mount Shasta, CA 96067
heartofthesun@snowcrest.net

Dedication

To the Brotherhood of the Magi who have fostered and preserved Magic on Earth - even in the most perilous of times

To the Magi of the Ruby Order - the highest magicians on the planet - who move subtle energy in service to Mother Earth and humanity

To Beloved Saint Germain

To Beloved Sananda Kumara and all of the Lords of Time

Thanks

The author wishes to thank the following for their heartfelt participation in the manifestation of this book: All of the wizards around the world who continue to enchant and activate me with their magic; my students, and those who have journeyed with me to magical places, for the fun we have had growing together; Neddy Thompson, Mary Kjorvestad, Sheryl Moore and Dery Dyer, for critically reading the manuscript; Francene Hart for another inspiring painting and the back cover drawing; Leanne Krause for the cover layout; and Suzanne James for loving support. To my family in Mount Shasta, Emma, Javier, Q'illa, Chaska, and Inti, who manage to hold things together in spite of me. Finally, and most magically, to my family in the Andes who have inspired the writing of this book. The characters are fictional (to the best of my knowledge) but the magic is real.

Jessie E. Ayani
January 1, 2002

Contents

**magic
happens!**

Pilgrimage

Leah cinched the cord on the hood of her parka, tightening it around her head. Driving sleet stung her face, already wet with tears of cold and fatigue. The entire expedition inched along the side of a mountain on a narrow icy path. They had dismounted their horses hours before. Leah, a veteran of many such journeys in Peru, was not concerned for her own well-being, though this was as tough as it had ever been for her. The group concerned her. A wrangler guided her rugged little bay, walking along the cliff edge. She held onto the rough rope bridle while walking alongside the mountain slope. Leah was in a light trance as she walked, weaving strength into the filaments of light that held her group of women in a communal place of surrender to the greater mystery. Ten of her beloved sisters followed behind her. Trusting the wisdom of horse and horseman in this perilous situation, she dared not turn to make sure of their safety.

Ahead of the women walked Susmo, Leah's spiritual brother and close friend. Susmo had been the bridge between Leah and the spiritual elders of the Andes in the more recent years of her spiritwalk. Susmo walked behind a band of young natives, descendants of the Incas, whose bare calves and sandal-clad feet, impervious to the cold, sent shivers through all of the women. The Indian men had met them in Pampacancha, east of Cusco, where the horsemen and Susmo's young apprentices had assembled the expedition. The young apprentices walked behind the women now as the wind of twilight howled down the mountain with considerable force.

A year had passed since this pilgrimage had entered Leah's dreamtime. The exact same dream had come to her four nights in a row. It was no less than a summons to make this journey to the elders, and each of the ten women with her had appeared in the dreams as well. Coming from around the world, these were sisters she had awakened, and then guided in their attainment of spiritual sovereignty. Leah's path was not that of a guru, but rather that of a liberator. These women had not been together before on such a journey, so the weaving of the group was barely under way when the storm hit. She and Susmo had planned the trip for dry season but their guidance had been adamant about moving that up to the end of April, when the weather was unpredictable in the mountains. Tuning into the group energy, Leah was assured that everyone was alert and strong despite the hardship.

Concerned about the next day's travel at even higher altitude, Leah focused her intent on Don Eduardo, the elder who had issued the summons. She saw him dipping his hand into his baby alpaca-skin coca pouch, a toothless grin upon his face. He pulled out three coca leaves, arranged them carefully between his index finger and thumb then held them to his mouth to infuse them with the power of his breath. Then he surprised Leah by calling out her name. He laughed again and told her that the storm was sent as a cleansing. When the group filaments unified toward the highest purpose of this endeavor, the storm would cease.

With this message came an intense energy that Leah used to fire her own core. The heat quickly spread out through her body, then into her entire energetic field, helping her to focus her intent more fully on the women. She sent the same powerful energy through the filaments of the group assemblage point to each of the women. She felt an immediate shift in that assemblage point as each one of them was able to see beyond the hardship to the greater purpose of their journey. Each one of the women received the message of the cleansing from Don Eduardo. Leah visibly relaxed. Energetically, they were in the clear.

Her thoughts turned to the filaments of light and the assemblage point, the most liberating of all the shamanic teachings. She had grown in the wisdom of this teaching over the years to know that it was central to all mastery of energy and that all esoteric traditions understood it, though terminology differed among them. An individual's reality is a composite of beliefs. At any given time, we call to us what we are willing to believe and this collection of beliefs guides our lives. When Leah was young, she believed that all people had to work hard for a living at a job they didn't like. This belief was based on messages she had received from both her father and mother. She breathed a prayer of gratitude that she had been able to change that limiting core belief for it opened to her the work of her soul. Soul work, she found, is not a task; it is her passion - her joy.

Leah had next realized that when she changed that core belief, her entire reality shifted. Eventually she came to understand that she had shifted her assemblage point, the place where all her core beliefs came together to focus her reality. The shamans saw that assemblage point as a focal point of light filaments. They taught that all things were made of light filaments because the Universe was a Matrix of light. They called our personal Universe the *wiracocha* or egg of light. Leah had come to understand that the light filaments of each person's *wiracocha* were that person's core beliefs. Each filament had its own frequency and each assemblage of filaments reflected the stage of their awakened frequency, or light-body activation. Everything a person draws to him or her - people, pets, material possessions either reflects his or her reality or challenges it.

Additional insight coming from her own Truth caused her to see that individuals could enter partnerships wherein they shared a collective assemblage point with the partner. This assemblage point, or reality, represents a collection of mutually held core beliefs. All too often she had seen partners lose their individual assemblage point to the partnership through enmeshment of each other's filaments. Just as devotees were expected to surrender their assemblage points to their guru, couples unconsciously gave their power away to their partner fostering co-dependency. Leah's understanding of a healthy relationship was individual autonomy in partnership, each partner conscious of his/her own reality and also aware that he/she shared a mutual, though not identical, reality with her partner. Conscious beings could not expect another individual or group to have exactly the same view of reality as their own. That was absurd. Leah championed individual sovereignty as a path to God, for only a sovereign being had the power to merge with the God-force in Divine Union. Anything else appeared to her as a trap.

Her reverie ended as the group reached the high pass. Behind them, invisible in the clouds but profoundly present were the powerful *Apus* Ausangate, Kayangate and all of their children. The rocky trail let them across the pass and down into a clearing which hung on the mountain side. A clear stream ran along the clearing near a stone hut. Susmo had mounted his horse and was directing his apprentices to make camp for the night. The wranglers piled up the saddles in one end of the hut and took the horses upstream to graze. Dry brush and dung stashed in the hut by the Indian guides the day before made a quick fire to warm the hut and cook dinner. Pitching tents and stowing gear went swiftly with the help of the young men.

When camp was set, glowing faces peered out of wet rain gear as the women gathered in circle before the hut. They rubbed each other between the shoulder blades and poured heart energy out to each other. There was no doubt in Leah's mind that Don Eduardo had called forth the perfect group of women for this pilgrimage. None of them had any idea where they were going, and none of them cared a bit. She fought back a laugh at the thought of their blind trust, but the women, so close to her and to each other, read her thoughts and started to laugh aloud. Soon the whole circle was in an uproar, releasing the tension and fatigue of the day with unbridled merriment. The young apprentices came to join them, soon followed by Susmo and the Indian guides. As the last of the group entered the circle, the low clouds parted, revealing the snowcapped mountain peaks which lined the valley below their camp. Bathed in the blue-pink light of sunset, the *Apus* shimmered magically. The group was one. The cleansing was complete. Tomorrow's path was in sight.

After organizing the tents for the night's sleep, everyone crowded into the stone hut to warm up and shed their rain gear. Several of the young men had brought in the cooking pots and had brewed coca tea. It felt good to hold the hot liquid and take it inside. Perched on piles of saddles facing the blazing fire, the women looked radiant. They had another full day on the horses and a very high pass ahead of them before reaching the first of the Indian villages. No one seemed tired. The gift of energy from Don Eduardo was gratefully appreciated, though not totally understood by one and all.

Her heart brimming with love, Leah looked around the room at the shimmering faces of these exceptional women. Having committed themselves unselfishly to the Mission of the Sisterhood, each one of their light bodies was fully activated. They were the Priestesses of Annu, Priestesses of the Sun, incarnate on Earth to hold the frequencies of Earth's ascension. These women were not the only women responsible for this great task, for the Sisterhood had incarnated *en masse*, in every race and on every continent, at this time. This was a soul lineage that was part of the great Monad of Christ Consciousness, a vast group of souls committed to planetary ascension. Leah felt these particular women had been chosen for this pilgrimage because they had reached the gateway of service in their planetary work. None of them were living for themselves any more. Realization of the greater work of their souls had come to all of them. This was a significant step towards enlightenment.

Susmo left the cooks to their work and wandered over to Leah. He put his arm around her and kissed her cheek. Her blue eyes sparkled as a great smile came to her face. Susmo was her dearest *wayki* - a true spiritual brother, and she addressed him as such.

"*Wayki*, we are so grateful for the strength of your young men, yourself and the Indians. It was an unexpected and challenging afternoon," she said, in fairly good Spanish.

"*Wayki* Leah, accept my apologies for the weather. All the intent in the world could not change it," he replied, in English, establishing his desire to try to speak their language.

"It was a *limpia*, a ritual cleansing, My Brother. We all understand and accept it. Don Eduardo was quite pleased with it," Leah answered with a chuckle. Susmo raised his eyebrows and all the women laughed.

"Susmo, I would like each of these beloved women to introduce themselves to you," Leah suggested. "A few have been with us in Peru before, but many have not, and they have had little time even to meet each other."

"Wonderful, Leah," he replied.

"*Buena,*" Leah said, with a smile. "Let's begin with Sonia, who will be our Spanish/English translator when we are in formal circle. Sonia," she announced with an official voice. "Front and center!"

Jumping down from her pile of saddles, Sonia brushed her shiny black curls away from her cheeks as she turned to face the group. A short, slight woman of Mexican-American descent, Sonia had a dazzling smile and dark eyes with a deep light. Having grown up in a bilingual household, the task of translation was not difficult for her. She had gladly accepted Leah's invitation to perform this service. Looking out at the expectant faces of the group, she began to speak.

"I am Sonia Sanchez. My home is in Albuquerque, New Mexico in the United States." Sonia paused, collecting her thoughts. "What can I say about myself? Well, I have had many careers in my life, including motherhood, but it was not until I found my real niche in this world that I began feeling fulfilled and joyful about life here on Mother Earth. So now, I live out my soul's purpose as a visionary artist, painting what I see in meditation and ceremony so that others might share in the experience. I feel like a bridge to the beauty and mystery lying within other dimensions and I try to capture that in the art. I paint most often with watercolor, but I also use acrylics and oils.

"I met Leah many years ago when she came to Santa Fe to present a workshop. Like many of us, I woke up from a deep and unhappy sleep that weekend and am continually integrating more of my Truth and light every day – to say nothing of continually detoxifying my body, mind and spirit," she said with a grin. The whole circle laughed with recognition of their intense cleansings. It was the only way to keep up with the frequencies coming to Earth from the stars, and it was one of Leah's favorite topics.

Sonia continued. "I was lucky enough to be with Leah at the mountain retreat when she gave us the story of the lineage of light, the Sisterhood of the Sun. I wonder what we will witness on this journey," she concluded.

Sonia gave Susmo a warm hug. Susmo, always deeply connected to his translators, sent a surge of love energy into Sonia's heart that brought tears to her eyes.

"Gracias, Wayki," she whispered to him as she moved to embrace Leah. Susmo was a charismatic man with a huge heart. It was impossible not to love him.

The next woman to step forward was Bridget, whose soft red hair fell in waves past her shoulders. A fair-skinned and delicate-featured native of Ireland, Bridget spoke with the charming lilt of the isles. She led the others to remember their Celtic soul roots, for the Sisterhood had incarnated as Priestesses of Avalon for centuries.

"Beloved sisters and Susmo," Bridget began, bowing to Susmo, "I am Bridget O'Brien, born in Dublin, but now choosing to live in Edinburgh, Scotland. To truly walk my soul's path, it was necessary for me to make some temporary separation from my family and its rigidly held religious beliefs. I married a Scot, Willie McIntyre, who has been incredibly supportive of my spiritual path. He was the one who signed me up for my first retreat with Leah in Glastonbury.

"Willie is a very special doctor, an osteopath and homeopath who sees through and into people. I am fortunate to have his help with my own work, and also to assist him with his practice. I have been taking healing courses for a long time and am a nurse and licensed body therapist in Scotland. Everything I had learned began making more sense to me after working with Leah and my British sisters. I could see the whole picture of health and vitality. When that happened, my hands became channels of a healing energy that clearly helped people come into balance. Willie gave me a room in his clinic and integrated my work into his practice. Now I am teaching others to bring this energy through their hands and hearts. The work is growing.

"I feel it is a miracle for me to be able to be here on this journey. Five years ago I was angry at the world, a big reflection of myself, and now I feel the love of God within me and know the meaning of acceptance. I am very happy in my life. It is good to see those sisters from the European retreats and to meet so many new sisters. Thank you."

Bridget bowed her head slightly then went to give Susmo a warm hug and kiss. Turning to Leah, she said, "I am so glad that you saw me in your dream, Leah."

"There was no way to miss your red hair, Bridget," she replied, smiling. In a quiet voice, she added, "Your work is magnificent, Beloved. You will find it even more rewarding because you are now fully anchored in your purpose."

Leah and Bridget kissed each other's cheeks before Bridget returned to her place. Leah nodded to a tall, blonde beauty who was leaning against the wall of the hut, wrapped in a lime-green fleece blanket. The woman smiled and stepped to the center. She towered over Susmo and Leah, but had no awkwardness about her. In fact, her grace and poise were inspiring for all of them to watch.

"I greet you all for my homeland of Sweden," she began. "I am Britta Stephenson. I was born in the north where it is very cold, but I now live in Stockholm. Please excuse the poor quality of my English."

"Get out of here, Brit," Sonia teased, "your English is perfect!" Brit bowed her head, pleased that she was being heard, then, tossing her long blonde braid over her shoulder, she continued.

"I was, for many years, a model in Stockholm. I made a fortune in modeling, but came close to ruining my body with starvation dieting and taking pills. I believe I was severely malnourished and know I was deeply depressed. Thank God, I have now learned to eat healthy food without fear. In recovering from that career, I sought out many alternative-healing practitioners in Sweden and around the world. I studied nutrition, movement and breath. I recovered to become a coach for others who had experienced a healing crisis like mine. Now I am moving into the fields of rejuvenation and youthful longevity. I love my work. I love helping people.

"I am also the mother of two children, a boy and a girl, who are still young. My body was not able to have children for many years and then – the two miracles came to me. My husband is a banker in Stockholm. He doesn't understand my spiritual work, but he does not oppose it. In my situation, that is support. He likes the transformation but is afraid to hear the details."

A number of the women gave her knowing nods of kinship with regards to the men. The work they were doing was little understood outside the Sisterhood. Therefore, support from loved ones was a particularly important issue. Most of the women on this journey had managed to manifest incredibly supportive partners, one reason they were able to be on such a quest. This was a journey without expectation, without rational explanation, and as far as Leah was concerned, without a plan. It was a test of fluidity, courage and dedication to the path.

After thanking the group for being her sisters and acknowledging both Bridget and Genevieve as friends from the Glastonbury retreat, Brit gave Susmo a kiss on the top of his head and tousled Leah's long blonde hair with affection. Leah had always adored Brit's playfulness. She was like a breath of fresh air in any group.

Genevieve took the cue and stepped forward next. Her English was halting, generously mixed with French, but her thoughts and expression were quite clear. She was a radiant woman of medium height, slim with bright green eyes. Long, wavy auburn hair was pulled together and fastened on top of her head in a charming way. Genevieve had the refined, almost chiseled, features of privileged blood.

"Good evening, Susmo, Leah and my sisters," she began. "I am Genevieve de Louise coming here from the little town of Saint Maximin la Saint Baume in Southern France. My life in Saint Baume was simple before I met Leah. I was and am still very dedicated to the Black Madonna and Mary Magdalen, whose cave of meditation lies on the mountainside of Saint Baume. My mother raised me in the traditions of the Black Madonna, the true Gnostic teachings of Jesus and Mary Magdalen, which was rare in our village of Catholics. I was not brainwashed by the church, though she cautioned me never to express my beliefs in public. Many have died in Southern France in the past for believing the greater Truth. I was so close to Mary that I took a part-time job as a tour leader to her cave and the tomb within our basilica. It was a good job, since most people came there in respect and awe. One day, Leah came to that cave and asked me to tell her everything I knew about the Black Madonna and Mary."

Turning her gaze towards Leah, Genevieve brushed away a few tears that had welled up in her eyes as she remembered that encounter. Gathering her composure, she continued. "As any of you might guess, I began saying things I had never known in my conscious mind about Mary, the Black Madonna, the Gnostics, the church she started, and the persecutors who sought to rid the area of her great Truth. Suddenly, I was a fountain of information coming from – I knew not where. Leah's presence seemed to connect me with a force that had been waiting to move through me. She held a space for me that allowed me to connect with my Higher Self and my Soul.

"Now I am aware that I was guided by the voices of the Sisterhood, those women who lived and worked with Mary in Saint Baume and those who had followed. I was fortunate that Leah was staying in the region for several weeks activating her own codes, for she kindly helped me to integrate what was happening to me. Otherwise I would have been afraid to continue or thought myself insane.

"Many women come to see me now to make their connection with Mary and the Sisterhood. My own gifts have opened further, giving me great opportunities to help them connect with their own wisdom and Truth. I offer these readings for a donation and God has taken very good care of me since the work began eight years ago.

"My daughter, Millicent, is just six years old. I am divorced from a nice man who could not live with my gift. My Millie is coming into her own gifts already. I am hoping she will be able to influence her father. I love him very much but need to follow my own heart. I can see that Millie and I share in our lineage deep feelings about the Sisterhood and Mary. Our family has been in the Languedoc since Mary's time, though branches of the family have been close to the throne of France. My mother believes that we are of Mary's blood. For me, it does not matter for we are all of her soul lineage. I am grateful to have found myself as a reflection of each of you. I am equally grateful to be here with you now."

Genevieve hugged Susmo and Leah before returning to the pile of saddles next to Bridget. Another dark-haired priestess jumped down from her perch and came forward. A veteran of many Peru journeys, she sought out a big hug from Susmo right away.

"*Wayki* Natalie," Susmo said, offering her to the group. Natalie laughed, bowed and stepped forward to speak. She had the unmistakable accent of a true New Yorker, offering her thoughts and feelings in a no-nonsense, matter-of-fact way.

"I'm Natalie Baylor from Long Island, New York. It is so great to be here in the Andes again. Thank you so much, Leah, for 'dreaming' this up," she added, getting a good laugh out of the group. "I inherited a little bookstore on Long Island. It's a kind of coffeehouse hangout for the locals, but we attract a lot of tourists during the season. My spiritual transformation has been reflected in the inventory, but more than that, I have attracted some very interesting people who became a regular circle of spiritual seekers. As I continued my search, they began looking towards me for guidance.

"I have to say that I was relieved when Leah came along. I heard about the Sisterhood through my sister, Helen, who hosted Leah in Boston. I got involved right then and it has been quite a ride since. This work has moved me into a place where I don't have to search anymore. I offer people that sense of stability and direction that Leah offered to me. Teaching came naturally, and I am happy to be conducting the beginning workshops for Leah in the East now that she has been working more internationally.

"It hasn't been my calling to marry or to have children. I like my freedom. I like to see open and fun men, but my real passion is sailing. The wind, the water, and this path have taught me the art of fluidity, the marriage of yin and yang within and around me, and the Divine Feminine that is my essence. I offer my support to each of you, since many have not been on a mountain trek before. Please call out with voice or thought if you need help," she concluded.

Natalie gave Leah a long, warm hug. Then she took her place once again, opening the floor to the next woman. The circle continued, bringing forth stories rich with transformation and not without humor. Carolyn Weston was an Australian lightworker who was an administrator for the Sisterhood in Australia as well as a workshop leader. Marie Louise Gerbouis was the proprietor of a unique rejuvenation spa in Geneva, Switzerland. Situated on a biodynamic farm, the spa combined thermal baths, body care and dietary reprogramming to help clients connect with healthy lifestyle.

Georgia Parrish was a breathtaking blend of African-American and Cherokee blood. Georgia had asked for and received foundation grant support to bring the work of enlightenment to those who would otherwise not be able to afford it. Each year, her funding had increased as the foundation saw how her programs fostered independence, courage and self-sufficiency among the participants. She had just been asked to put a program together for the Cherokee Nation to empower women of Cherokee blood in five states. Georgia was pure inspiration.

Liu Chow, a second-generation Chinese-Canadian, was a writer from Vancouver, British Columbia. Writing with an obvious passion, Liu was a powerful spokeswoman for the Sisterhood through the written word. Ellia Theiran had co-created a blossoming aromatherapy company in Santa Barbara, California with her partner, Greg, and the kingdom of the Devas. Their products were sought after for their high frequency and effectiveness in moving energy. Ellia also had a nice sideline business practicing Feng Shui, the art of moving energy within space. She had a sense of vitality about her that was stunning. She and Greg had two boys with families of their own. Both she and Natalie had been working with Leah since the beginning of Leah's formal teaching.

When Ellia had finished her introduction, Leah asked Susmo to introduce himself to the group. He had been leaning against Leah's pile of saddles twisting his mustache throughout the introductions. Without moving, he nodded to Sonia indicating his desire for translation, then began to speak. His Spanish was delivered in a poetic cadence coming straight from the heart.

"*Wayki* sisters, I am Susmo Manaja. I welcome you to the Andes and to a very mysterious expedition. When I was a boy, my father often took me to the lands of the Incas. We were sworn to secrecy about these journeys because these Indians had never been found by the Spanish or by the church after the conquest. Their teachings were pure Inca, kept whole from the times before the Incas became corrupt. Their Quechua dialect was ancient. My father was a dealer in antiquities who always found beautiful weavings and artifacts on our journeys. We never went empty-handed. Our horses were always loaded with blankets, food and simple farming tools.

"These Indians' lives were and are austere and rugged, for they had chosen to live in the high mountains where there is cold wind, snow and where little food could be grown. They chose to do this to protect the Truth and live in peace. My father's passion was to learn the legends and histories of the people. As my father learned about the tribe and their history, I began hearing my Truth. I chose a life following in my father's footsteps, inheriting his little shop in Cusco. When my father died I was forty years of age and a respected member of the business community of Cusco. Receiving the written legacy of his secretive work with the Indians reconnected me to my Truth in a way that was sudden, almost desperate. I found within me a hunger for the Truth that I had been ignoring.

"My wife learned to run the business and I began arranging weeks of free time in my work when I could be in the mountains searching out the elders. My wife and children understood this as my need to heal the wounds of my father's death, but that is not what I was doing. I felt guided by my father and, in a way, was as connected to him as I had been when we journeyed together. The tribes of the high mountains received me in keeping with the memory of my father and I was soon apprenticing with many of the *paqos* (shamans). I arranged more and more time away from Cusco until, with the teachings inside me, I had no desire to be there. Now it is different. I have learned to live in both worlds, but I prefer to take people into the mountains to experience their awakenings.

"You might imagine that my family thought me crazy to be in the mountains so much and they felt a little abandoned as well, I am sorry to say. But I was a driven man. Now I understand that the time was at hand for the Truth to reach the world and that I was to be a bridge for that Truth. However, at that time, I even questioned my own sanity. I have been fortunate that it has all come to pass as a surrender to the greater Truth - that is to say that I left my rational mind behind and gave myself wholly to the unfolding Mission. I think all of you know that this is necessary. My eldest son, Lobo, is apprenticing with the Indians, free from the constraints of the cultured world.

"Now the time of bridging is complete and I await the next part of my Mission. This journey we are undertaking, this pilgrimage of Truth, may hold the keys to the future work of those in this group. Don Eduardo would not call people to him who were not to be of assistance to the Mission. So, as we walk and ride tomorrow, I ask you to clear irrelevant thoughts from your minds and focus your intent on service. We will mount our horses at nine o'clock tomorrow morning following breakfast. Let my warriors pack up your tents and load the horses. They will overtake us in no time at all. You all must save your strength – and focus your intent. If all goes well we will reach the village of Don Eduardo before dusk."

Susmo waited for Sonia to complete the translation, then turned to Leah. "Neither Leah nor I," he said, "knows the intent of Don Eduardo. We simply concur that we all must be here at this exact time. I cannot tell you more," he concluded.

"That is quite true," Leah added, "and it does not surprise me that the timing of this pilgrimage coincides with the auspicious planetary alignment. We will be under the influence of this grand conjunction of eight planets for the entire trip, but we will be particularly mindful of it May 3rd through the 5th, when this fortuitous stargate, a portal to the higher dimensions, opens. My suspicion is that certain energies important to the Mission will find a universal doorway through that conjunction. It has all the makings of a co-creative wave of cosmic energies. I think we all understand that the experience will be intense, but all we women have to do is show up and be receptive." She gave Susmo a little pinch on the cheek and added, "we'll see what happens to the men."

The group laughed and applauded while rising to receive the steaming hot bowls of *quinoa* soup being served by the young warriors. After a dinner filled with the chatter of new friendships and free-wheeling speculation about the journey, everyone retired to their sleeping bags carrying hot water bottles and instant heat packs inside their coats. The Indians were left to sleep in their way-station hut. A number of the women shared tents for added warmth and less gear to haul.

Leah preferred to sleep alone to accommodate the frequent insights and visions that came to her during the night. Maintaining some distance from the women allowed her to be clear about the status of the group assemblage point as well. It was a simple truth that moving energy required a kind of focus that could not be social. Susmo, on the other hand, had no qualms about disturbing Lobo in that way, or the whole mountainside with his snoring. The importance of falling asleep before the men became quickly apparent to the eleven women.

At seven-thirty the next morning, the women were called to the doors of their tents to receive steaming hot tea from the warriors. They would find these little acts of attention to be outrageously luxurious under the circumstances and most welcome.

By nine o'clock they were packed and ready to mount the horses again. The warriors would break camp, allowing a little more time for tent moisture to dry then join them by lunch. A crisp, clear morning set the stage for a warm and beautiful day. The group was encouraged to dismount and walk when they were traveling downhill, easing the strain on muscles that comes with two days on horseback. The treacherous walk the day before had spared no stress for anyone.

Having overtaken the group at midday, the young men stopped in a natural clearing to prepare a feast of guacamole sandwiches and fruit. Riding into the clearing, the group found lunch spread upon a tablecloth beneath a monolithic slab of rock that jutted out of the earth like a mountain. Susmo asked them to look at the rock, then above it at the snowcapped peak they were ascending. The rock was a miniature of the mountain. There was the everyday magic of the Andes.

Not long after lunch, the Indian guides reached a junction on the path and were joined by another band of their tribe. Susmo went ahead to speak with them and returned to inform the group that, after crossing the high pass before them, they would not be far from Machabamba, the first of the Indian villages. Men from the village of Don Eduardo who were returning from Cusco had joined the guides. It was a five-day walk to Cusco for the Indians of the high mountains. They did not ride horses, and the blanket-wrapped goods on their backs were heavy. Dropping their loads to give a hearty greeting to Susmo and his friends, the travelers welcomed a short rest before throwing their packs back over their shoulders. Soon they started off across the rocky terrain, leading the group towards their village.

Leah and the women stopped to layer up because the wind in the exposed areas was fierce and cold. They had ridden out of the protection of the mountainside. What greeted them was breathtaking. Snow-capped mountain peaks sparkled above the high country where icy streams sliced through the rock-strewn mountainside. Home to the condors and eagles, these mountains were a sacred family of *Apus* and *Ñustas* the male and female spirits of the mountains. Each peak had a name and was the guardian of all that lay below. The highest peaks in the Andes were great *Apus* where the elder shamans who tended the great *Apus*, communicated with the stars. Don Eduardo was such a elder.

Just before dusk, they arrived at Machabamba, the first of a string of villages tucked in the green valleys of lofty mountains which spread towards the jungle. Dismounting their horses, the group walked the last hours of the journey single-file down the footpath into the village. Children began appearing from the herds of llamas and alpacas, surrounding the visitors and grabbing their hands. It was the warmest kind of welcome for the road-weary group, and many felt tears stinging their eyes. Coming to greet them next were the men who offered them warm potatoes, while their shy women watched from the shelter of their doorways. The wranglers took their horses away to graze, freeing the group to join fully in the festivities. It felt like coming home to all of them. Met by pure spirits, who wanted nothing from them beyond a smile, a laugh, and a traditional hug, the group was fully in the moment, the rigorous journey forgotten.

Susmo gave Leah a warm hug, announcing that her women were true warriors. Arriving at a plateau above the village huts, he asked Lobo to supervise the establishment of their camp. Don Eduardo would greet them in circle after a dinner served in an abandoned village hut next to the clearing. There was enough time to get tents set up and maybe have a little nap before dinner.

As the women waited for the warriors to pitch their tents, their attention was drawn to the snow-capped mountain peaks above them as the last rays of the Sun sent radiant light from the *Apus*. Leah sent a prayer to the sacred mountain, which guarded the village, on the steam of her breath through the chilly air.

"Beloved *Apu Señor Waman Lippa*, may we hear the voices of the stars, may we be as children receiving your grace, and may we surrender without hesitation to this unfolding mystery, the greater Truth. Be as guardian and oracle to your children, beloved *Apu*. We have come here to receive and to serve.

"Beloved *Ñusta*, show us the way of balance and receptivity. May we be blessed with the ability to co-create the future. May we never forget the Mission we serve and those who have held the light for so long on *Pachamama*. Blessed Be."

White Hearts

Close to full, the Moon hung over the mountains to the east as the group left their crowded dining hut after dinner. Susmo led them up and down the steep paths through the community of rectangular thatched-roofed stone houses to a larger stone building at the far edge of the village. Village men were gathered around the entrance of the building awaiting the visitors. After a ten-minute round of hugs and cheek kissing with all of them, the group was ushered into the fire-lit stone room. Larger than the homes, it was reserved for community meetings and ceremonies. Two young boys tended the fire pit. The fire's smoke rose through a hole in the thatched roof. In spite of their excitement about the strangers, they maintained a serious attitude about their chore, stealing looks whenever they could.

As Susmo and Leah entered the room, they saw an old *wayki* talking to two villagers. Leah was shocked. "Brian Stafford!" she cried, quickly holding a hand over her mouth to muffle her voice. "What on Earth are you doing here?" Leah grasped Susmo's arm, dragging him towards the tanned, sandy-haired man they had known for years. Brian lifted Leah off the floor and twirled her around in his arms. He set her back down next to Susmo with a kiss, and then grabbed Susmo. After the two *waykis* had finished greeting each other, Brian stood back a bit to look at them.

"Leah, I have not seen you in three years. You are younger and more fit than ever."

Leah laughed. "Thank you, Brian. That always sounds good coming from you. How long have you been here?"

"Susmo left me here about a week ago." Brian said.

Leah looked at Susmo suspiciously. "You are difficult to surprise, *Wayki* Leah," Susmo offered sheepishly, " but I think we have succeeded this time."

"That you have!" she replied. "What brings you here, Brian?" Leah asked, touching his arm lightly.

"Well, Leah, I had a dream. I was sleeping under some palms near the ocean one afternoon so I cannot tell you if it was a dream, a journey or a vision, but I clearly saw Don Eduardo who told me precisely when to be here."

Leah smiled inwardly, acknowledging Don Eduardo's masterful method of invitation. " It looks like life on Maui agrees with you," she added.

"I miss Santa Barbara, but the energy is similar and the weather is more to my liking," he laughed.

Brian was just a bit taller than Susmo and Leah, of muscular build with luminous blue eyes. He was forty-two years old to Leah's fifty-five years. Susmo's vanity prevented him from revealing his age, though she guessed him to be in the mid-forties given that Lobo was nineteen.

"I sent an e-mail to Susmo," Brian continued, "who agreed to arrange my safe passage to the mountains, and here I am. By the way, Susmo, we are not alone. Another *wayki* arrived yesterday afternoon. He had come up the trails from Paucartambo to the east villages and worked his way to Machabamba. I have not formally met him yet, but I've seen him and do not know him."

Susmo's eyebrows were raised nearly to his hairline. It was obvious to Leah that he had been surprised as well – no doubt by Don Eduardo. Susmo's dark eyes sparkled and the wavy black hair of his *mestizo* lineage framed the olive skin of an expressive face. He looked from Leah to Brian and replied, "We should have taken that route ourselves. We were given a severe thrashing by the sleet spirits to eliminate the need for any cleansing ceremonies."

Brian laughed and asked them to join him as he finished speaking with the village men. They joined Emanuel, Juan and Jose, three of the *alto mesayoqs,* or high priests of the tribe. These were men in their forties and fifties who tended to the spiritual needs of the village. The elder priests like Don Eduardo, were the messengers of the stars who held light for the planet. In addition to the titles and duties of the priesthood, which was part of the tribal tradition, *paqos* (shamans) possessed a quality that was cultivated and expressed in their work and life. One might be a seer, while another might be a *curandera* or healer. Don Eduardo was a *ylloq'e*, in fact the highest and most respected magician in the Andes. He had trained all his life, through the *pampa mesayoq* (master herbalist) aspect of the priesthood, as a magician. It was his calling.

Directed by the young warriors, the women were seating themselves in a semicircle opposite a low altar when a commotion outside the door drew the attention of Leah, Susmo and Brian. Through the doorway entered an obviously exceptional man. In the physical, he was over six feet tall, a good-looking man in his late fifties, with a tanned face, close-trimmed graying beard and mustache and soft green eyes. Handsomely streaked with silver, his dark, wavy hair was drawn back in a ponytail, presenting a subtle contrast to his black fleece jacket. In fact, like Leah, he wore only black. He was dashing, Leah mused – a charming blend of Jedi Knight and Zorro.

His physical appearance was lost to no one, but more importantly, his energetic presence held them all spellbound. For those who could see energy, this man's golden aura pulsated rays of violet and indigo light, while a huge, filamentous White

Heart was present deep within his heart chakra. Leah had sensed the presence of a heart like that in Susmo, but this stranger's field was as bright as that of Don Eduardo, whose White Heart had always been a mystery to her. The minds of the group came alive. Where did he come from? Who was he? What part would he play in the unfolding mystery of the journey?

The stranger smiled as their thoughts reached him and, tactfully freeing himself from the grips of five children who had accompanied him to the ceremonial hut, he came towards Leah, Susmo, and Brian. The *alto mesayoq's* silently backed away to take their places on the altar side of the circle. As the stranger neared her, Leah felt her entire body fill with a blissful current of energy. His smiling eyes were meeting her own - every step of the way. She felt as if she were looking at someone she had lost a long time ago, but she had never laid eyes on this man before this night. Acknowledging deep and mysterious emotions within her, she extended a trembling hand towards him. He bypassed it entirely and wrapped her fully but gently in his arms. When he drew away, she was smiling brightly, brushing away the tears that had rushed forth when their energies had met.

"You must be Leah," he said, in a rugged version of the Queen's English.

The only place she had heard English like that was 'Down Under'. Her mind expanded to review all of her Australian friends, students, teachers and their stories. She narrowed her eyes to study his face. "You're not Christian Kramer, are you?"

"Delighted to meet you, Mate," he said, laughing heartily. "How did you know?"

Leah laughed. "A good guess. On my last visit to Perth, one of my students gave me a flyer for your workshop as I was leaving for the airport. She told me you had lived with the Aborigines in the bush for two years and then with the Maoris in New Zealand."

You must have been in Perth last October. I could feel your presence," Chris offered.

"You could?" Leah replied, stunned. "You didn't even know me. How could you detect my field?"

"Remind me to tell you sometime, Love," he replied, winking. "Aren't you going to introduce me to your friends? Oh, and please call me Chris."

"Of course," she blushed, turning to Susmo and Brian. "This is Susmo Manaja, my spiritual brother and dear friend. He grew up in contact with these Indians and has been training with them for a long time." Addressing him as brother in Spanish, Chris gave Susmo a long hug. As the two *waykis* pulled away from each other Leah saw the White Heart within Susmo's energy field come alive, as if it had been charged. He too had tears to brush away.

"*Wayki*," he said, "it feels like I have known you forever."

"No surprise to me," Chris replied in perfect Spanish, grinning from ear to ear. "This Mission's been a long one."

Turning to Brian, Leah continued. "Chris, this is Brian Stafford. Brian roams the beaches of Maui when he is not connecting people with the dolphins, the whales and their own inner knowing. He's a remarkable healer as well - an energy-balancing wizard." The two men embraced as Leah watched Brian's energetic field flair dramatically.

"*Wayki*, it feels good to have you with us," Brian said, warmly.

Only the muscles of his angular face betrayed Chris' emotion at meeting Brian. Leah wondered if she were witnessing a small reunion of the Brotherhood. She wondered at the meaning of the White Heart? Snapping herself out of her mind, Leah directed Chris's attention to the semicircle on the floor. "Chris, these are my beloved sisters. Carolyn, do you know Chris Kramer?" She asked.

"I've certainly heard of you, Chris. Nice to finally meet you," Carolyn waved from the circle. The other women called their names out to both Chris and Brian.

"What a gift to be in the presence of this much feminine light consciousness," Chris remarked, acknowledging the women. "How did this group come together?"

"We have not all been together before this journey, though I have worked a long time with each of them. We all appeared together in a dream that I had for four consecutive nights. We were with Don Eduardo and Susmo. I had no vision of Brian, nor of you."

"A little mystery makes the game interesting," he replied, winking at her. "I dreamed only of Don Eduardo. I had met him once when I was here trekking with a group from Melbourne. We had little time together, but Don Eduardo definitely wove his filaments into my field. I dreamed him many times, but this last time was a summons. It was very clear to me to be here at this time, though not exactly right here. I was already in Paucartambo, ready to begin climbing into the high jungle, when I received a further message to meet Don Eduardo here. So I waited until some of the Chua-Chua villagers showed up in the market. I was scrambling to keep up with them on their way back up here. Then it was a matter of moving from one village to the next, looking for Don Eduardo."

"Perhaps Don Eduardo has something up his sleeves?" she whispered as the revered elder entered the room.

Don Eduardo was in his late eighties. Aside from a toothless smile all too common in the Andean elders, he didn't look or act a day over forty. Walking with a spring in his step and a bundle under his arms, the tiny man came towards them. Leah was visibly delighted to see him again as she watched his radiant light-body engulf the entire room. Colorful wool tassels from his knit hat framed the noble bronze face of the Inca. He wore the traditional black knit long shirt and knee-length pants of the mountain men under a poncho woven in the deep red, green and black diamond pattern of the tribe. A felt hat in the shape of a haystack topped off the tribal garments.

Speaking only Quechua, the *ylloq'e paqo* honored Leah with the first greeting, the traditional hug, and a mischievous wink of the eye. She had to chuckle to herself, wondering what he really had up his sleeves this time. Don Eduardo's manner brought remembrance to Leah of the many lessons he had taught her about the ego. Those unaware would have thought him a peasant, for there was no way to ascertain his true power in his demeanor.

He had a hearty embrace for the three men who bent low to receive him then he motioned for all to be seated. Don Eduardo sat before the altar and directed Chris to sit on his left side with Susmo, then Brian, to Chris' left. Leah wondered how Susmo felt relinquishing his usual place next to the *ylloq'e*. He looked undisturbed, but she detected a bit of ego pain. Chris, she thought, would have been comfortable hanging from the rafters. He didn't seem to stand or sit on protocol.

To Don Eduardo's right were the other elders of the tribe, and the rest of the *paqos* in order of rank. To these people, one station in life was as important as another, eliminating competition and hierarchy within the tribe. It was as noble to be a coca leaf reader as it was to be a high priest. One pursued one's calling, not a cultural idea of success. However, there were recognized levels of spiritual attainment, as with the Incas, that perpetuated a natural rank.

Leah sat directly across from Don Eduardo in the middle of her sisters. When everyone in the room was seated, the village women, moving silently, entered the room and filled the space behind the visiting women. Breathing an affirmation of their sisterhood, Leah turned to greet the women with her eyes. "Now all feels complete," she thought.

Gazing across the circle at Leah, Chris breathed his own affirmation. "Now all feels complete." This woman, who had been a part of his dreams since childhood, sat before him with enchanting transparency. Her light was immense, but soft, aligning her with Venus and Sirius, and all of the Sun cultures including the Incas.

When Leah had first come to the villages of the high mountains, the women had never before seen a blonde, blue-eyed woman. In their oral history were stories of the White Gods, missionaries of the stars, prompting considerable embarrassment for Leah and lengthy dialogues among the women and Susmo. Since that time she and her women had been embraced as sisters, trained and awakened, fostering a kinship most welcome at this moment. It seemed important to her that they balance the powerful energies of the men in this circle. Her eyes met Don Eduardo's, whose imperceptible nod affirmed her thoughts.

In the wink of an eye, beautifully woven mesa cloths appeared on the earthen floor before the *paqos*. As Don Eduardo spoke, Susmo translated to Spanish then Sonia gave the English interpretation though Chris appeared to be fluent in both Quechua and Spanish. So it would be for the duration of their time together. Don Eduardo explained that the *paqos* were going to prepare two offerings, or *despachos,* one for *Pachamama* (Mother Earth) and the other for the *Apu.* These two *despachos* would align everyone's filaments between Earth and the stars. Leah and many of the women knew these ceremonies to be potentially cataclysmic realignments of an individual's assemblage point for the uninitiated. However, for this group, they would be a welcoming home.

Many of the women reflected on the first such ceremony they had attended. On the surface, it didn't seem as if much was happening, but on the level of the light body, they had been catapulted out of lower frequency realities into realities more aligned with their souls. Without appropriate preparation, reentry into their old lives was lovingly referred to as "crash and burn".

Two of the highest-ranking tribal women *paqos* carried bundles to the men. Leah knew these women well, for they had come many times to be in ceremony with those she brought to Peru. Doña Felicia, Don Eduardo's wife, was the tribal wise woman. She was older than her husband and nearing her time of completion on the planet. In Leah's heart, she held a place of absolute honor. Margarita, twice struck by lightening, was the High Shamaness of the village. Though much younger than Felicia, she had earned her position by surviving both experiences, having incorporated the lightening into her luminous body. Margarita was a seer who spoke to the stars.

One *mesa* cloth was opened to reveal a mound of coca leaves that Susmo had purchased for Don Eduardo in Cusco. The *despacho* offerings were referred to as the magical ordering of the coca leaves. There were hundreds of different *despachos* in the Andes. Moving to sit alongside the men with *mesas* before them, the two *paqo* women opened bundles filled with herbs, tiny colorful candies, string, llama wool, flowers, trinkets and more. Making the *Pachamama* offering was the men's task - primarily Don Eduardo, accompanied by social chatter and laughter. Ordering the items in the gift was the domain of the women *paqos*, many of them *curanderas* and *brujas* (herbalists) in the community who had gathered the herbs and flowers from the mountains to the jungle with their apprentices. Doña Felicia and Margarita prepared the *despacho* for the *Ñusta*.

In time, each person in the circle was given a *kint'u,* three coca leaves held together at their stems. Putting their individual intent into the *kint'u,* each member of the group returned the leaves to Don Eduardo, who added them to the *despacho*. Soon the gifts came into form and the mesas were closed. Doña Felicia and Margarita returned to the outer circle of women while, one at a time, the visitors came before Don Eduardo to receive a *limpia,* a cleansing. Wiping each person from head to toe, back and front with the mesas, he prayed in Quechua then blew into the crown of each head, bringing into everyone's consciousness energetic messages from the stars.

With a flood of light, the initiation brought the entire group into a high frequency assemblage point meant to serve the purpose of their being together. When everyone had come forward to receive the *limpia,* the gifts were taken away by the *alto mesayoqs* and burned in a very hot fire. The group sat in meditation until the men returned with their affirmations to Don Eduardo that the *despachos* were received well by the spirits.

Don Eduardo thanked the two men as they rejoined the circle. Rising, he took a very heavy bundle from the altar and brought it to the center of the circle. It was the bundle he had carried under his arm when he arrived.

"Perhaps it is not what he has up his sleeves, but rather under his arm," Leah mused to herself.

With great respect and tenderness, he unwrapped the object within the bundle. Light danced from the weavings as the object, a stunning, life-size golden skull, caught the light of the fire. Within the eye sockets of the skull were two enormous and perfect rubies. No other adornments were obvious, but as the circle drew forward to observe the skull, a band of glyphs, like a headband, circled the cranium. Leah recognized the language of the star beings, the *Akhus,* in the glyphs. She had seen similar glyphs on the stargates, portals to higher dimensions, which she transited through often in the deep trance of interdimensional journeying.

The demeanor of the villagers indicated that the older men and women had seen the skull before, but the younger ones had heard only the legends. They came forward for a better look when Leah's group and the three men had returned to their places. Leah's eyes met Susmo's – both were surprised by this well-kept secret. There was no way to judge the age of the skull, though, to many, it felt ancient. Its aura of white, gold and magenta pulsated like a beacon into the circle. Those people sensitive to frequency felt the energy in the room shift dramatically into higher consciousness. Those less sensitive felt the changes in other ways, like a blurring of vision, ringing in their ears, a slight headache or nausea or change in breath that stabilized rapidly.

Don Eduardo followed the energies in the room until all was quiescence, save the static signals emitted by the more curious of minds. He drew three coca leaves from his baby alpaca-skin pouch, arranging them like a hand of playing cards. Holding this *kint'u* before his lips, he breathed his power and intent into it, then passed it to

Chris, bestowing on him the highest possible honor. Receiving the *kint'u* with reverence, Chris put the leaves in his mouth and formed his own *kint'u* from the pile of coca leaves on the mesas before them. He blew his power and intent into the *kint'u* and offered it to Don Eduardo, who took the coca leaves in his mouth and chewed them. This ancient ritual proceeded around the circle until Don Eduardo's filaments had touched all of the visiting *waykis* and their filaments touched his. At the same time, the villagers performed this ritual for each other.

Nodding to Susmo, who would translate the Quechua, and speaking from the core of his spirit essence, Don Eduardo opened the circle for the evening. Susmo shot a glance towards Sonia, who opened herself to service as the group's translator.

"How good it is to see that you have all found your way to this obscure collection of stone dwellings," he began. "Welcome to our home. I see some *waykis* who have been here before and others I have only dreamed. In the Dreamtime we all know each other well. I have called you here for one specific reason, but true to the nature of life, a number of purposes will be accomplished in our time together. We will not be staying in the village long, but long enough. We have an important event to attend elsewhere at the time when the planets converge. Until that time, we spend every moment in preparation. As with any event of magnitude, there will be tests."

Leah could feel the stirring of emotion amongst the women, but held a steady gaze across the room. Her eyes shifted from Don Eduardo to Chris, Susmo and Brian, then back again. The men showed no fear.

"Women," Eduardo continued, "you will be asked to hold the power of the stillness. You will be asked to weave a Dreamscape for the men – a dreamscape of the highest order. That is why you were asked to be here. You are all dreamers. That will be your test. Oh, of course, there will be lessons for you along the way as well," he added with a playful grin. The circle responded with laughter. Everything in life brought lessons, but especially these journeys. "Doña Felicia and two of her women will join your circle as the journey progresses." His words caused Leah's heart to swell with feelings of love for Doña Felicia, who had been a dear friend, spiritual mother and teacher from their first meeting.

"These three men to my left are going to discover their true identities. Each one of them has been, like all of you, moving through life towards the *Hanaqpacha* (Higher Consciousness or Fifth Dimension), gradually removing the masks of ignorance. All of you have been shattering the limitations of a race consciousness that have kept you asleep for a long time. Though these men have accomplished much in this way, they are, to varying extents, still wearing masks of powerlessness. During this time when we are together, all illusion will be dispelled. The veil of ignorance will be lifted and the conclusion of an ancient Mission will be set in motion.

"These three men are brothers of the soul, just as you women are sisters of the soul. There are a number of members of our brotherhood who are incarnate at this moment in both male and female bodies, and there are many other incarnate souls who serve the Brotherhood of the Magi. The head of this brotherhood, the Amethystine Order, has mastered many dimensions. He manifests a body as needed from the ascended state. There are many brothers who are not on *Pachamama* at this time. Most of the souls of your Sisterhood are on *Pachamama* now to weave the dream of the *Hanaqpacha,* creating that new reality. That is unusual for the Sisterhood."

Leah watched Chris, Susmo, and Brian closely to ascertain how much recognition each had of Don Eduardo's information. Chris seemed introspective, Susmo was obviously excited, and Brian was completely confused. She intuited that Chris had some information previous to this meeting and was putting pieces together for himself. Susmo had probably been prepared over time by the elders, so anticipated what was next, but dear Brian had not equated his love for Susmo nor his reaction to Chris with something deeper than friendship. Brian's preparatory work would be intense. His light-body was activating at higher levels as Don Eduardo spoke. Leah threw a protective cloak of Feminine Energy around her dear friend and let her eyes shift back to Don Eduardo. On the way, they were bathed in the soft light of Chris' eyes. Again she felt the blissful energy stir within her and a rising of light in her own heart chakra.

Don Eduardo continued. "You are all part of a great soul energy, an essence, that serves *Pachamama's* quest for higher dimensions. All of the creatures of *Pachamama,* including human beings, are part of the organism of *Pachamama.* We are, collectively, her eyes, her ears, her feelings and her mind. To separate yourselves from that Truth has been your undoing. To separate yourself from the animals and plants, the rocks and birds, has not served you either. At the same time, I affirm that you are all from the stars. Can you see that you are both? The essence you bring from the stars becomes one with *Pachamama* through embodiment, the taking of human form. Denial of this truth will cause failure of your Mission. Since you do not act alone, but through a vast group of souls, your own failure jeopardizes the greater Mission. Am I clear?" he asked.

Every head in the circle nodded agreement and the great *ylloq'e* talked further. "So, what of this skull? What connection has this skull with any of us?" he mused. "What is its purpose? It holds a frequency. It contains a message. It anchors a Mission. It is the skull of the Order of the Ruby. In the past, many brotherhoods were active on *Pachamama.* A few of them remain active, but most have lost their Truth to the great illusion of power.

"The Order of the Ruby, within the Amethystine Order of Magi, is affiliated with other authentic orders, the Order of the Red Hand, the Order of the Seven Rays, and the Order of the Emerald Cross, to name a few. Each order has a different quality, like the *paqos* in our tribe. The Amethystine Order, which a number of us serve, is one of *ylloq'e cuna,* magicians, wizards, and magi. The Order of the Ruby are the highest magicians amongst the *ylloq'e cuna.*

"There are many words to describe the quality of the Ruby *ylloq'e cuna.* They are Masters of energy. In their complete power, all of nature is at their command. Importantly, the ruby light in their hearts brings forth compassion and love, *munay,* in much the same way as the Sacred Heart of Jesus. These *ylloq'e cuna* can step out of the cycles of lives and continue their service from the ascended state. Their greatest virtue is impeccability, for the balance between light and dark can be precarious. Unlike the entertaining magicians who amuse with illusion, the Master *ylloq'e* dispels illusion to bring forth the Truth. It isn't always amusing."

Don Eduardo's eyes reflected his coyote medicine as he glanced around at the serious faces in the circle. He had been direct, even a little stern with his words, but now cackled and slapped his knees in amusement to break the enchantment of his message. Alertness was his objective. To mesmerize the group would not have served the Mission.

"How do the *ylloq'e cuna* work?" he continued. "Their power is energy and all things are energy. You and I are energy, light that has been intended into form by deliberately diminishing its frequency. You have all attained a certain amount of liberation from that form through the integration of higher frequencies, but the *ylloq'e's* work is to completely liberate himself or herself from it - to use the power of the Universal Matrix itself to accomplish this magic.

"It is true that there are many *ylloq'e cuna* in the Andes and around *Pachamama*. What makes the *ylloq'e cuna* of the Order of the Ruby different? There are codes within the order, codes of integrity and service. Once conscious, if a *ylloq'e* of the Ruby uses his magic in a way that is not impeccable or in a way that does not serve the people or *Pachamama,* he will lose his power. They do not have the option of black magic, for their own souls will put them to death. They cannot serve themselves. The greater Truth does not invest a man or woman with this kind of power to see it abused. The Soul is aligned with the greater Truth. Death provides the opportunity to reevaluate the Mission and begin again."

"The *ylloq'e cuna* of the Ruby have another sacred duty, and that is to activate the light within the Sisterhood of the Sun and to protect these women with their lives. Like most of the magi, the brothers of the Ruby Order are soul-contracted to activate the women by providing them ceaseless dramas meant to instigate realization and ascension. They are not always conscious of this service." Don Eduardo scanned the women with twinkling eyes and a wry smile. Leah smiled in agreement for all of the dramas that each of them had been forced to transmute.

"It is service to the Mission as guardians of the evolution of human consciousness," Don Eduardo continued. "You will discover that this order has been instrumental in anchoring advanced star energies for mankind. Each time a star energy is anchored, we are one step closer to our full potential. The veil that causes humans to slumber becomes a little thinner. You must understand that *Pachamama* is becoming a star. To serve her is to serve the highest purpose and to become a star as well. Remember that we are *Pachamama*. Our bodies are of her soil and return to her soil when we die a human death. Our consciousness may be from *Pachamama* or the stars. Some people are of *Pachamama* completely. The *ylloq'e cuna* of the Ruby are from many star systems. Many energies have been called together to serve the greater Truth.

"This order is part of a larger brotherhood of magicians who support the *ylloq'e cuna* of the Ruby and train those who would work with energy. It is the Amethystine Order of the Seventh Ray of Ceremony and Magic. The Ruby *ylloq'e cuna* are their magician warriors.

"This great brotherhood and those others I have mentioned are part of a still greater brotherhood, the Brotherhood of the Sun. Many of you know this order as the Great White Brotherhood. This includes the priests and priestesses in all galaxies who serve the light that is the Source of all life.

"How would you know the Ruby *ylloq'e cuna*? If you can see energy, you will know them by their filamentous White Hearts. They beat strong and bright in the luminous field of those magi who know who they are and who they have been. Though most of the souls of this order incarnate in male bodies, there are always women with White Hearts to help hold the balance of the warrior energies. Generally, they are willing to serve on the front lines of spiritual evolution. This White Heart is woven of the filaments of Christ Consciousness. It vibrates at the frequency of the

Hanaqpacha. It is in alignment with the greater Truth. *Ylloq'e cuna* use the power of this heart to heal the human hearts around them. Once activated, this heart cannot be used to serve one's self. It is the heart of a spiritual warrior.

"Where did the Order of the Ruby begin? How long ago did it begin?" Don Eduardo, who had been expressionless during his teaching, started laughing. It was a free and joyful laugh. He laughed so much that tears sprang from his eyes. Brushing them away with his coca pouch, he regained his composure. His arm swept around the circle as he said, "You people ask so many questions!" It was a reference to reading their minds; for, indeed, these questions were being projected from most of them. They laughed uproariously when Sonia translated, then everyone seemed to relax.

"The order is very old," he continued, slipping a few coca leaves into his mouth. "It is so old I cannot tell you about it tonight. The story is too long and I want to make love to my wife." Again the group went wild with laughter. Don Eduardo was a practiced comic and loved to see people laugh. Those close to him knew he was probably speaking the truth and Doña Felicia, well into her nineties and ordinarily reserved, revealed her toothless gums in a girlish smile.

Don Eduardo asked them all to come again the following night, when he would tell them the story of the order in the ancient times. They would remain in the village for the transmission of the oral history of the *ylloq'e cuna* and his tribe. Then they would begin a quest of destiny.

Springing to his feet, the ancient *ylloq'e* bundled the golden skull in its weavings and dashed out the door. The *alto mesayoqs* put away the mesas, coca leaves and makings of ceremony as the village women slipped out to tend their hearths. The young warriors announced that breakfast would be served at eight o'clock the next morning, and Leah added that her circle of women would meet right after breakfast in the dining hut. She wished everyone a deep and dream-filled sleep, reminding the women to pick up their hot-water bottle from the cooks on their way to bed. She had activated a couple of heat packs in her pockets just before the ceremony started to keep her hands warm. More than ready for bed, she left the group to pick up her hot water and have a little tea at the cook's fire.

As Leah slipped out into the moonlight, she felt a hand touch the center of her back. Her body warmed from head to toe instantly. She stopped in her tracks savoring the warmth. It felt delicious, almost sinful under these circumstances, like indulging at a spa when you really couldn't afford the luxury.

"Mind if I walk with you, Leah?" Chris asked, his hand moving around her to grasp her shoulder.

"Not at all. I'm grateful for the warming. I sometimes get bone-chilled on these treks. Where were you in that sleet storm yesterday, my friend?" she laughed.

"I was sitting with Don Eduardo, holding fast the filaments of your group. You were all truly magnificent."

"Why didn't I see you when Don Eduardo came to me during the storm?" she asked as they began to climb through the village towards their campsite.

"I have a preference for invisibility," he chuckled.

"I see. Tell me about your life in Perth, Chris?" Leah asked. "It is one of my favorite cities."

Chris was open and at ease, like an old friend. "Well, I masqueraded as a professor of Anthropology at the University of Western Australia for a lot of years," he began.

"That was how I managed to connect with the Aborigines and the Maori people. My department sent me into the bush to gather some data. Next thing I knew I was into a walkabout that taught me more than I ever wanted to know about being a warrior.

"Luckily we were on break when that stage of invisibility was called forth. The Aborigines operate in 'no-time'. In fact, I don't see that those in the bush are at all constrained by the Third or Fourth Dimension in their everyday lives.

"Well, for some reason the Aborigines were interested in me, which delighted the university. I received a grant to research more extensively and was given a two-year sabbatical to do it.

"Lately the Aborigines are being considered a national treasure in Australia – this, of course, after approved genocide nearly annihilated them. The story is much the same as that of your Native Americans. Now that world attention has been focused on their culture and tourism exploits them, the government is suddenly concerned about their survival.

"What I found out right away was that they are going to leave the planet when they darn well feel like it. Until that time, survival was not their issue, but ours. This they stated, pointing to the heavens. My understanding was that they were fully informed about the ozone layer and had no fear that the Sun will harm them."

"So the grant results were in right at the onset?" she quipped.

"You could say that," he laughed. "Beyond that I had an extraordinary time with those light beings. I met my physical death more than once and was tormented by my own mind until I gave up the idea of rationality. After that, we had fun."

"And the Maori?" Leah asked, visibly amused.

"Again, it was the call of duty," he offered. "It developed into an initiation of spirit. The Aborigines set me right with the world and the Maori set me right with my soul. That was the part about knowing who you are and who you have been. It was the end of denial. It was also the end of my job. Now I teach, just as you do, and take people into the bush to find themselves. Have you been to Ayer's Rock at Uluru, Leah?" He asked.

"Not yet, though I have wanted to activate to those energies. I will plan to go there on my next tour of Australia," she replied.

"I'd like to take you, Leah."

"How lovely, Chris. I accept."

She felt the warm tingle of bliss move through her body again. It was not invasive, not sexual, but more akin to happiness and harmony.

"Chris, do you think the Aborigines and the Maori knew about your affiliation with the Order of the Ruby? When did this big White Heart come into being?" Leah asked, slightly touching the front of his jacket around the heart.

Chris stopped and faced Leah, holding her hand where she had placed it. "They must have known, Leah," he replied, "but I did not feel the force of its energy until I passed my final test with the Maori. Have you ever been lured by the dark side, Beloved?" he asked.

Leah's heart beat wildly as she answered. "In a way I have, Chris. The choice was to market my light to the general public at the cost of my integrity. It was not a difficult choice because I had seen how those who took that path stopped growing. What you are talking about is more traumatizing. I can tell by the way my heart is beating."

"It is all relative, Leah. I am not sure what dimension I was in or if my senses had left me completely, but I came to this place of despair with my soul. Did you ever doubt the path?"

"Many times. My ego was in reaction from observing the actions of others on the path. I struggled for some time with their integrity before I understood that my integrity, my Truth, was my only real concern. I think we all go through something like that. But tell me what happened to you. It was huge, wasn't it?"

"There is a place in doubt and despair, Leah, where you can confront the essence of evil. It appeared to me as a masked shaman dancing around a fire. He played with my filaments and robbed me of my power. As he was weaving my filaments into an assemblage point of the ego-centered sorcerer, I felt him taking my life. In the beginning I was somewhat fascinated with it, like a sci-fi film, but when I felt my life force ebbing, I went into fear – bad idea. I saw fear fuel the flames of his fire and he quickened his work. If I had given myself to this energy, it would have killed me, for, as we have just heard tonight, we don't have the option of black magic. If I had not done something to save myself, I would have died anyway."

"Please still my heart." Leah pleaded. "What did you do?"

"I heard the voice of the Maori magician who had been training me. All that he said was "Love". With his utterance of that word, a great rush of energy overtook me. A glorious vision of Jesus and his Sacred Heart came before my eyes and I knew that I shared the power of love as Jesus had manifested it. I knew who I was in that moment and the power of it threw that shaman in his own fire, liberating me from despair. Love became my power, a force within me, and my personal Mission was clear to me. Of course, my teachers had led me into that Dark Night of the Soul. That shaman was the same being as my magician teacher who had spoken the word "Love". He was light and dark, and so was I – no more illusion. The evil was of my own creation, the child of doubt and fear. True to Universal Law, it turned on me to destroy its creator. It had a life of its own at that point.

"The darkness is real and it exists in all things including you and I. We magi walk a fine line balancing our light and dark. Evil is the work of humans. The object of the game is to walk the high road, the path of light, and avoid seduction by that darkness without denying it. The magi learn to use the darkness to move energy. The distinction is whether or not you succumb to its seduction. Sorcerers may choose the powers of the darkness. They may even do this knowing that there is no return from that prison of power. I, like all Brothers of the Ruby, had no choice. It was light or death."

Leah turned towards the cook's hut. "Let's go to the fire, Chris. I am suddenly chilled to the bone," she said in reaction to his story.

He drew her back again. "Not until you tell me how your White Heart came into being, Leah."

"My *what*?" she asked, in disbelief.

"The enormous White Heart in your field, Leah. Right here," he said, placing his hand on her heart where the Solar Disc of the Sisterhood radiated from her heart chakra.

Again her body warmed to his touch and the fire lost its allure. "I was not aware of this heart, Chris. I don't feel much like a warrior so it doesn't make sense, does it?"

"Tell me why you came as a woman this time?"

"Chris, that is exactly the question Don Eduardo asked me when I first met him. I had no answer for him then and I'm not sure I have one for you now. I am happy being a woman. It feels right. Your story seems appropriate to you and your path, but not to mine. It is good to be soft this time. Perhaps this heart came into being when I learned to be sensitive to others, to use my heart in a way that could help them heal their wounds."

"That is quite true, Leah, but I sense more. The brothers have always activated the feminine codes of consciousness but it has been on a small scale. Not many sisters have been on the Earth at one time until now. Consider the depth of the wounds caused by the patriarchy to the feminine collective consciousness. How could a man resurrect a woman's power when we consistently fall into mythic patterns of dominance and fear? I believe it is best for a woman to activate the codes of consciousness in the women. Now women are activating each other."

Leah was silent, deep within herself. "Leah," Chris whispered, "don't you remember making this commitment?"

"Yes," she sighed. "Chris, did you know that the ruby is really a sapphire? The sapphire is the stone of the Sisterhood."

"I understand, Leah. Sometimes we carry codes and sometimes we activate them. This time, you are doing both. We are all part of the Monadic Consciousness of the Christ Initiative. Some of us have chosen the heart of a spiritual warrior."

Chris gave her a gentle kiss on the top of her head as they turned towards the cook's hut. Many events and qualities in Leah's life suddenly made sense to her. But who was this man who seemed to know so much about her? He was fearless, gentle, filled with love energy, and he seemed to be able to speak about what he had experienced from a place of non-ego, a place of detachment from it all.

Suddenly they became aware of the rest of the group coming around the last village dwelling towards them. Leah and Chris began to walk again.

"I am not sure what will happen on this quest of destiny, Chris, but I admit to being a little concerned about Susmo and very concerned about Brian."

"You love them. I know. So do I. They will have their tests because they must be fully activated to fulfill the Mission of the Order. This is why Don Eduardo called me to be with all of you. My previous vision had me in a place different from the villages here. That is why I was already in Paucartambo. I am here to serve, as are you and your women. I will have my own lessons, truths and visions. I trust that Susmo and Brian will be true to their calling."

"This is going to be quite the interesting journey," Leah mused as they entered the cook's hut. Its power and purpose, though still unknown, felt like a storm gathering force.

"May we begin tonight?" Chris whispered. "Would you open your Dreamtime to me, Leah?"

"A tempting invitation," she replied, with a smile, "but I am not much of a sleeper on these treks."

Chris placed his hand on the back of Leah's neck until she felt a deep peace settle within her body. Sleep would not be denied. "You need to rest well for what lies ahead, Leah," Chris said softly.

"You win, Chris," she replied drowsily, "We will start work tonight."

Dreaming Paths

Leah's sleep was deep and replenishing. Reluctantly, she awoke to the call of her name, having to convince herself that it was not part of her dream. Holding the dream in her consciousness, she unzipped the flap of her tent and stuck her hand out to receive hot tea from Lobo and the young warriors. While they poured herbal tea into her thermal cup, she studied the sky, estimating how long it would be before the Sun hit her tent. Guessing half an hour, she thanked the warriors, closed the tent flap, capped her thermal cup, and zipped herself back in her sleeping bag. The tea would have to wait until she was ready to dash to the outhouse. In the meantime, she propped herself up on her elbows and began to write down the dream in her journal. Leah had experienced an unprecedented solid night's sleep, but the dream work had been intense.

Her first dream had been simple - a release from the unconscious of a repeated loss. She felt it symbolized her preparedness to detach even more from the present reality. With the second dream she shifted into Power Dream mode. She could remember every Power Dream she had ever had though the details of some of them eluded her. This time the details were being recorded. Chris appeared right away. They journeyed together to a monastery high in mountains that looked like the Himalayas. There he introduced her to a group of Master Teachers who worked with energy. She went off with several of the teachers while Chris left with the others.

In the dream she was shown several secrets of moving energy, not on the level she had already learned, but on the level of the magi. One master, Mukda, seemed to take charge of her training. She could see her White Heart and rays of violet emanating from her dream body in the mirrors of their practice hall. Her body changed from that of a woman to that of a man and then back again. She was taught how to bring an immense energy through her hands and heart. As the energy was projected at the mirrors, it came back to her. One strong projection knocked her down. Leah learned to take care with the energy – to use it subtly and never to abuse it.

Near the end of this nightlong dream, Chris reappeared in the Hall of Mirrors to observe her. Soon they were fencing together with the energy, reminding Leah of the Jedi Knights and their light sabers. She found it exhilarating and fun. Chris would turn into a woman and she into a man, working two energy paths of consciousness at once. When they were back in their Earth bodies at the end of the sparring, Chris embraced her and would have kissed her if she had not heard her name being called. Try as she might, she could not hold the dream. That part was not meant to be. Not now, anyway.

Rolling over to contemplate the dream, Leah's thoughts turned to Chris. Their attraction was cosmic – intimately linked to the Mission. She was most curious about his training, for even Susmo, born among the Indians, had not realized Chris' power.

It was wrong to compare. She knew that, but ignored it. Susmo was easy to read. His power was his *munay,* love as a force. When he was in *munay* it was impossible to be with him and not be in the love frequency. When he was not in *munay,* he was a Latin man playing out archetypal themes that enchanted then infuriated women. It was as if he lived the two lives of his *mestizo* lineage. They danced a strange dance within him, which veiled his growth with illusion. Like all of her women and herself, family lineages were ready to be healed for Susmo, but he was in denial.

Brian's power, on the other hand, was his creativity through his mind. He was a genius with body energy, finding new ways to hasten healing through balancing the energetic field. He understood new physics and how to apply it to link the mind and body. His ability to do that while standing in Truth and integrity was astounding.

Yet Brian ran away from every relationship he entered, including parents, lovers, business partners and friends, fearing commitment of any kind. Leah saw an energy chasing him, an elemental created of his own fear. Fear of what? Losing himself? Maybe so. Because his lower self operated out of fear, Brian's Higher Self could barely condense a consciousness in his heart.

Leah knew she and her women's circle would play some critical role as dreamers. However, she also suspected that they were there to instigate some major changes for the men – and then there would be the women's personal work as well. These trips were powerfully transformational group encounters.

Then there was Christian Kramer. What was his power? Could you name just one? One would think he had them all. He seemed a realized man and, however new he might be to it, a true Magus of the Order.

What was his weakness? She could not put her finger on it, but it was there. When she needed to know it to help him, it would be revealed.

Leah's role was clear to her from many meditations with Don Eduardo. He would be moving energy on the level of the cosmos, the stars. She was to move it within the group assemblage point and within the dreamers' luminous fields, assisted by the powerful energetic egg to be created by Doña Felicia. Perhaps Chris would be able to guess what they were doing, but no one else would ever know. The group would feel protected and powerful. Leah wanted nothing for herself, learning long ago the grief brought about by self-absorption. She lived for the Mission, not for herself. She knew that inescapable lessons awaited her as well, and that they would undoubtedly involve Chris.

Thinking back through the Power Dream, Leah wondered about its purpose. Were the instruction and practice valuable in this Third Dimensional reality? How could she know? Deciding to test the power of the dream, she held her hand over her heart and set her intent on warmth. She knew this would attract filaments of warmth from the Universal Matrix. Within seconds, her body was filled with the same warmth Chris had gifted her, with all of the blissful feelings. White light filled the tent as her heart swelled with energy. The tent walls became transparent and she saw the Sun rising over the mountains, shining right in her eyes.

Soon her energy moved out of the tent to merge with the Sun itself. In similar situations Leah had learned not to break the energy with panic. The feelings were intense, as if her heart were exploding. Bypassing fear, she moved into the bliss and then to ecstasy. She felt oneness with creation.

Removing her hand from her heart, she allowed the pulsation of life force to continue through its natural ebbing. Maybe one day, when her cellular energy was able to hold it, she would integrate ecstasy completely and become God-present. For now, she was content to realize God in these rare moments of peaceful perfection.

•

On her way to breakfast, Brian emerged from the dining hut as Leah approached. "Leah, good morning," he said, giving her a firm hug. "You are radiant. Have you seen God?"

"Truly I have, Beloved, right in your eyes," she replied, smiling. "How did you sleep, Brian?"

"Like a bear – well, what's new?" he said, laughing. "Actually, I had the most amazing dream, Leah."

The excitement in his voice informed Leah of his need to tell her the dream. "Do you mind sharing," she offered, sensitively.

"Not at all. Maybe you can make something of it," Brian began, eagerly. "In the dream, I was having a ball riding in on a big wave with my boogie board. I was on my favorite Maui beach. Anyway, Chris is standing on the shore when I get in there. He's waiting for me. Chris tells me that we are going somewhere – to leave my board on the beach and come with him. Well, I kind of hemmed and hawed a little bit until he started disappearing, then I said, 'Hey, wait for me!' And suddenly we were disappearing together.

"Immediately, we appeared at the doors of a building, like an ashram. He took me inside, put some white robes on me, then he escorted me to a meditation room. Chris sat on the floor behind me while he guided me into a meditation that took me out above my body. I was asked to observe my warrior's heart. I could barely see it. Then Chris enveloped me in a white light he was projecting and I began to see the violet filaments of the heart in my field. It was as if we were constructing the heart together. The key thing he told me was that the heart would not survive in fear, hate, greed, lust, envy or ego. The heart would thrive and strengthen with courage, impeccability, integrity, sensitivity, authenticity, justice, and right action. These were the codes of the Brotherhood of Magi."

Leah nodded. She was somehow not surprised that Chris could fragment his consciousness in the Dreamscape.

Brian continued. "We stayed there – well, it seemed like all night; he instructing me and I hanging in the air looking at myself. I admit that I wanted to run away, but how could I? It was as if he knew me better than I know myself. In the end, he told me that I had a genius for magic and asked when I would cease denying my gifts to the world. He really had me over a barrel, Leah, but I didn't know how to commit to the greater truth. I think it is something I am coming to, though."

Brian stood staring off towards the mountains. "Susmo is leading us up towards the glaciers today. Leah, I am a little reluctant."

"Good, Brian, then adrenaline will be on your side," she teased. "Actually, it sounds to me like you have found in Chris someone who knows you well enough to open a few doors for your soul. How lucky you are, My Beloved Friend!"

"I would expect you to find something hopeful in all of this," he replied, sounding less worried.

"However I can serve you, Beloved," she replied, smiling. "Hey, am I too late for breakfast?" She added.

"There is enough soupy oatmeal for an army."

"See you later, Brian – and have a good day in the mountains."

After kissing Leah on the forehead, Brian started back towards his tent. Leah entered the dining hall to find Susmo entertaining the women with his stories of daring deeds and metaphysical wonders. Her beloved brother was a charismatic storyteller, with an untiring interest in women.

Studying the group for just a moment, Leah observed Susmo drawing the filaments of some of the women into his field, and sending his into theirs. It was invisible, and as with most people, he was not consciousness of his actions, but it was obvious to her. Regrettably, he was engaging old behaviors that had caused him grief in the past.

She opened the breadth of her vision and saw that Chris stood against the wall, discreetly watching Susmo as well. Was Susmo being guided to act out his dark side by this mysterious dreamwalker, or was Chris simply an observer? If he was guiding Susmo, it was on an energy level undetectable to Leah – high magic. She felt him completely capable of it.

Without creating a distraction, Leah moved along the wall towards Chris and gently laid her hand on his back behind his heart. Intending warmth, she could feel the heat entering his body through her hand and bliss taking over her own. "Could the bliss be equated with the merging of one's self with another, whether that other be God, the Sun or another living being?" she thought. "After all, we are all God made manifest."

Chris drank in the gift of energy, closing his eyes to Susmo's ego. Leah dropped her hand to grasp his elbow and stretched to whisper in his ear.

"Mr. Kramer, who is Master Mukda?" she asked.

Chris smiled, opening his serene eyes to her. "You are a quick study, Leah. Mukda is a wizard and a sage, someone I have worked with in the Himalayas."

"The Himalayas?" she repeated flatly. "You forgot that part of your story."

"Another invisible episode, I'm afraid," he replied, with a sheepish grin. "The Aborigines taught me how to navigate the Dreaming Paths. In that way I was blessed to find Mukda's ashram, and so were you."

"Well, thank you. Did you sleep well?"

"Quite."

"Dreams of your own?"

"Many – one quite interesting. I was navigating a Dreaming Path, tracking the sound of an infant in distress. On the side of a mountain, I encountered a mother puma, pacing back and forth with raging, yet bewildered, eyes. Her baby was crying from within a cave, the entrance of which had been blocked by a rockslide. Above the cave I could see the path of an avalanche that advanced the rocks. The mother had no strategy to remove the rocks, though she did not lack the strength. Susmo, Brian and I will ride out to this place this morning. Because I found the pumas on the Dreaming Path, I am now responsible for them. My brothers have agreed to come with me."

"Do they know what you are looking for?" she asked, her eyes wide with disbelief.

"Not exactly," Chris replied, with a slight smile.

"Oh my! I would love to be flying overhead for this one," she whispered. "But duty calls with my women."

"I promise they will have good stories to tell," he said, nodding toward Susmo.

"Indeed. How will you find them, Chris? The mountains are vast."

"Navigation in Dreamtime and time/space are not much different, Leah. We are meant to find them."

"I know you will. We women will be sitting with the weavers this afternoon, learning about the fabric of the dream."

"I would like to be flying over you," he exclaimed.

"No doubt you will be, *Paqo*," she laughed. "Say, if you have one of these mornings free, Chris, would you come to sit with our circle and share of yourself?"

"It would be great to meet your women. In fact, tomorrow might be best. Susmo and Brian will be laying low. Those stones are going to be mighty heavy today," he replied with a grin.

"Wonderful. Well, I need to get some breakfast before we begin today's circle. I'll see you later, Chris."

"It is time we were leaving for the mountains. I will pry Susmo away from the women."

"Make sure he leaves with all of his own filaments and no one else's," she added with a quick smile.

Chris stroked her cheek as she turned towards the cooking fire, chuckling to himself. She was obviously in her element. The Goddess of his lifelong dreams was a pretty sharp lady. Curiously, he wondered if she had ever tried to live with a so-called normal person since coming into her power. In her own fashion, Leah was entertaining the same speculation about Chris.

As she stood before the cooks waiting for her bowl of oatmeal, Leah saw him walk up behind Susmo to break up the stories. As Chris laid his hand on Susmo's shoulder, all the women's filaments shot back into their own energy fields at the same time Susmo withdrew his filaments from their fields. She knew Chris had soul level permission to enter his field in such a way; in fact, it was vital to the Mission.

"He certainly makes that look easy," she mused to herself, observing Susmo's startled expression.

Opening her morning circle to questions, Leah invited comments about the journey, the previous night, or anything that was troubling the women. For Leah, it was a time to work with the group assemblage point, strengthening the ties between them, and to learn from all of them as they learned from each other.

"Who will be first?" Leah asked, scanning the circle of beautiful women. Everyone's hand shot up at once, sending the circle into peals of laughter. It was not their custom to raise hands. "Okay, is this a conspiracy?" she asked, laughing.

"We have been overstimulated by Susmo!" Natalie offered. "It's such an invigorating way to start the day. Seriously, though, I have a question about Don Eduardo's teaching last night."

"All right. We'll start with you, Natalie," Leah said.

"I'm curious about the complete liberation from form that is part of the *ylloq'e's* path. That appears to be connected to the idea of knowing your Authentic Self, the self that is, necessarily, free of illusion. Care to comment, Leah?"

"Ah Natalie," Leah sighed. "There are so many facets to that question. Take, for example, invisibility. On one level it is about subduing the ego, not being so full of yourself, and on another it is really about being so totally free that you can fly. On yet another it is ascension. All are liberation, but at different frequencies.

"A *ylloq'e* would need to be liberated completely to project his double, would he not? How could you separate and project your luminous body without killing the form? Only if you were liberated from the form could both survive. That requires mastery of the luminous field.

"To begin to know your true identity is to be aware that you are not your ego. Ego creates the illusion, so to be self-realized is to dispel the illusion and bypass the ego. Higher Self regards even the slightest bit of ego reaction or ego pain as a curse cast upon the horizon of your enlightenment. Which isn't to say that you should not have a personality – just realize it's not in charge. Don't give it power."

"Thank you, Leah. A little reinforcement never hurt anyone," Natalie smiled. She placed the palms of her hands together before her heart while bowing her head in respect.

Leah returned Natalie's gesture and asked for another question.

Bridget spoke next. "I know I keep asking questions like this and, one of these days, I am really going to understand the answer, but there it was again last night. I still get twisted up inside about it. Leah, would you please remind me of the difference between evil and darkness?"

"Beloved, I understand the twisting. Your assemblage point still contains some filaments of fear-related dogma from your upbringing. It is natural, but it may be time to ask those filaments to spin out of there.

"My guess is that you are going to experience some things on this journey that will force those filaments to change. Why? Because those low frequency beliefs are not assisting the Mission. The Truth will be demonstrated to you in such a way that it cannot be denied. Until that time, this explanation will have to do. You will notice that I am not altering the context of Don Eduardo's teaching, just expanding on it.

"We all contain the darkness. At any given moment half the Earth is in darkness and half is in the light. This is fundamental cosmology. Considering God as the All That Is, the Matrix of Creation, how can we separate out the dark and call it something other than God?

"Yet, within this Matrix of light and dark there are frequencies, and many of the dark forces of the Matrix have attached themselves to low frequency. How or why that happened I couldn't tell you. It simply is. It is a balance of cosmic energies, for the intention of God is to experience God-Self in all ways at all frequencies, and to magnify, with that experience, the magnificence of Creation. It is God increasing God. It is the Greater Truth becoming greater. The Truth is light *and* dark. We are part of the God experience, created in God's image as light and dark.

"When we were created by God, from God, we were sent out as beams of light to experience the Matrix. Our great Soul Systems split into Monads of Consciousness, then into Soul Groups, and finally into Individual Souls. At some point on the journey, we split into two Rays of light – the Masculine and Feminine, and created a mirror, one for the other.

"Each of us has a Twin Ray. That other part of us represents our darkness as the unmanifested, until each of us has elevated his or her consciousness to the magnitude of God-remembrance. Why? That separation of light has caused us to forget that we are God. How would we recognize God in something that we perceived as darkness? With enlightenment comes the recognition of the unmanifested and the call to Union. When the two shall be one, we enter into the Divine Light of Creation. Twin Rays must ascend together.

"In a primal sense, the darkness was a creation of splitting souls - of separation itself. In the Taoist cosmovision, the Tao (God unmanifested) birthed the Tai Chi (Duality) from the Wu Chi (The Void). Within the Tai Chi, the Yin and Yang are becoming each other, complementing each other and contain a small part of each other. It is so within ourselves. We are neither fully masculine or fully feminine. We are neither fully manifested or unmanifested but a perplexing paradox of both. The two combined were originally sent away from the Oneness to experience individuation because the probability of every soul returning to God as the magnitude of a star was not outlandish. God is patient, after all."

The women laughed as Leah continued. "Now, evil has nothing to do with any of that. Evil is the creation of the human lower mind. Higher mind is the vehicle of consciousness rather than the instigator of mental process. In the slumbering masses, lower mind is the slave of ego and desire. Remember, evil does not exist in the *Hanaqpacha*. Its frequency is too low. It is Third-Dimensional mindlessness or black magic. It can exist in the disembodied state, like a haunting or possession, where evil is directing the disembodied soul, or it can hover around human beings.

"When a person obsesses about something, like hating his neighbor, the filamentous structure of his mental body becomes disturbed. He attracts to him many energies of low vibration, energies of anger, rage and hate. Those emotions are not innately evil, but they do have low vibration.

"Eventually, these energies gain a power and take form as an elemental. As this person continues to obsess, the form supports the obsession, and this empowers it to grow larger, stronger. This form becomes a parasite, at first in the person's field and then it is so strong it can leave the field and live off others. The person has created an elemental energy, which is evil. It is not anger, rage or hate, but it eats them for breakfast, lunch and dinner. It was birthed from the lower mind of an unenlightened individual. This elemental can become large enough to parasitize race consciousness. Don't forget that Earth is a free will experience. It has been intended as a school of conscious evolution and attainment.

"That brings us to evil and black magic. A black magician plays with personal power, the seduction by low-frequency energies like greed, desire and ego gratification. Sometimes he is directed by disincarnate souls, but often it is by his own desire for power.

"The evil elementals he creates are deliberate - premeditated. Perhaps they are meant to hurt others, to protect his turf, or maybe to seduce others into his radius of power. Black magicians engage each other in battle rather like sport, and they will try to eliminate those who would bring the light of the Truth into their work. They operate in the shadows because their intent and their tools are low vibration. But what they create with their lower mind is evil, and, believe me; it can be powerful. Personal power is an ego game. If you sell your soul to that lust for power, you may never find out who you really are.

"Remember, the consciousness of the Matrix is moving towards Union with the Divine, so Universal energy will challenge those who acquire power. All *ylloq'e cuna* are seduced by the darkness. It is the test of power. However, it appears that the Codes of the Ruby Order would prevent, through death, the possibility of a *ylloq'e* creating evil. My guess is that it would endanger their ancient Mission by weakening collective energy. They are mighty souls from a vast number of star systems, but they are also mortal humans who, like us, are born on this Earth without remembrance of their true essence."

Leah had drawn the group assemblage point into a new frequency by weaving a tight concept of integrity. The circle sat silently for a few minutes while the filaments shifted. Then Brit, sensitive to the shift in reality, commented. "I like this idea of creating a Dreamscape for these men, even if it does present us with tests. It truly feels like the work of the sisterhood."

"It does," added Ellia. "The Fifth-Dimensional filaments are all around us in the Matrix, the same potential exists as with every other assemblage of reality. How simple it could be to weave them into the fabric of the now. Perhaps it will feel like a ghostly Camelot until enough souls are ready to make it their reality too, but I am all for having it here and now."

"Here, here," they all cheered, raising their teacups.

That discussion spurred others about the White Hearts, the power of love, the power they each felt from the golden skull, and the brotherhoods.

Near the end of their time together, Sonia asked if Leah knew the identity of the head of the Amethystine Order, the Ascended Master.

"I have an idea about that, and I am going to let you have yours. I would not spoil the way this journey is unfolding for any of you."

"Well, then tell us about Chris. Who is this mysterious guy?" Sonia pressed.

"What an excellent idea, Sonia," Leah replied, enthusiastically. "I will let you ask him yourself when we sit together tomorrow morning. Chris has agreed to share with us."

Leah broke the energy of the circle by asking Georgia to lead a little Cherokee song that they loved to sing together. This left plenty of time for hiking, meditation or journaling before lunch. Leah planned to find a sunny rock where she could take flight through the Dreaming Paths in search of Master Mukda.

•

After journeying almost three hours, the three men were close to their destination when Chris suggested they stop for a rest. Susmo, a worthy *caballero,* enjoyed riding and protested mildly, but Brian was grateful for the break. Leaving camp several hours before, they had followed a narrow trail through the rocky terrain south of the village. In the last hour they had begun to climb up towards the snowline, though they were still some distance from it.

Sitting on a group of low rocks, the men prepared to eat the lunch that the cooks had given them. Chris pulled a stack of sandwiches from his pack, Susmo produced fruit from his, and Brian brought out some jerky and trail mix. Chris ate lightly, as was his habit, avoiding the jerky and energizing the food before eating it. Susmo was oblivious to Chris' ritual and habits, but Brian's interest in his own training was being rekindled as he watched the attention Chris gave to the energy of the food he was consuming. Chris seemed to be fully conscious every moment - waking and sleeping.

"Any idea where we are going?" Susmo asked Chris.

"Maybe three kilometers beyond that ridge," Chris replied, fixing his gaze on a low ridge ahead them on the trail. "Say, Susmo, maybe you can help me understand something?"

"Maybe. What is it, *Wayki*?"

"I am curious about the condor who's been following us for the last hour."

Susmo and Brian scanned the heavens for a great bird, but saw nothing. "What condor, *Wayki*?" Susmo asked. "Have I been so self-absorbed that I missed it?"

"Missed *her*," Chris replied. "Without being obvious, look about halfway up the mountain to your left where some mighty boulders are huddling together. Sitting atop the boulders, staring at you is Lady Condor."

"On my mother's grave," he breathed, sighting the giant bird. "She is the symbol of spiritual greatness, freedom and vision to my people," he added.

"But what does she want from you, Mate? She's been following *you*."

"How do you know she isn't following you?" Susmo asked.

"She told me she was trying to get your attention, My Brother," Chris replied. "There is something that is not yet in your consciousness, a realization, which she would like to gift to you."

"I don't know what she wants from me," Susmo said, shaken. "I have nothing to realize."

"Well, let's call her down here and ask her. I believe it is in your best interest to resolve this, but if not for that reason, then we will call upon her to release me from the tedious task of being the go-between for the two of you."

"Whatever you say, *Wayki*," Susmo replied, with a touch of sarcasm in his voice.

Brian watched Chris carefully as he focused his eyes on the eyes of the condor. Closing his eyes, Chris sent a tremendous energy from his heart to the bird. It was received as a sound wave, an invitation from the heart, in the language of the condor. The great bird spread its five-foot wings and was soon aloft circling over the three brothers. She circled lower and lower until Susmo could feel that she wanted him.

"I am willing to hear," he whispered to Chris.

"She knows," he whispered back.

The condor flew low to the north then, turning, approached the men. Landing a few feet away from Susmo in a cloud of dust, she stared in his eyes until tears sprang from them. Silently he repeated a mantra, *"Madre de Dios"* (Mother of God) over and over, while the bird tried to communicate with him. In time he became more receptive.

Chris watched, fascinated, as the patient spirit-bird began untangling filaments of light in Susmo's lower chakra. In the Inca tradition there are only three chakras, appearing as bands of light. The lowest, at the navel, was *llankay,* the power center of manifestation. Susmo's *llankay* looked murky and dull. His heart chakra, *munay,* was radiant, and his third chakra, *yachay,* at the Third Eye, was a little weak but clear.

The lower center was cluttered with bundles of filaments. Chris knew that they were connected to control, desire and ego, and the bird was cleaning it all up for Susmo. He had the filaments of every woman he had ever invaded energetically tangled up with a fear-based sense of identity and the need to protect that illusion. In addition, many women had had expectations of him and had forced their filaments into his energetic field as well. All of these were interwoven with the foundational filaments of his upbringing. That magnitude of clutter kept pulling him down into the lower body, which lacked integrity. This condor was a priestess, a healer, and one who had been with Susmo and his father for many years. She was an Emissary of the Order of the Ruby who had protected Susmo from the spirit world, though he was never aware of her until this moment.

Brian was unable to move. Quite beyond his comprehension, the entire scene was like a dream. The bird was huge, wild, and sitting in front of Susmo cleaning up his filaments. Excitedly, Brian became aware that he was seeing the filaments for the first time in his life. He had the fleeting thought that he might be in shock from the situation, but he watched it all like a starving man. Brian's eyes fell on Chris and observed his filamentous connection, White Heart to White Heart, with the bird. Chris was magnificent in the purity and strength of his luminous body. Brian could see the perfect balance of his energies, the high pulse of their flow, and his energetic field, which was expanded for miles.

When the bird had finished her work cleaning up the *llankay* chakra, she turned her attention to Susmo's light body. Brian and Chris watched her reweave his *wiracocha* (luminous body), drawing in new filaments from the Universal Matrix and the Earth to complete the weaving.

When she was finished assembling the light filaments of his *wiracocha,* she turned away from Susmo to look at Chris. Brian observed their White Hearts swelling and merging, then disconnecting entirely.

Chris reached over to their spread of food, picking up the last piece of jerky. Offering it to the bird, he said, "For you, *Mamita,* with our gratitude."

She took it from him gently, then left them in the swirling dust of her beating wings as she flew back to her perch.

Standing up, Chris brushed the dust from his black fleece pants, using the brim of his expedition hat. Running his hand over his hair, he place the hat snugly on his head to temper the wind and shade the Sun then casually asked, "Shall we be going, Mates?"

Brian put the leftover food in his pack along with the wrapped garbage, while Susmo stood up, wiping his eyes. He immediately fell over, as if drunk from a bottle of Pisco, a strong Peruvian brandy. Chris helped him to his feet again, brushing him down with his gloved hands.

"Steady there, Mate," he said. "You have a drastically different assemblage point. Why don't you lean against that rock, and get your bearings, *Wayki?*" He helped Susmo over to a boulder behind them, and then went to help Brian pack up.

"You know, Chris, I scan the heavens all the time and did not see that bird," Brian commented, quietly. "She would be a hard bird to miss."

Chris gave Brian a soft slap on the shoulder. "Don't be so caught in form, Brian," he replied. "The bird is more liberated than you are. She is a *ylloq'e* who takes on the body of the condor at will. It was not my place or yours to do what she did for Susmo. Service has a million faces, My Brother."

"Chris, you communicated with the condor," Brian added with a little awe.

"No, Brian," said Chris, gazing up at the great bird, "I communicated with my Sister."

While they were eating, the grazing horses had strayed down the mountainside. Chris walked in their direction, sending forth a sound unfamiliar to either Brian or Susmo. The three horses came trotting up the hillside at a brisk pace to stand before Chris. Each one received a gentle stroke on the side of the head as he gathered up the reins.

Susmo and Brian were standing together as Chris brought the horses to them. A credit to his training, Susmo had managed to ground his new assemblage point and was ready to move on.

"Chris," he asked, "can you tell me what happened to me with the condor?"

"The content of your interaction remains between you and Sister Condor. The condition of your luminous body is of interest to me, because the Mission of the Brotherhood of Magi binds the three of us to each other; however, the nature of your struggles is none of my business.

"You received an initiation, Susmo, the incorporation of high-frequency filaments into your consciousness. Your life will not be as it had been, My Brother. I would be happy to speak with you about it at any time, should you wonder at your own behavior," Chris concluded with a grin as he mounted his horse.

While riding towards the ridge, Susmo was still lost in his experience with the condor, Brian was wondering how much of the entire event was manifest by Chris' power, and Chris was sending filaments out from his heart to Mother Puma. Each of them was focused in a different way - Susmo in process, Brian in question, and Chris in energy.

When he first heard the cries of the puma cub, Chris pulled up the reins on his horse and dismounted. He motioned for Brian and Susmo to follow suit, then led the horses to a small clearing between outcroppings of jagged rock. He made it clear to the horses that this was a place out of danger, and the horses seemed to understand.

Chris took a length of heavy rope he had tied to the saddle for the rescue and wrapped it around his waist so nothing would be dangling from his body. He laid his backpack on a nearby rock and motioned for Susmo and Brian to do likewise.

"We have reached our destination," he whispered to Susmo and Brian as he rejoined them. "I will need your help in creating a space of calm and safety for a very nervous mother."

Susmo raised his eyebrows curiously, but Brian looked positively worried. "What are we doing, Chris?" he demanded.

"Well, Mate, we are going to try to rescue a little one who cried out to me through the Dreaming Paths. His mother is frantic, full of rage, but manageable if we can control our own emotions."

"Like what kind of emotions?" Brian asked.

"Fear, Mate. If we cannot calm the mother, we will not be able to save the child. If we cannot be calm, centered, in our power, the mother will attack us."

"Are we talking about a big animal, Chris?" Brian asked.

"Big enough, I would think. *Wayki* Susmo, how big are pumas, anyway?" Chris asked, casually.

"*Madre de Dios,*" was all he uttered.

"Here is the strategy," Chris explained, ignoring Brian's reaction. "The mother is blocking our way to the den. She has been pacing from den to clearing for several days. The cub was trapped in the den by a rockslide while mother was hunting. Mama Puma has already lost her other two cubs to a whim of nature and the father was killed while culling a llama from a herd near the next mountain village. She is a bit touchy at this moment and really frightened that she will lose all she has left.

"She will sense that we are her only hope, but she will react to anything we project at her. So, we need to be invisible, transparent to her senses."

"Count me out, Chris," said Brian, sharply. "I don't get along with house cats."

"Will you place yourself in the Cauldron of Magic, My Friend? Or will you fail the Mission?"

"This isn't the Mission, Chris, it's an animal in distress, and a dangerous one at that," Brian reasoned.

"Brian, to a magus, his life is the Mission - every moment of it. Everything he encounters and is led to by the greater Truth *is* the Mission. The choice is yours, both of yours, to live or to continue being dead."

"Chris, dead is what we are after she mauls us," Brian pleaded.

"Dead is what you have been all your life. You have the potential of realized men, but you are operating at less than five percent of your power."

Searching inward for a moment, Brian asked, "How do I get rid of my fear?"

"Focus on love, Brian, *munay*. It is that simple. All of creation responds to the power of love. Love begets love, while fear, the absence of love, begets more fear."

"I may die," he sighed.

"You may live," Chris answered, holding Brian's eyes steady with his own.

"What do we do?" Brian said, with resignation.

"Susmo, how do you feel?" Chris asked.

"I have my own problems," he admitted – "a lot of fear, but not of pumas. I fear not knowing who I am, not being recognized and respected, not being heard, not being attractive to women, not winning the game, and not being liked, to name a few, but pumas are good *waykis*."

Chris grabbed his shoulder pulling him closer to himself and Brian. "I expect those fears don't hold quite the magnetism that they used to, Mate. Now, here is the plan. We walk slowly, carefully into the clearing, focusing on love, staying completely clear of emotion – even the sadness of hearing the baby's cry. Keep your arms close to your bodies. We will each pick a spot and quietly sit down within range of her pacing – close, and increase the intensity of the *munay* we send to her. We should be able to sense when we have gained her confidence so that we can move along the cliff side towards the den.

"I've got this rope around my waist to tie around the rocks. With the strength of the three of us, we should be able to move them. The path is very narrow, puma style, and the cliff is steep. We need to be alert, not worried about mama, while we are out there. Clear?"

"What if fear comes up?" Brian asked.

"Get rid of it. She'll know. Your body cannot be rigid or her muscles will tense. You and the puma are one light, Brian. She is closer to that realization than you are because all animals experience the bliss of Oneness, but, since fear has blocked that knowingness, we need to help her bring it through right now. Susmo and I will be sending love too. Place your confidence in brotherhood."

"Okay, let's get on with this."

"We'll try to be telepathic with each other in this situation. I don't think language will help. Whatever you do, don't yell," Chris added.

Brian looked pale as the three men walked quietly towards the clearing. They had been talking behind a rock outcropping more than a hundred meters from their destination. The mother became visible to them and they to her at about thirty meters - a serious disadvantage for this mother who was too distressed to have heard a hunter at close range.

They began projecting *munay* from their warrior hearts. Chris added the vibration of harmlessness and compassion to his *munay* as they approached the puma. Her eyes were fierce, yet intelligent about her helplessness. The cub cried out as they neared their sitting places, causing the puma to charge defensively down the path to the den. Chris could tell she had taken no water in days and had not eaten for some time. She sent him that information through the filaments of compassion that he had extended to her.

Sitting soundlessly towards the left of the path, Chris motioned to Susmo to sit opposite him and for Brian to occupy the spot next to him and opposite the path entrance. When the puma came into their circle, she paced around it several times, her senses fully opened. Could she accept their help? She was unsure. She paced the circle again and came to sit in front of Chris. Silently he communicated with her.

"Mama Puma, I have heard the call of your cub while riding the Dreaming Paths. I share your sorrow of the loss of those you love. Will you allow me and my companions to move the rocks from your den and reunite you with all that you love?"

"I trust you, Friend. I am grateful that someone heard my child. I am not sure of your friends," she replied.

"Test them if you must, Sister. They have good hearts and do want to help you."

The puma walked across the circle to sit before Susmo. Susmo did not react. He poured *munay* from his filamentous White Heart, a heart that grew bigger and whiter with each passing moment. Satisfied, the puma moved to sit in front of Brian. Chris did not interfere with Brian's test, but observed both cat and man keenly while continuing to pour forth the love. Brian held his own projecting the love and staying clear. He was visibly relaxed.

The test was completed when the puma yawned. Brian reacted spontaneously to the huge open mouth in front of his face. He lost the *munay* to fear within a nanosecond.

Chris saw tension come into Brian's body at the same time the cat's hind quarter began to twitch. He felt Brian struggling to regain his composure, but by then the puma was panting. Chris felt adrenaline surge into the blood of puma and man. He glanced at Susmo, who had shut his eyes in an effort to focus his *munay*. He was calm and centered. The cub cried out again, but the mother was locked into Brian's emotional field. In *her* eyes, he had failed the test.

Chris had to hand it to Brian for remaining silent, but the situation was escalating rapidly. Letting go of the human need to come up with a solution, Chris opened a portal to his cosmic body. He became one with the puma, Brian and Susmo, as well as the condor circling overhead, the mice running between the rocks, and the rocks themselves. He found himself, in an expanded moment of time, seeing through the eyes of the puma, who was calculating the risk of attack with two other men present.

She had not eaten in days, and this weak man feared her - an easy prey. She felt the *munay* held in the circle by Chris and Susmo, but Brian's fear pulled her into her animal instincts; survival, hunger, helplessness and her own fears for her own life and that of her remaining child. In the next moment, that instinctual force overcame her and she sprang off her hindquarters towards Brian.

Coming fully into the power of his heart, Chris brought forth a sound that was both primal and terrifying. The sound echoed off the mountains, causing the great condor to dive from the sky into their circle, taking her place at the head of the path. The puma brought Brian to the ground with the thrust of her leap, but went limp, collapsing upon him as if she had been sedated. She was still conscious, but she had released her desire to kill him. She began licking his face instead, and Brian promptly fainted.

Susmo was wide-eyed and alert, the sound having carried his White Heart out to the mountains and back several times. He watched the condor land next to him to guard the path to the den and Chris, his light fully expanded and shimmering, rising to assist Brian. Chris coaxed the puma from Brian's body but asked her to watch over him while they helped her child. She eased herself off Brian, and lay attentively at his side watching his breath.

Chris motioned to Susmo, who rose silently to join him at the path. The condor flew up to a rock overlooking the den and the two men inched along the path to the rockslide. A timber wedge would have worked beautifully, but there were no trees at this elevation. Chris unwound the rope from his waist and made a lasso with it. One by one, he and Susmo roped up each rock and dragged it onto the path where they could push it down the cliff. Of course, more rocks slid down from above the den as they removed them, but eventually they made some progress towards clearing the door. The cub could squeeze through the entrance if he was strong enough, but the mother would not have been able to enter and their home would be lost.

After they had heaved several more rocks over the edge, one big rock remained, but they were unable to move it by themselves. They needed Brian's help. Chris glanced up at the condor as he moved along the path back to the clearing. She was reminding him that he could use light and sound to move the stone. After all, how did he think the pre-Incas built their cities?

"My Sister, you are correct," he silently replied, "but I have not written off this magus yet. Surely he will be tested again, but I would offer him a chance to save face."

"As you wish, Brother," she replied.

Brian was conscious, eyes opened, but he was afraid to move a muscle with the cat at his side. Chris squatted next to the cat and began to stroke her head and back. She rolled over to offer him her underside, freeing Brian from her steady gaze. Chris gave Brian the nod to get up, indicating he was needed on the path.

He hobbled over to the path, his knees weak from fear. Susmo grabbed Brian by the arm then explained the situation with the rock. Soon Chris showed up with the puma, who sat on the path waiting for her child. Susmo held the rope close to the rock it circled, Brian grabbed the middle and Chris grasped it close to the far end. At the count of three, they began to pull.

"This is like tug-of-war with a Mack truck," Brian complained.

"Focus," Chris shot back at him.

The rock started to move – not much, but it moved a little. They took a breath and began again. At the count of three, the puma grabbed the loose end of the rope and pulled with her teeth as well as her mother's passion. The rock moved quite a bit.

On the next try, the rock moved past the entrance of the den, freeing the cub, but now it blocked the path. Changing their strategy, the men began to push the rock towards the cliffside while the puma sat on the path, waiting. They were in a dangerous situation, since a good hard push would send them all tumbling down the mountainside.

Hesitantly, the cub poked its head out of the den, to see three dirty men resting against the hillside looking back at him. Frightened beyond belief, he cried out and ran back into the den. Chris glanced to his left and saw the body of the puma flying through the air in a tremendous leap. She cleared the rock in front of them, landing at the door of the cave.

"Maybe this rock will give them a sense of protection," he offered, with a chuckle. "Soon another male will show up to mate with her."

"I think you're right," Susmo replied. "Why don't we leave them alone?"

Chris gathered up the rope and headed back towards the clearing, with Brian and Susmo following. He called the horses to them, uncertain that Brian would be able to walk that far. When they were mounted on their horses, looking somewhat the worse for wear, they glanced back at the path towards the den. The condor was gone - nowhere in sight, and the mother puma stood upon the rock with her squirming cub dangling from her mouth. Chris felt a pulse of compassion flow through his heart, reconnecting him with their hunger and thirst. He dismounted and walked towards the puma with his water bottle. Slowly, he poured it out before her into a shallow bowl-shaped depression he'd noticed on the rock. She gazed at him with powerful but grateful eyes, and then dropping her cub on the rock, she began to drink.

About halfway back to the village, the men stopped to eat the rest of the fruit they had brought. Brian still looked pale, beyond exhaustion, while Susmo was serene and renewed. They would have several hours to rest before dinner and their evening with Don Eduardo. Brian hoped it would be enough, for he was becoming even further exhausted chastising himself for his failure.

Chris sensed Brian's feelings and assured him there would be another chance.

"Do I want another chance?" he asked.

"Your soul is committed to the Mission, Brian. It is what you have been born to countless times. Your personality, the ego, is not committed. In fact, it blocks commitment of any kind. That, in addition to fear, is your weakness, your supreme limitation. You must ask yourself what lies at the core of this weakness and destroy it."

"What if I don't know?" Brian asked.

"Your ego is asking me that question. Who you really are already knows. Get in touch with who you really are and start asking questions. Make use of your

Dreamtime," he added, raising his eyebrows slightly. "I wouldn't waste time with the task either. You will not know when the next test is at hand."

"I will get on it, Chris. Thank you for saving my life."

"I didn't save your life, Brian. The forces of nature saved the puma a little embarrassment and a great deal of karma."

Susmo laughed heartily as they packed up their trash and walked to the horses. "Where did the sound come from, *Wayki?*" he asked Chris.

"It is our oldest language, *Wayki,* but one we have forgotten. It is the language of the heart."

"What did you say?"

"Nothing. The heart does not speak in words, My Brother. It speaks in feelings and emotion."

"What feeling then, *Wayki?*" Susmo asked persistently. "I have never felt anything so powerful. It brought the condor diving from the sky, stilled the puma and burst my heart. What was it?"

Chris mounted his horse. Then, looking down at Susmo with the kindest eyes, he said, "The sound was peace, My Brother - *tranquilidad.*"

•

Unusually reserved during dinner, Susmo ate with a feeling of contentment not experienced since he was a baby. He was reflecting on his unwillingness to share the experiences of the day with the women. It was not just some code of the brotherhood, for secrecy, he knew, was arbitrary. There was something deeper. He felt he had been released from the need to engage them or project at them. What is more, he realized he had been doing just that. Instead, Susmo ate quietly, fully aware of the feminine presence before him and willing to be nurtured by it.

Studying Susmo from the circle of women, Leah saw an image take form behind him. It was an older man with a mustache and a goatee, whose wavy, black hair was streaked with silver. He beckoned to Leah. Casually walking to the fire for a little more soup, she returned by way of Susmo who greeted her with a kiss on the cheek.

"*Hola, Wayki,*" he said, cheerfully.

"Thank you, My Brother. How was your day?"

"My day was interesting – very worthwhile," he replied, vaguely.

Leah eyes moved to focus beyond Susmo's left shoulder. "*Wayki,* I need to tell you that there is a man standing with us who cares a great deal about you."

"What man?" he asked.

Leah described the man to him in detail.

Susmo chuckled, "How appropriate that my father would visit me today. I will meditate with him tonight, but tell me if he wishes to convey something to me right now."

"He does, *Wayki.* I don't know what this will mean to you, but he is grateful that you have released him."

"I released him?" he asked, dumbfounded.

Leah listened to Susmo's father and conveyed his message to his son, sentence by sentence. "He is speaking of many filaments that he and you shared during his life. These filaments remained within each of you after his death. He feels they were inappropriate and would like to apologize for being so invasive when you were growing up. He says he is sorry that you took on so much of his pain, but joyous that you have let it go, that you have broken the cords that bound the two of you."

Susmo allowed his welled-up tears to flow. "*Oh, Mi Padre,*" he breathed, "how much I have been like you. I did not see it, but it is true. We have both been liberated today."

As the image faded, Leah placed her hand on Susmo's shoulder. "What an interesting day you must have had, *Wayki,*" she whispered in his ear. Then she walked back to her seat across from him, feeling blessed by the aura of his liberation. "What a beautiful being he is," she thought to herself. Susmo's White Heart had grown immense that day, and now radiated his contentment and gratitude.

Brian showed up at the end of dinner, still pale but with two hours of restorative sleep. He was definitely in no mood to discuss the day's events, so wandered into the kitchen to eat leftovers alone. Deep in thought, he was caught halfway between the day's experience and the work of self-examination that lay ahead.

Chris never showed up at dinner because he had been called to the home of Don Eduardo to begin preparations for the coming journey. Like an orchestral conductor, Don Eduardo was keenly aware of the day's events and all their nuances.

Motherland

When the group assembled in the community hut, the energy was subdued. The women had spent the afternoon absorbing the cosmology of the Incas as it was woven into the fine *tejidos* of the tribe. The weavers, whose skill at the loom reflected their spiritual wisdom, had given them a great gift. Doña Felicia had supervised the teaching, turning it into a ritual of the cosmos and *Pachamama*. As the village women moved into the hut to silently fill the space behind the eleven Sisters, many eyes between the two groups met, acknowledging, with reverence, their time together.

Not long after all of the participants were seated, Don Eduardo entered the room. Chris was at his side and the bundle containing the skull under his arm. Don Eduardo asked Chris to set the golden skull in the middle of the circle exactly as he had the previous night, while he scanned the circle of faces around him.

Chris glanced at Leah as he adjusted the skull to face her. His eyes bathed her in love, but then betrayed some concern. A bit confused, she looked to Don Eduardo, who motioned for her to come before him. The great *ylloq'e* asked Leah to sit before him on the loose straw covering the earthen floor and connect her heart to his heart. As she did this, she felt a great swoosh of energy enter her heart that sent a ripple through her entire energetic system. Don Eduardo smiled at her and said. "Welcome back, *Wayki*. You were not in your body."

Leah laughed and thanked him. "I've had an interesting day, My Beloved Teacher," she said, with the twinkle back in her eyes.

"You too?" he asked, glancing towards the men.

"No wonder I had seen Susmo's father," she reflected silently.

ack to her place and called Brian forward. Asking him
circle with his eyes closed, Don Eduardo produced a
tile flower water used in ceremony and, in Latin culture,
swig of it into his mouth, the *ylloq'e* blew a fine spray of it
rcled around Brian spraying it everywhere in his field. As
umistakable scent of cleansing ceremonies, the group held
ce of love. Finishing the cleansing, the *ylloq'e* stood side by
ve him a tremendous slap on the back – right where his
ass.... acted the physical body. Surprised, Brian lunged forward,
and then rig... elf before stumbling into the golden skull.

"*Listo,*" Don Eduardo announced crisply, letting everyone know he was ready to begin his teachings. Now alert and energized, Brian took his place between Susmo and Sonia. The *alto mesayoqs* had spread a mesa full of coca leaves on the floor before the *ylloq'e* who selected three leaves to form the *kint'u*. This night he chose to honor Susmo by offering him the first *kint'u*. Susmo was not expecting the gift, so received it with some surprise. He reciprocated by offering three leaves to Don Eduardo who then went around the circle of guests weaving the assemblage point for the evening with the coca leaves. He ended with Chris.

Don Eduardo then asked Leah if she had brought the sapphires of the Sisterhood with her. Leah wore a beaded doeskin amulet around her neck that she pulled from her layers of fleece. The *ylloq'e* asked if she would be willing to anchor filaments of Truth from the Universal Matrix around the golden skull, setting a six-pointed star grid with the stones.

"As you wish, Beloved Teacher," she replied.

She moved to the center of the circle to rest upon one knee before the skull. Spilling the large sapphires into her left hand, Leah closed her eyes and breathed her intent to the Universe before blowing her power into the stones. Chris saw a blue flame rise up from the stones in the etheric realm, an indication that Leah's soul had chosen the power of the Blue Ray of Love and Wisdom during this Earth walk. Then she began setting the grid around the skull, beginning with the apex of the first equilateral triangle that pointed towards Don Eduardo.

After the first triangle was in place, she set the second, anchoring its apex where she sat in the circle. When all six stones were in place, she connected them with the Universal Matrix, using her intent and the light from her own hands.

As she completed tracing the triangles three times each, her hand reached up, securing the star in the Universal Matrix. Chris observed the star jumping above and below the floor to form a three-dimensional star tetrahedron, the Merkaba. The geometry was fully anchored in the Matrix of light, holding the intent of Truth as it expanded to hold everyone in the room within its geometric space.

Sitting down at her place again, Leah tucked the beaded pouch inside her shirt and raised her eyes to find Chris watching her. She felt the warm tingle within her again as she received his love, closing her eyes for a few seconds to acknowledge it.

Don Eduardo then asked Chris to produce the six rubies of the Ruby Order. Chris pulled his own pouch from around his neck, much to the women's amazement. "Well, why wouldn't there be six rubies?" Leah thought to herself with amusement.

Chris was asked to set his six-pointed star grid around the circumference of the room, activating it to its three-dimensional Merkaba with the intent of wisdom and protection. When he set his intent, Leah saw a flame of deep blue light activate the rubies. She was surprised that Chris was not traveling on the Violet Ray of Ceremony and Magic, the Ray of the Amethystine Order of the Great Solar Brotherhood.

The ruby Merkaba shot filaments of light into the Universal Matrix at the same time it connected with the points of the sapphire star tetrahedron sending them into opposite rotations. Energetically, the room became filled with dense, humid air. Then, just as suddenly, a wind moved around them and up through the thatched roof taking all of that air with it. The grid lines were luminous with the sparkling blue light. Leah and Chris' efforts offered a backdrop of co-creation for the evening's work.

His eyes twinkling with delight, Don Eduardo seemed pleased with the magical light show. "I believe we are ready to begin," he announced. Everyone settled their bodies into their places ready to absorb the oral tradition of the tribe while the *ylloq'e* reached into his baby alpaca-skin bag to being chewing the coca.

"I have been fortunate," he began, "to know many of you *waykis* who have been able to help me put these legends into a context you will understand. In our tradition, you would not hear me name continents or places, as you know them. Even the oceans are referenced in ways that identify their quality and power, rather than a name. Naming is the gift of your culture. Our people have difficulty placing things in time for we know time is not linear. It is the same with space - direction. That is why I am so fortunate to discuss these legends with those of your people who are knowledgeable of such things. In this way I have come to insert the names of places and spaces that will have meaning for you. *Claro?*" he asked.

Everyone was right with him. "I also refer to the experience of the ancestors as my experience, because we have the mind of a tribe. I am my ancestors.

"People have speculated about the origins of our tribe," he continued. "You will understand their confusion as this very complicated story unfolds. We came from the stars, a long, long time ago, maybe one hundred thousand years ago. We do not know exactly. In Quechua, the name of our star is *Chaska* – the Eye of God. In fact, we came first into this solar system to another planet that we also call *Chaska*. It was from this planet, the one you call Venus, that we arrived on *Pachamama*. In the traditions of our astronomers, Venus is a star and *Pachamama* is also. If we could see these two planets from the distance of our original *Chaska*, the star you call Sirius, they would appear as stars.

"We came from Venus to a great land in what you call the Pacific Ocean. On Venus we lived in the Fourth Dimension and still maintain a civilization there that is now moving into Fifth Dimension. The focal point of the Mission on Sirius is in the Sixth Dimension.

"You can see that our Mission on Venus was similar to that of *Pachamama*, to help the planet ascend. We do this because each step in ascension takes us closer to Union with the greater Truth or God - as you prefer. Our Mission, and that of most of the star systems in the Universe, is to heal separation and move towards Union with Creation.

"In our villages, we have always lived with that intent, both personally and collectively. When our starseeding came to this land in the ocean, we landed in starships and continued to live in the Fourth Dimension. We developed a great civilization dedicated to ascension. It was never our intent to live in the *Kaypacha* – this present Third-Dimensional reality. That came much later.

"The continent in the Pacific was called Mu, which, in the ancient language, means the Motherland. You would call it a Paradise or, more appropriately, a Golden

Culture. We lived to be very old - several hundred years old - remaining vital young men or women. We had a science that was used only to enhance the Mission in the name of the greater Truth. Our priests were initiates of the higher dimensions and greater mysteries who used their wisdom to assist the government of Mu, her people and all living things. They were in communication with the High Council of *Chaska* at all times, meaning that the Mission was carried out through the priests.

"These priests were impeccable. They did not in any way live for themselves, but as servants of the Mission. We had a king and queen who lived in service to the people. Conflicts were few and easily resolved, because the purpose of our lives was never forgotten. If your priests today were communicating with the stars and serving their people, no one would be separated from their purpose," he added, waving a coca leaf at all of them.

"On Mu, we lived in peace and spent our time working with the vibrations of the plant beings, the stone beings and the animal beings to activate a higher vibration in all of them. This would have taken eons to accomplish which is not necessarily a long time, but the Siriun High Council predicted that we would not accomplish our purpose in time to coincide with the galactic timetable of *Pachamama's* ascension.

"It was determined that *Pachamama* could not be lifted out of her Third-Dimension frequency because of the negativity existing on her. My people in Mu were living in paradise, but around this planet there were many starseeded cultures that had fallen into great negativity. Even much of the animal life had taken on this negativity. They were living in the Third Dimension with no memory of who they were or where they had originated.

"Even though our powers were great, it was too much to expect us to heal this ugliness. In our tradition, the *Kaypacha* (Third Dimension) was created to give us the experience of density as a way to grow closer to the Greater Truth. The risk is to become a slave to the density for the gratification of the desire body. The High Council informed our priests that there would be a great change on *Pachamama,* because she needed to shake the density off her skin to be able to walk into her future. She would convulse as many times as would be necessary to accomplish her purpose. On Mu there was never any question that *Pachamama* was a living being with consciousness. That is how she was treated.

"Our priests were informed well in advance of the impending changes on *Pachamama.* We built underground cities in safe places to withstand her shaking and flooding. We also sent colonies of people to live high in the mountains that you call Tibet in the Himalayas, taking with them the records of our civilization and our Mission. We were told that certain parts of the Motherland would not be affected initially, and so our people were moved to those parts of the land. Records, temple stones and sacred items were moved as well.

"We have calculated the time of the first disaster to be around thirty thousand years ago. The Motherland split up into pieces because some of the land fell away and the ocean rose over much of the rest of the land. The largest island was renamed Lemuria, as a daughter of the Motherland - Mu.

"After this first great cataclysm, we resumed our work with the frequency of all living beings. It was easier than it had been, but still difficult to project when we might expect success.

"During this time, a fleet of flying ships visited my people. I believe you would call them aircraft or spaceships. We greeted a group of gigantic men and women, almost four meters in height. They were extremely intelligent masters of light and sound who had come to *Pachamama* from *Chaska* many eons before we had arrived there. They too were associated with Venus but, unlike our race, were blonde and blue-eyed giants living in the higher dimensions. You all know that the soul does not know color, but that races exist to focus different consciousness and purpose on *Pachamama*.

"Their purpose was different from our own, for they had established a great civilization in what is now the Amazon jungle. In the region of the upper Madre de Dios River, their hidden cities still exist. Some say that there is still a population of extraordinarily beautiful people there. However, their purpose was to use light and sound to leave a legacy of wonder in stone, to walk *Pachamama* preaching brotherly love and to gift civilization to many groups upon *Pachamama*.

"They were the Plumed Serpents, *Quetzalcoatl, Pachacuti,* and those of many legends throughout the Americas. Associated with the Dragon or Winged-Serpent Wisdom, through *Chaska,* they were referred to as the Great White Gods. You can imagine the impact of nearly four-meter men and women on my race of people," he laughed. "We soon found that they had superior intelligence and many powers that we did not understand. We came to call them the Elders or Ancient Ones.

"The cataclysm had pushed the land upward, making the former city and the subterranean chambers of the mysteries of the Elder Race inaccessible. Soon the jungle grew over it until it was completely *salk'a* (undomesticated). This place is known as Paititi today and there are tribes in the jungle, who remember, as we do, these blonde giants.

"These noble people had wandered *Pachamama,* but had never deliberately colonized. Our people had colonized extensively to support our Mission and to protect the treasures of wisdom brought with us from the stars and developed further in the Motherland. We welcomed them into Lemuria as a colony of Superhumans. Our races were different and our soul Missions as well, but we had this connection with *Chaska* that made us as brothers and sisters. Naturally, our work with frequency accelerated greatly.

"In their air ships, the Elders had brought treasures from Paititi. One of these treasures was a gigantic golden disc of the Sun. It is the same disc that hung in the *Qorikancha* in Cusco during most of the Inca Empire.

"It was more than a golden disc– much more. The Disc of the Sun acted as a portal to *Chaska* (Sirius) and other star systems. It was made of transmuted gold. An entire temple filled with people could be transported to the High Council.

"Even more astounding was a flaming crystal called the Maxin Flame that contained the Seven Rays in one flame - the Permanent Ray. It recreated the Light of Creation. They brought many scrolls of wisdom written in the glyphs of the stars. They created a language from which the Aymara language, a language that still exists around Titicaca Lake, was derived. This mysterious language could translate any language into another language. I am told by the *waykis* that the ancient language resembles advanced computer languages, though I have never experienced a computer. However, they also retained the pure language of the star seed written in glyphs on the many scrolls. Of course, they brought their flying ships as well, and continued to send their teachers out around *Pachamama*.

"The Elders' priests and teachers were the Lords of the Seven Rays, who brought with them the sacred Solar Brotherhoods. Their magicians brought this golden skull, which eventually came into the hands of my people. The glyphs on the headband are part of the star language," he added, filling his coca pouch from the mesa before him. Leah shot a glance at Chris to ascertain his knowledge about Don Eduardo's last revelation. He looked just as surprised as she felt.

Don Eduardo continued. "There came a time when these powerful beings completed their Mission. The Elders left their treasures in our competent hands and found a path through the portal of the Disc of the Sun to the Sixth Dimension, ascending as a group.

"Some of their race was not prepared to ascend because they had acquired karmas and Three-Dimensional thought patterns that had not been cleared away. Others made a commitment to serve. These Elders found themselves trapped on *Pachamama,* continuing to teach and protect the wisdom. They were still very advanced men and women. One of these men was Lord Aramu Muru, who stayed behind with his Feminine Aspect, Arama Mara. He became the high priest of the temple on Lemuria and was the guardian of the sacred scrolls, the flame, the skull and the Disc of the Sun.

"In time, other survivors of the cataclysm found their way to our shores. We were bound to take them in by our Codes of Service, but they brought with them lower frequencies than we had experienced. Our healers and magicians worked tirelessly to transform their density, but the magnitude of their fear and hatred eventually penetrated our society.

"Eventually we fell even more into the Third Dimension, with friction between brothers, lack of integrity, and hoarding. Many people entered the darkness in all its forms.

"Our people had known that there would be further upheavals of *Pachamama* which would eventually destroy our land. That did not occur for some time, but, as a precaution, another large colony had been established in the Himalayas in the ancient land now called Tibet. There we kept the wisdom and customs alive for future generations and continued to follow our purpose of raising *Pachamama's* vibration.

"We had also established a large colony on this continent of South America on an inland lake. This sea had formed from the waters of the ocean as the land rose up around them. The colony, on Titicaca Lake, was and still is called Tiwanaku.

"The village was prosperous because the lake was filled with fish from the sea. The climate was similar to the high jungle, and the plants provided good food. We have estimated the establishment of these two large colonies to be seventeen thousand years ago.

"In the colonies, there was marriage between our colonists and the remnant people, many of whom were former colonists from Mu. The need to survive and the mixing of blood caused most of our people to lose sight of their purpose.

"Within the temple cultures of Lemuria, Tiwanaku, Tibet and our small colonies in America, the British Isles, China and India, the magicians held the higher frequencies without fail. Some of the other priests were able to hold a vibration of integrity and Truth also, but most could be seduced by power. The culture was deteriorating.

"Some time before any of the ancient starseedings, the High Council of *Chaska* and the Galactic Federation, the governing body of the galaxy, anchored light on *Pachamama* to stabilize her and prepare for her ascension. The Permanent Light Ray was split into its Masculine and Feminine aspects – like the splitting of a Soul into Twin Rays. The Masculine Aspect was anchored in Tibet. The Feminine Aspect was anchored at Titicaca Lake. That is why we colonized in those places. In each place the magician-priests participated as guardians of each aspect of the Flame of Creation.

"Lord Muru was such a magician. The Elders had brought the Brotherhood of the Sun and its many other brotherhoods to Lemuria to safe-keep the mysteries. Lord Muru became head of the Brotherhood of the Seven Rays, the South American branch of the Amethystine Order and the Order of the Ruby near the end of Lemuria. He was the one who had been left behind when the Ancient Ones disappeared, but one who very quickly ascended into higher frequencies when his position gave him access to the mysteries.

"During the last days of Lemuria, Lord Muru, Lady Mara, and those brothers and sisters of integrity who followed them packed the sacred scrolls, the Maxin Flame, the Disc of the Sun and other sacred stones and golden pieces like our skull into one of the Elders' ships. All of them flew to a part of Lemuria that would remain after the final cataclysm. This place is now the home of our *Wayki* Chris - Australia," he said lightly grasping Chris' shoulder. "Not surprising, is it?" he asked with a laugh.

"Not surprising at all," Leah affirmed for the group with a big smile. Everyone in the circle had some ancient Lemurian land connection, either by birth, choice or calling.

"Am I boring you?" Don Eduardo asked the group, looking very serious.

Nearly everyone contributed to a communal "Are you kidding?" response.

"All right, I will go on. I warned you that this was a complicated story," he said with a wink. "My many *waykis* helped us determine that the final upheaval of *Pachamama* occurred around twelve thousand years ago. Lemuria disappeared, except for some remaining scattered islands and Australia - Oceana. *Wayki* Brian lives on one of these islands and *Wayki* Chris on the great remaining landmass of Mu. What about *Wayki* Susmo?" He asked, not wanting to ignore the third brother.

"*Wayki* Susmo decided to be born in the land of the Incas. Who are the Incas? They are my ancestors. I wanted you to know that I have not forgotten about my original purpose with this story." Again the group loved his humor.

"First we have to learn about the fate of Lord Muru and Lady Mara. They and their followers flew their ship to Tiwanaku after the deluge subsided. Here they found that something very interesting had happened to our colonists.

"Several thousand years before the arrival of Lord Muru, a man of tall stature, though not four meters, came to the village. He was a white man, with blue eyes, blonde hair and a great, fuzzy beard. He was thought to be a God, for the remnant people held this concept of God from the Elder Race who had come to the planet in their ships at the beginning of time. This man had come from across the sea, which you call the Atlantic Ocean, stopping first in a place called Atlantis. His name was Mak-Ma and he was a master of building with stone using the power of light and sound.

"Imagine the reaction of Lord Muru, who was also such a Master. Mak-Ma guided the initial building of the city of Tiwanaku, including the Great Pyramid, which he modeled after those he had seen in Atlantis. He moved monolithic stones using only sound and light.

"It was a beautiful city, dedicated to the Sun, but it had suffered during the final cataclysm when the altiplano was formed and Titicaca Lake was elevated to its present height. After that upheaval, the mountains became calm but the city of Tiwanaku, as you can now see, was no longer on the shore of the lake.

"When Lord Muru arrived at the lake, he found small villages scattered on her shores. The villagers were profoundly moved by the appearance of Lord Muru because their oral tradition spoke of Mak-Ma and the Elder Race. They took him to Tiwanaku, which he had observed from the air, to speak with their priests.

"It was there that he heard the stories of Mak-Ma and the culture he had brought to the people. Tiwanaku had once been the thriving center of a great Sun-culture civilization. It continued to be a center for spiritual teaching and ceremony. Lord Muru established a temple and monastery on the Island of the Sun in Titicaca Lake and Lady Mara established a temple for her women on the Island of the Moon.

"Celebrations were held on the Sun Island, where Lord Muru had placed the golden Disc of the Sun and the crystal of the Maxin Flame in a temple built using light and sound. The Elder Race did not die as we do. Aramu Muru came from Paititi to Lemuria with the original immigration, and he did not leave the planet until recently.

"After Lord Muru's temple was established, he used the Disc of the Sun to communicate with the High Council on *Chaska* asking them about Mak-Ma. They told him that another starseeding had come to *Pachamama* from Sirius after his Elder Race had immigrated to Lemuria.

"This starseeding came to the Earth to begin another initiative of ascension similar to that of Mu. All of these efforts had originated on *Chaska*. There were other star systems seeding *Pachamama* as well, but for different reasons.

"Mak-Ma was the son of the two starseeds, Aman-Ra and his sister-bride, Mir-An-Da – Osiris and Isis. He had come across the ocean from a fertile land that became a desert after the last deluge. You call this land Egypt. The sacred place of the Feminine Aspect of the Permanent Ray had now been touched by two starseedings of *Chaska* and the Elder Race. Most of you are descendants in blood of that Egyptian starseeding.

"Many of the women in this room are part of a Sisterhood of the Sun. This was not a racial lineage, but a soul lineage of the Feminine Spirit that moved through many of the starseeded descendants. Lady Mara was a high priestess of this Sisterhood, as was Mir-An-Da. Later in our tradition, many of the Inca priestesses were part of this Sisterhood. Like the Brotherhood, it moves on the soul level, to the places where the Mission is evolving.

"But, to return to my story, Mak-Ma did not stay at Titicaca Lake forever, since he was called home to report on the findings of his journey. Yet something quite curious happened right after Lord Muru settled at Titicaca Lake with his treasures of antiquity. Two Beings manifested themselves from the waters of the lake. The people called them *Wiracocha* (Foam of the Sea) and *Mamacocha* (Mother of the Sea), thinking them to be the Shining Ones, the Elder Race, returned.

"Like the missionaries of the Elders and Aramu Muru, *Wiracocha* and his sister-bride *Mamacocha* were tall, blonde, blue-eyed and he was bearded. The Elder teachers like *Quetzalcoatl* had said they would return to the people, and my people believed it was in the form of these two star beings. In fact, they had never completely left, for Lord Muru and Lady Mara lived among them and welcomed the new *Akhus, Wiracocha* and *Mamacocha,* as Elder souls incarnate in yet another race.

"When the new starseed greeted Lord Muru and Lady Mara, they were received as brother and sister. Lord Muru knew of their coming from the High Council. *Wiracocha* and *Mamacocha* were part of a royal lineage to be established in the Andes for the future Incas. Their kingly codes were of service to the people, identical to the Egyptian starseed.

"*Wiracocha* was not a magician. He was a king. When this king and queen arrived at Titicaca Lake, Lady Mara was free to merge herself with Lord Muru, her Twin Ray, because *Mamacocha* was there to carry on the sisterhood.

"This was the first stage of liberation for the two Elders. When this occurred, Lord Muru's power and integrity increased dramatically.

"*Wiracocha* and *Mamacocha* left a legacy of government, economics, and culture, freeing Lord Muru to guide the building of great cities and temples using light and sound. Lord Muru and *Wiracocha* established a priesthood that would, one day, guard the mysteries after their departure from the planet. With the marriage of their children, the original starseed of the *Wiracochas* continued for some time after the royal couple disappeared on the waters of Titicaca Lake. However, eventually it was necessary to merge their blood to form the Inca race, bringing a unique genetics into being.

"That is where my people re-enter the story. We were people of the original Motherland - Mu, who had originally immigrated to Tibet. We journeyed to South America from across the sea several thousand years after Lord Muru had come to Titicaca Lake in his airship. Lord Muru came to our mountains in his ship to retrieve certain of our scrolls and sacred objects that were from the stars.

"With him flew the brothers of the Order of the Red Hand. They were one of the original Solar Brotherhoods. This order was guardian to those sacred records of the stars. They selected certain young people to accompany them back to Titicaca Lake. That is how the blood of Mu and the energies of the Masculine Aspect of the Permanent Ray were merged with the blood of the lineage of *Wiracocha* and *Mamacocha*. From the mixing of our blood into the royal lineage, the pre-Inca people were born.

"This is a good time to mention that the Elder Race never mixed their blood with any other race. Our tradition states that they were not of exactly the same species and their methods of reproduction were far more advanced than ours. Yet, Lord Muru oversaw the mixing of blood that would protect the sacred mysteries into the future.

"Tomorrow evening, I will conclude the telling of our history with the story of the Incas and our tribal legends and prophecies. I hope that it is clear to all of you that the Mission is ancient upon *Pachamama*.

"The Elder Race, who were called True Men, perhaps a superior genetic form of man, came to *Pachamama* in ancient times, when she was first inhabitable. I am told that was about a billion years ago. It was at that dawn of *Pachamama's* dance with humans that the Order of the Ruby came into being here. At that time it was already a very old Order in this galaxy.

"The Sisterhood of the Sun came also within the Feminine Aspect of the Lord of the Ruby, the title of the high magician of the Order on *Pachamama*. In the times of my story, she was Arama Mara, the Twin Ray of Aramu Muru, who passed her legacy to *Mamacocha*. The Sisterhood was very strong in ancient Egypt as well, where another lineage was seeded to safeguard the activation of ascension on Pachamama.

"The Elder Race left *Pachamama* when their racial Mission was complete. However, the souls who lived in the bodies of that race as the magicians and the high priestesses of the Sun and many of the other ancient orders have continued to incarnate through the Sisterhood and Brotherhood to complete a Mission far older than the Elder Race. That Mission is Union with the greater Truth and Light - what you call God. It is the Mission of *Chaska.*

"*Listo,* that is all," he concluded, abruptly.

There was a holy silence in the stone room. All eyes came to focus on the golden skull, which seemed to be radiating a violet light. Suddenly Leah remembered the Merkabas in which they were spinning and reentered the light filaments of their geometry. The ruby eyes of the skull, which had been staring at her for two evenings in a row, suddenly came alive and pierced her heart with a laser-like beam of ruby light.

Chris watched what was happening on the inner plane from across the room. Part of him wanted to rescue her, from what seemed an invasive energy, and another part of him was fascinated that she, conscious of what was happening, seemed to know what to do with the light.

She shut her eyes and wove the light into her luminous body. When the skull was finished transmitting, she opened her eyes and took a deep breath. She looked at Don Eduardo, who nodded his head in approval. He then asked Chris to deactivate the ruby grid, bringing the opposing Merkaba spins to a stop. Then Leah removed the sapphire grid, dropping the stones back into her beaded pouch. The stones felt as hot as coals against her skin as she tucked them inside her layers of fleece.

"There will be no need for a hot pack tonight," she thought.

After Don Eduardo wrapped the skull in its woven bundle, Leah thanked him, as spokeswoman for the group, for such a clear and profound speaking of the greatly modernized oral tradition.

Don Eduardo slapped his knees again. "My ancestors would not understand a word of it," he laughed, "but they would trust my version because they know I have not deserted the Mission."

Leah also thanked Susmo and Sonia for bringing the story into English from the Quechua in a way that did not diminish its elegance. As she was leaving the community hut, her eyes turned toward the starry heavens, Brian threw his arm around her and started walking her through the village. He was still energized from the cleansing and anxious to talk to her about something.

"What is on your mind, Brian?" she asked.

"This day seems like an eternity," he commented.

"Well, we just covered a billion years or so of guarded history in two hours," she laughed. "I could see how you could feel that way."

"That was truly incredible. However, for me, many things that happened to me earlier today, with Chris and Susmo, have caused me to look at my past, Leah."

"No wonder you looked so pale at dinner, Brian," she replied.

"There was more, but I am wondering if you could spend some time with me tomorrow. I know that you help your women identify things in their past that are still blocking them. I need some help in that department."

"What's this about?" she asked.

"Commitment, I guess."

"Don't guess, Brian. You have to be absolutely sure about these things. There isn't time for six sessions of therapy here, and, anyway, that is not my calling."

"Right," he muttered staring at his feet. A moment later, he looked into Leah's eyes. "Okay, the problem is commitment – commitment to life at its most fundamental level."

"I have known you a long time, Brian. I won't pretend that I haven't thought about the patterns you have created. If I can help, I would be happy to serve. As you are falling asleep tonight, why don't you ask for guidance about it and we will talk after lunch."

"Thank you, Leah. I have to rid myself of fear if I am to complete this journey."

"Or die in the process, I imagine?" she mused.

"According to Chris, I've been dead my whole life," he answered, "and the fear is keeping me from living. He thinks it is tied into commitment."

"That could be true for most of us, Brian. How do you feel about that, personally?" she asked gently.

"I think he might be right."

"Don't think about it, Brian, how do you *feel* about being described as dead?" she insisted.

"I stopped feeling when my father died, Leah."

"How old were you?"

"I was five. He was the age I am right now."

"That explains a lot. It is about time you started living, My Friend. Think about your father in the morning, the circumstances of his death, your mother's feelings and reactions with you – all of that. Think about every woman you have ever loved and tried to live with – all of it. Okay?"

"Okay. I will meet you after lunch," he said with resolve. "Sweet dreams, Leah," Brian added, kissing her on the cheek.

"Good night, Brian."

Leah walked to the dining hut to fill her hot water bottle for the night. Lobo and his young friends had slipped out of the community circle quickly to be there for those wanting water or hot tea.

Like Brian, Leah felt it had been a very long day, though it was only nine o'clock. She thanked the young men and started walking towards her tent. Writing a few notes about the day and the evening's teaching seemed an important way to pull the filaments of her experiences together. Something very strange had happened with the weavers, almost too strange to describe in writing. She wanted to talk to Chris about it when she saw him the next morning.

Suddenly, he appeared alongside her on the path to her tent. "My God, where did you come from?" She cried, holding her hand to her heart.

"Didn't mean to scare you, Mate. I thought I heard you call my name and was surprised to see you passing right by me. You had a question of some kind. What was it?"

"As a matter of fact, I did," she replied guardedly then she laughed. "I am sorry, Chris. I am tuned into people all the time, I just don't get the two-way version very often."

"It's nice for me too, Leah," he said, slipping his arm around her shoulders. "Now, what is your question?"

"I haven't thought how to put this into words, so here are the pieces. After circle this morning I journeyed off to find Master Mukda. In the dream last night I felt a presence, something very familiar to me in that monastery. It was not Master Mukda, but something invisible.

"Connecting with him again was not difficult. He led me to a small temple where I was asked to contemplate the power of the White Heart. When I had completed the meditation, I was free to go. Many insights came to me in that meditation, but the interesting part of the journey was my return.

"Instead of retracing my path to the temple, I mistakenly turned the other way and soon found myself in hallways quite familiar to me. I came to the doors of a teaching hall where an unconscious part of me has spent most every night of my life. Mind you, I am 'seeing' it all for the first time, though I know an aspect of self belonged there.

"I did not enter the hall because I had not been invited, nor had I deliberately requested to be there. That wasn't my purpose, anyway. Willing myself back to my body, I ended the journey abruptly.

"So, this place where I met you last night is not a monastery at all, but the ashram of Lord Sananda, the ascended Jesus. It exists in higher dimensions, and I have just become visually aware of it. How can I thank you, Chris," she said, pausing to catch her breath.

"No trouble at all, Leah," he replied. "Go on with your story."

"Thank you, Chris. This is so incredible. Ordinarily I have no one to talk to about these things," she continued, rubbing her hands to warm them. He took them in his hands while she finished her story.

"The next part of my remarkable day was with the weavers and my women. As they were explaining how they wove their cosmology into their *tejidos,* I kept falling into a trance. I was being pulled out of my body without consciously willing it, which is why Don Eduardo had to bring me back into my body. It was a very strange experience, but my guidance told me it was Divine Will – all part of the plan. Doña Felicia saw what was happening to me and moved a pile of weavings next to me to help me relax my body.

"The next thing I know, I am flying - flying high above the mountains. Then I felt you calling me and I was suddenly standing in front of Susmo, confronting him with all of his womanizing, egotistical behavior – and loving him so much as that was happening. Into my awareness came all of his pathology. The image that came to my consciousness was that I was shoveling manure. Throw it here. Throw it there. Let *Pachamama* eat it, but get it out of him.

"This went on for a long time, until he felt pretty clean. Then I saw his filaments shifting and changing, reassembling themselves into a reality of higher frequency. He looked pretty good, and I got to fly off again.

"I just know you are going to put this all together for me, so let me finish before you comment," she said, feeling his desire to speak his part of the experience. He acquiesced and she continued. "Well, I am flying around feeling like I am the queen of the sky, when I hear this sound. It gives me chills to think about it right now. It was primitive but strange beyond words.

"Startled, I lost the beat of my wings and fell from the sky. Susmo was there again when I landed – albeit more like a chicken than the queen of the sky, I can tell you. I felt very connected to him and the frequency of the focus that he was holding with his luminous body, so I held it with him. That is all I remember.

"No one seemed to care that I had fallen into this deep trance sleep with the weavers. Doña Felicia helped me up when I became conscious of my surroundings again, and the afternoon progressed as planned. Tonight at dinner Susmo was not his usual self, causing me to study him with my second attention. Unbeknownst to me, this attention was not in my body, so I was able to see the spirit of his father standing behind him. He wanted me to communicate something to Susmo, which I did, and then he disappeared. The end," she said with a big sigh and a smile.

"Sounds like an ordinary day to me," Chris laughed. "I am glad that you went to the ashram and realized where we were last night. There is much work to do there with the Master Teachers and with Lord Sananda. Certain aspects of the Mission are being directed from that center, and it is important that you remember your experiences there. Asking to be there is one thing, remembering the experience is quite another. That's wonderful, Leah.

"The other experiences, all relating to Susmo, were part of the Mission. Susmo has many things to release before he can realize himself and come into the full power of his White Heart. He has had incredible *munay* coupled with a messed-up desire body. It has made for a lot of confusion.

"I say this to you because I know I am not telling you anything of which you are not fully aware. The Order requires that every filament of our luminous field be of the frequency of the White Heart. That would be Christ Consciousness frequency.

"Your love for Susmo and desire to serve him motivated your double, under the direction of your Christed Self – your own White Heart, to journey with us as a condor – a fancy piece of shape shifting, by the way. That required you to coalesce a whole new collection of cosmic filaments -that of the condor's luminous field - and shift your consciousness to them. Why? Because none of us - not you, not me, not Don Eduardo, nor Brian, could confront him with his stuff. The condor could do it. His father could do it. In truth, Susmo's Higher Self orchestrated all of it to assist him in his self-realization."

"I understand what you are saying. I also know that there is a teaching in this for me, Chris. Can you help me with it?" She asked as they came to stand facing each other in front of her tent. "Energy is shifting too quickly here for me to want to make the mental effort with it."

"It's the same lesson as the ashram, Leah," he suggested.

"Seeing?" she asked.

"Exactly - expanding consciousness. Train yourself to remember every detail of the journeys, the dreams, the projections of consciousness. The condor experience was very complicated but in the future you will be able to remember everything that has happened, not just your role in it - and direct it. Your consciousness is all over the place – just like the rest of us, and you have no idea what you are doing out there."

"You're suggesting that I am carrying light codes for pretty advanced perception, aren't you?" she asked.

"If you only knew what you were carrying, Leah," he breathed, grasping her shoulders. "Right now, your codes are being activated fully. When the gifts become of service to the world is, as you know, dependent on the timing of your Mission.

Your experiences indicate that this expanded perception is something you can work with now."

"Chris, Brian told me that you were in his dream last night too, in the same ashram. Do you remember the details of both dreams?"

"Technically, they are not dreams. If you were not awakening this perceptive gift, you would not have remembered the dream. Previously you have not held a vision of Lord Sananda's ashram, even though you hang out there nightly. Now that you have connected with that reality, the vision will be with you. So these are realities being lived by aspects of us. My training is to be aware of what my total consciousness is doing at all times. The Dreaming Paths are like the highways of consciousness, Leah. The training is to be able to drive on more than one highway at once."

"So in other words, you remember being in both of our dreams," she said.

"I do. I was also traveling a Dreaming Path with the puma, among others. It's just expanded consciousness, Leah. In truth, we have the ability to be aware of all things in the Universe. This is minimal consciousness for one with your capabilities," he said tapping her heart.

"Have you no memory of being in my dreams?" he asked.

"When have I been in your dreams?" she asked with surprise. "Obviously, I have no memory of it. Have I?"

"You have been in my dreams for most of my life. I would guess from the time you were born."

"Are you kidding me?" she asked in disbelief. "Why weren't you in mine?"

"I was. You didn't remember," he said smiling. "I'm telling you this is really important."

"Is that how you knew I was in Perth?"

"It is. I knew your vibration from the Dreaming Paths, and I could feel your presence in the physical."

"Chris, I wish I had remembered. I wish I had known you all that time," she replied.

"All things are as they should be," he laughed. "You would not have liked me, Leah. In this reality I was as much a scoundrel as Susmo. In the Dreamscape I lived my higher purpose."

"How lucky for us all that they seemed to have come to a harmonious agreement," she smiled.

"Not without a struggle, Leah. Can I share with you that I survived that Dark Night of the Soul because you filled my dreaming world?"

A few big tears sprang from Leah's eyes. "I am in awe of the Mission, Chris, and grateful to be of service."

Chris took her in his arms and within his White Heart. She felt universal love for him in that moment, a true connection to God.

"What about the sound, Chris?" she whispered.

"You were connected to my cosmic body, Leah. We were in an unacceptable situation. It could not be resolved in this dimension so I surrendered to Divine will and the sound came forth to discharge negative energies."

"It felt ancient to me, invoking a primal reaction that broke my flight. Were you familiar with the sound?"

"Absolutely," he said, holding her at arm's length to look into her eyes. "It is part of an ancient language that speaks from the heart. As you guessed, it is not a language of words, but sounds that invoke visions. It is the first language. Learning this language was part of my training. Few people know it."

"I've heard it before."

"Of course you have. Would you like to experience it again?"

"Not so loud this time, okay?" she whispered conspiratorially while glancing around at the peaceful campsite.

He laughed. "You will not even hear it, Leah," he said, pulling away from her. As he activated his cosmic body, Leah was bathed in his expanded luminous field. He never uttered a sound, but the frequency he projected entered her field as a vision. She saw a flaming heart open wide to receive her. Within the heart she felt protected, supported, beautiful in every way. She was at peace.

Her body tingled from head to toe and out into her field. Before her eyes, Lord Sananda appeared to her as a radiant being in golden robes. His soft blue eyes became a source of nourishment for her soul. She felt *unconditional love.*

When Chris returned to his previous state, he saw her in expanded awareness. She was radiant and tranquil. The ruby light she had taken in from the golden skull pulsated in her field. "You have heard?" he asked.

"I have heard. Thank you, Chris. I do know this language."

"Anything else on your mind?" he asked, leaning towards her slightly.

"Maybe one more question, if you don't mind," she said shyly raising a gloved finger.

"If you're not uncomfortable, I can stay out here all night with you, Leah."

"I'm getting a little cold, so this will be it."

"What is it?"

"When the ruby light filled my heart tonight I felt like it should have been given to you. Have you already received it?"

"Maybe you were connecting to the ruby energy in my field. I had a similar experience at Ayer's Rock. Seeing it enter you tonight helped me understand what happened to me. It was lovely to watch, and it leads me to believe that a second golden skull might exist within Ayer's Rock. Legends say that the Lemurians left information encoded in a great crystal within the rock – information explaining the true history of the Earth."

"Some of which we just heard tonight," she added.

"No doubt Lord Muru designated Ayer's Rock as the keeper of those sacred mysteries. I happen to believe that the Incas were given as much as they were capable of holding and retelling. There are many more revelations hidden around the Earth."

"Beneath the Sphinx, perhaps?" Leah offered.

"Absolutely, but in other places as well."

"To be revealed in accordance with the Divine Plan."

"Exactly. Just like the story we heard tonight. I can't believe you don't have questions about that," he exclaimed.

"Many, but I think the women will bring most of them up tomorrow. I'm glad you'll be there to help answer them."

"Wouldn't miss it for the world. What are you doing in the afternoon?"

"Brian wants me to work with him for awhile."

"Good. I'm glad he has engaged you."

"We've been friends for a long time, Chris. I can probably help him get some clarity. Why do you ask?"

"There is a place I would like to show you – maybe an hour's hike. We would have to start by two to get back before dark."

"No problem. Brian loves to get sidetracked, and I love to nail him when he does. We should be finished by two."

"We'll meet outside the community hut then. Would you like some deep-sleeping energy before you turn in?"

"Lovely," she replied. "Throw in some heat, too. I am feeling lazy tonight, and my hot water bottle is turning into an ice cube."

"You're not lazy. It's just been necessary to focus our energies in the higher mind tonight."

Chris took off the glove of his right hand and slipped it behind Leah's neck. She closed her eyes to receive the energy as deeply as possible. When he had finished with the transmission, he pulled back her fleece hat and kissed the top of her head.

"Good night, Love, I will see you on the Dreaming Paths."

"I will try to remember everywhere I have been. Sleep well," she replied.

Chris began to walk away, then turned around after a few strides to look at her again, smiling. "You know, Leah, when a man is trying to kiss you on the Dreaming Paths, and you are receptive to his advances, it is considered bad protocol to allow someone else to distract you."

"Yikes!" she cried, covering her blushing face. Then they started laughing together. "It's all in the timing, Mate," she said, in good Aussie imitation, "and that's your department."

With a charmingly crooked smile, he waved his hat to her as he strode away towards his tent. It would have been easy to take her in his arms right there to satisfy the longing he had had for so many years. However, since his boyhood, she had come to him in Dreamtime as a Goddess, and he would not treat her as anything less.

Rubies and Sapphires

Leah awoke with a start. The Sun was already on her tent, bathing it with light. Holding every detail of the dream in her mind, she fumbled around for her travel clock. There was still time to write before her circle met at nine o'clock. Recording her experience was far more important than breakfast. Layering from the waist up, she sat up in her sleeping then taking up her journal and pen she allowed the words to spill out onto the empty pages.

"The dream began in the garden of Lord Sananda's ashram. I was sitting by a reflecting pool, when Brian came to sit across from me. It was as if he were keeping his appointment with me in the dream. He began telling me the story of his childhood in a way so touching and profound that I realized I was hearing it from his Higher Self. There was no confusion, no blaming, and no pain. Instead he spoke with compassion, forgiveness and clarity.

"Brian had had a deep love for his father. His father had been his best buddy, spending all of his spare time with him. Brian's mother supported their relationship because they had waited such a long time for a boy. Brian's dad was already in his forties when Brian was born.

"Then the illness in his father's heart came. His father passed to the other side very quickly. From his ascended state in the dream, Brian saw the purpose in his father's life and death. He also saw his own emotional trauma, and that of his mother.

"As a boy he felt abandoned, cheated by his father's death. In his own life he refused to let anyone get too close to him. He had learned that loving someone very deeply meant that they would disappear or that his whole world would be destroyed.

"Brian told me that his mother smothered him completely, fearful that something might happen to him. Her grief went unresolved beyond her death at seventy. When she died, Brian felt free for the first time in his life, but he didn't know how to be truly free. He was locked in the old structures that had been and still were his prison.

"He told me he was ready to forgive them both – to be free of his blood forever. He felt the illness in his own heart and wanted to be free of that as well.

"He asked me what he could do. For a split second, I stared into the reflecting pond and saw Master Mukda and Chris, walking along the ashram in an enclosed walkway, similar to a cloister. Suddenly I was there with them, peering through the windows of the ashram where orange-robed monks were holding strange yoga postures.

"A beautiful man came towards us, guarded by four men as if he walked in a square of men. His light was so bright I could not see the faces of his guardians, but his face was magnificent. He was a radiant being who held the softest presence I have ever experienced in a man. His eyes were dark but luminous, and his hair long, wavy and dark brown. His golden robes radiated peace and love.

"I felt such a longing when I saw him – a deep aching inside – that I stood still, expanding my heart to capture the moment. He smiled at me and I went into bliss. After he passed, I ran to Master Mukda's side and demanded to know whom we had seen. Master Mukda looked at Chris, who shook his head.

"Where did you see someone, My Child?" he asked. I turned around to show them, and saw myself sitting with Brian at the pool. Suddenly I was back with Brian at the pool, feeling very bewildered.

"Brian asked me if I was all right. I passed the experience off to him as a daydream then focused myself on his situation. He would need to cut the cords with both of his parents, for even death had not given him his freedom.

"Core beliefs that he had about losing those he loved could be changed to beliefs about risking his heart to find true love and happiness. Core beliefs about fear of inherited illness could be changed to beliefs in his Divine perfection. That would best be accompanied by energetic healing of the genetics. Core beliefs about needing to fulfill his mother's expectations had to be changed to surrendering to his own soul's purpose. Changing these beliefs would change his reality to one better able to serve him and his Mission.

"He thanked me, then walked off towards the ashram to meet one of the teachers there. I looked in the reflecting pool again, and saw Chris waiting for me in the Hall of Mirrors. I was there instantly and we practiced fencing with the light again. Delighting in knocking me down, he showed his playful warrior side to me.

"When we had finished our practice, I asked him about the man I had seen with him. I was told again that there was no man when we were walking. "Is there another man?" he asked, stilling playing with me. I stood there completely confused.

"Chris came to me, lifted my chin, and kissed me very deeply. It was another experience of bliss as our White Hearts expanded to hold each other. He walked away from me backwards, holding his eyes on me as his image faded. I heard his voice tell me that my morning tea was turning into ice."

Leah dropped the pen and journal as she fell back into her sleeping bag.

"Unbelievable," she thought. There were clearly three Dreamscapes in the principal dream, all of them unrelated, or so it would appear.

There was Master Mukda and Chris in the cloister of the ashram, the Holy Man, and the fencing with Chris at the end. Two of those Dreamscapes were accessed through her meeting with Brian at the well, which was, presumably, the principal dream. The Holy Man with his guardians may have been a vision, or a fourth Dreamscape accessed through the Dreamscape with Master Mukda.

Perhaps the most unnerving part was turning around and seeing herself at the well again.

"Is it possible that I have experienced four different aspects of myself living out their own realities?" she asked herself. "Was any more real than the other? The kiss was real. I felt it, and the bliss, bleeding through to this reality, but what of the many falls while fencing? My body feels none of the bruises. Perhaps the content is not important, but merely the fact that I have remembered all of the dreams in the dream. Or have I? And who was that Holy Man?" she wrote.

Leah finished dressing, figuring she would ask Chris about the dreams when they hiked that afternoon. Chris mattered to her. She had had no one to engage in this reality at this level of consciousness, and she was grateful for the companionship. She recognized that her strength was the use of Truth to awaken others, in keeping with the Sapphire Ray. At the same time, she saw Chris as the magician who expands consciousness experientially. He challenged her to be more than her calling – to move outside this reality altogether, where the Mission became cosmic.

She did not need to be in this reality to experience the kiss. In fact, in this reality, the experience would have been totally different, colored by the nature of the Earth walk. In the dream, his passion was clear to her, as was his integrity and the depth of his love. He showed a reverence for her that she did not understand, though it meant a great deal to her.

Unzipping the tent to put on her boots, Leah found a metal teacup sitting in front of her door. A ring of ice clung to the edge of a full cup of tea, reflecting the rays of the Sun. She laughed out loud. "Well, ain't life just a gosh darned mystery!" she exclaimed to the mountains, while standing up in her boots to tie them.

Leah entered the dining hall at nine o'clock to find her women already in circle and Chris speaking with Brian and Susmo near the fire. The cooks had saved a few pieces of *pan* for her, which she spread with guacamole and topped with chunks of goat cheese. Taking a cup of hot tea with her, she went to join the women, who had already finished eating.

"We were about to check your tent, Leah," Bridget said, concerned. "It's not like you to be the last one up."

"Thank you, Beloveds. The dreaming has been intense. How have all of you been sleeping?" she asked, directing their inquiring energy back at them.

Everyone had something to say about the camping experience, and some of it was quite funny. The women spoke of lighthearted things until Chris finished talking to the men and came to sit next to Leah.

"I am at your service, Leah," he said, softly.

"Wonderful! Who would like to begin the interrogation of this wizard?" she asked with a twinkle in her eye.

Chris laughed while his eyes made a study of the floor. He had known that Leah would test his ego and integrity in this session with the women. He knew it was important to her, so he had agreed to do it.

He also knew that the women were not aware of the energies that Leah had been able to observe around him. However, there was enough feminine energy in the room to cause the fall of an empire. He would have to be careful.

"Tell us how you learned to love and respect women, Chris?" Sonia, boldly asked - but with an enchanting smile.

"How do you know that I do?" Chris replied, a little embarrassed, but not opposed to sparring with women.

"It is obviously the most attractive thing about you," she replied.

"There is a vibration around you that feels safe," Ellia offered, easing Chris' discomfort.

"Okay, okay," he pleaded, raising his hand to the group. "You've found me out." The women laughed as he began to explain.

"I'll try to answer this question. I am blessed that you can perceive something that cost me so much. Before I took up with the Aborigines, I was what I would call a scoundrel. That is to say, I had a monster of a mind, shot off my mouth with useless information, and had no clue how I felt about anything. Thinking I loved women, I was, in fact, a dreadful womanizer.

"I realize now that it was all a performance of the ego. It's not uncommon you know and Aussie blokes have that reputation to uphold," he added with a smile.

"When I found myself in the 'Outback' on a walkabout with the Aborigines, I was forced to leave all that behind to my experience. I found that to survive, you needed to be in touch with your feelings and to be empathic with tribal members. It could cost you your life to be otherwise. I learned about instinct, intuition, tribal mind or telepathy, and respect for each individual.

"To be sure, I didn't just walk into the bush without my mind, but my continual efforts to focus my mind reached a torturous level of frustration. I had to break through that need to think in order to become telepathic.

"I literally lost my mind. In my everyday reality I would have been institutionalized as a psychotic, but the tribe understood. The shamans and the women helped me recreate a multidimensional reality for myself that did not include self-importance.

"I am so grateful to those strong and beautiful people for busting my limitations. In the Polynesian cultures, like the Maori, women are the Dream Weavers. They sit on the earth anchoring the dream while the men journey out to navigate the Dreaming Paths.

"If the women didn't hold the dream, there would be no paths for the men to navigate. If the men failed to navigate the paths, what was the point of the dream? So, I learned a lot about men and women co-creating reality. Neither of us has to go it alone.

"I am just about finished with my tale. However, I have to tell you also that I have known a Goddess in my Dreamtime since I was quite young. She used to come and sit with me when I was sleeping - like a Guardian Angel. During that time on the walkabout, she was my greatest teacher. It was as if she had waited patiently all of those years for me to open myself to my potential. She really showed me the power of the feminine."

"Do you still dream of her?" Carolyn asked.

"I do. She is My Beloved."

Chris glanced at Leah, catching a glimpse of astonishment in her eyes.

Then Natalie, sensing some emotional tension, switched gears. She spoke up, asking both of them to share what they knew of the Elder Race. Chris was relieved to be off the topic of his own life. Leah gave him the nod to go first.

"I admit to being amazed at the oral tradition as Don Eduardo delivered it last night. Many pieces of an old puzzle came together for me. I remembered stories of the Hyperboreans, a race of giants who walked the Earth in ages past. It is where I first heard of Lord Muru as well. The story was about one man's metaphorical journey of Union with his Divine Feminine, his Lady Mara. When I get back home, I'm going to reread it with greater insight.

"I have heard that the faces of Easter Island and Marca Huasi are the handiwork of these giants. There are too many stories of the White Gods to write it off as fantasy. What can Leah tell us?" he concluded, turning towards her.

"I have known them as the Lords of Time and the Plumed Serpents, *Kukulcan, Pachacuti* and *Quetzalcoatl* from the Incan and Mayan Sun cultures," she began. "They conquered time and moved into the higher dimensions.

"In the esoteric literature they are the Kumaras, the Dragon Lords from Venus. Sanat Kumara has been the Oversoul of the Earth for a long time, assisting her ascension from an astounding heart space that envelops the entire planet.

"Lord Sananda, our ascended Jesus, is a Kumara as well. Beloved Mary Magdalen was mistress of the Dragon Wisdom. The Elder Race has left the planet, but aspects of the souls of that great lineage incarnate in human bodies to demonstrate how we might ascend.

"I cannot believe that Lord Muru and Lady Mara were left behind because of karma and density. It seems to me that they stayed behind to leave us a legacy of the Union of the Divine Feminine and Masculine. They were, I believe, in service as Bodhisattvas for the races that followed them."

Liu had something on her mind, so Leah asked her to speak.

"If either of you has an answer to this one, I'd appreciate it," Liu began. "I have retold our story of the Sisterhood many times, Leah. I have written articles about the Sisterhood and the Mission, as I think many of us have, in order to find our sisters. I don't often meet with negativity, but every once in a while someone goes into reaction about White Gods, and the whole Hitler/Master Race thing comes up. It seems hideous to me that they would dream of associating something this spiritual with that evil man, but there are strong feelings out there born out of fear and shame that get in the way of people's ascension.

"This isn't a white ascension going on right now. What do I tell them? I don't want to go into reaction."

Feeling little affinity for Liu's question, Chris gave Leah the high sign to tackle it.

"Let me tell you how I try to move energy for people who have confronted me with their reactions and opinions, Liu," Leah said. "I'm at an immediate disadvantage, with my blonde hair and blue eyes," she added, laughing. "That story, like Don Eduardo's oral tradition, came through me for two reasons. Most importantly, it activated the Mission and helped to locate the awakening women who are part of that Mission. Secondarily it was a healing – for my bloodline and for my soul lineage.

"Don Eduardo's story is a healing for his bloodline, and as that story is retold generation after generation, the blood remains healed. My bloodline hadn't been healed since Jesus resurrected to do it. The soul lineage story accomplishes the same purpose as an oral tradition – to keep the Mission alive.

"My particular blood and soul lineages began with the *Akhus*, the star beings, who were blonde, blue-eyed Caucasians. It was the seeding of the Caucasian race.

"Don Eduardo's story was the seeding of the Asian race, which was also from Sirius. Each race has a consciousness and a race Mission. Perhaps someday, someone will reveal the lineages of the other races. That's the blood.

"The soul lineage has incarnated into every race, on every continent, on our sister planet, Venus, and in a multitude of galaxies. It is timeless, boundless and without malice. The soul is not related to the blood.

"Now, why the Siriun High Council chose to start a new race is a good question," she said. "Why they chose to bring those genetics to Titicaca Lake in the form of *Wiracocha* and *Mamacocha* is obvious. The *Akhu* genetics, soul and blood lineages together, held key codes to the elevation of human consciousness that were needed – apparently to merge with the genetics from Mu, since they had fallen into the Third Dimension.

"The Siriuns could well be responsible for the Elder Race, which was also Caucasian, but a race of Cyclopean/Avian origins in the Universe. Oh, sorry, I forgot to mention that," she laughed. "Yes, Cyclops with really well developed Third Eyes. Cyclops are always getting a bad rap, but there you have it, the most advanced beings to have ever inhabited the Earth were, in essence – serpent-born white giants with wings - dragons.

"The Siriuns, by the way, have boundless imaginations and a more cosmic command of genetics than our beloved scientists could ever hope to have." The group reacted with amusement - none of them bound to the illusion of the Third Dimension.

"So, look at the bloodline of Jesus," she continued. "The Master was a descendant of the *Akhus* in Egypt who came in service to mankind. He was born into the Bird Tribes, the Winged Ones who guard the heavens. On Earth the Bird Tribes have followed *The Way* as the Essenes and many other orders like the Essenes.

"Jesus was born to them, but not of them. He was born into the Tribe of Abraham but was not of it. Jesus was sent to re-inform our genetics. There's a tremendous genetic weakness in the bloodline of King David where consciousness is concerned. Though tremendous esoteric wisdom has evolved in the culture, they couldn't hold onto the Grail Codes for more than a few generations after the Golden Age in Egypt. I am referring to all of the sons of Abraham for Arabs and Jews began with the same starseed. Fortunately, the blood, re-informed by Jesus, disseminated around the Earth to integrate new etheric genetics for consciousness in most of our matrices.

"Those codes have had a timing, and the alarm clocks are ringing right now, insisting that we all wake up. Light codes at the soul level are activating as well in those who elevate their consciousness to the appropriate frequencies. There is a Divine Plan at work here that doesn't see color, only frequency.

"Jesus was more than an *Akhu*, he was a Kumara, a Soul affiliated with the Elder Race. However, a mere aspect of his complete self incarnated as Jesus, the man. A greater aspect descended into form at the Resurrection. His complete self could not have been comprehended by humanity, and therefore was not brought forth incarnate in our lineage.

"A true *Akhu* is not only a Winged One, but a hybrid of bird and serpent – a dragon. I have talked about the great wars of the heavens and the division between the Dracos or reptilian beings and the 'so called' *Akhus* or Winged Beings. Perhaps they are better referenced as the Bird Tribes.

"That war has been translated into our reality on Earth as well. It is the archetypal struggle of separation – of dark and light – the fallen angels. Remember it has nothing to do with evil. In the Andean tradition, it is the complement of difference, *yananti*; in the Taoist teachings it is the Tao - the yin and the yang - the unmanifested and the manifested. What the Kumaras, or Elders, represent to humans is the healing of this separation, though in actuality they may never have experienced the Fall.

"The Elder Race beat time and moved into realms beyond that division because they were Ancient Ones born of both. Metaphorically, they were the plumed serpents - with the wings and head of a bird and a reptilian body. It's not how they looked in this reality, of course, but it was the essence of their lineage. Maybe they never experienced the space wars, the fall, and the pain of separation at that level.

"Earth was prepared for humans by the Elder Race - benevolent missionaries of the light. They did know separation, though, because their arcane teachings were focused on the healing of our Divine Feminine and Masculine, and uniting with our Divine 'other'. The splitting of one ray or essence into two represented an earlier form of separation from God."

Liu was still writing feverishly as Leah finished speaking. Chris leaned over to Leah and whispered, "Look what happens when you spend your nights in Lord Sananda's ashram, Beloved."

Leah blushed. "Sorry. I've been known to get carried away," she replied.

"Don't be sorry. Be grateful for consciousness, Leah," he said.

Leah begged Chris to add something to the discussion.

"All right, Mates. I would add a word about Hitler - from the magus' perspective. Hitler was an occultist who could actually access pretty high magic. He presents us with a sterling example of misuse of power - black magic - evil. On the other hand, it is beyond our comprehension to know the greater workings of the Divine Plan and what role he might have played in steering humanity towards greater consciousness. Remember how the dark is necessary to bring the light forth? Surely the lives of those who abuse power offer us the most poignant mirrors of our own egocentric petty tyrants." The group laughed heartily.

"I am also fascinated with the distinction between the soul and blood as it relates to Don Eduardo's story last night. It seems the Sisterhood and the Brotherhoods existed amongst the Elder Race. When the Elder Race inhabited the Earth, they were unto themselves, but since then, the incarnating souls of their magi and priestesses have adopted human bodies – which is to say, the human race. I find that interesting, though I don't know exactly what to make of it.

"Perhaps it is the true path of the Bodhisattvas. It puts things into perspective though, to know that we have been working on this Mission for over a billion Earth years. You'd think we would be much smarter than we appear," he concluded, sending everyone into laughter.

"Chris, what of the Order of the Ruby? Can you explain its role on a more galactic scale?" Carolyn put forth.

"That's kind of a tricky question for me, Carolyn. Without revealing that which would jeopardize the Mission, let me say that the Order of the Ruby is an elite warrior force of magi that works under the guidance of the Kumaras and at the direction of the Galactic Federation and the High Council on Sirius. Our weapons are energy and the magical use of that energy."

"Sounds like the Jedi to me," Natalie remarked.

"A little bit," Chris replied with a smile, "but imagine a Jedi who can see through the illusion of light and dark. Rather than fighting against the dark, this Ruby Jedi embodies it and enchants the dark and light into Union. Well, that represents the high side. On the low side, some of us are still trying to embody our Missions."

Chris revealed little of himself as the morning session continued. The women inspired him with their dedication to the spiritual path and the wisdom that they all held in their hearts. The group talked until the cooks came in to prepare lunch, at which time they wandered out along the edge of the village to meditate and enjoy the Sun.

•

While the women's group was meeting with Chris, Susmo was speaking with Don Eduardo. He had known Susmo's father well, prompting Susmo to seek out the *ylloq'e's* counsel. He told the Elder about his encounter with the condor and his father's message through Leah later the previous day. Then he began to describe a dream he had had that night.

"In my dream, my father appeared to me in the garden of my childhood home. At first, he said exactly what he had said through Leah. Then, having my attention, he continued to talk to me. He was very sorry that he imprinted me with his patriarchal values. Even though we appear a matriarchal culture, in our country it is important to prove one's self as a man and to keep a steady watch over that supremacy. In this respect, our culture is very sick, but I understand that similar seeds were sown in all patriarchal cultures.

"The way I saw him prove he was a man was through political power and power over women. My father had many mistresses at all times. He was trying to tell me that he was sorry to have made me so much like himself – sorry that my wife would hurt as much as my mother hurt. He asked me to look at what I was trying to prove - what kind of satisfaction it gave me to attract women to give myself importance.

"It was a very sad dream, *Mi Maestro*, not just because of my father's remorse, but because of my own. He took me in his arms and we wept together. Can you tell me why, at this time, my father has suddenly communicated with me in this way?"

"Susmo, can you see that a higher aspect of yourself agreed to have the condor begin this process for you?" the *ylloq'e* asked.

"It could be," he replied. "But why now?"

"*Wayki*, you must recognize the power of women if you are to navigate through their dream work. You are being asked to shed your personal, racial and cultural prejudices in order to be who you really are.

"If you think that women are something to conquer the way your ancestors conquered the Indians, there is little hope for your future with the Order of the Ruby. If you are willing to release your inauthentic behavior, then maybe there will be hope for you."

"I honestly feel that the condor released me, *Mi Maestro*. I feel differently towards the women today. Do you think my old ways will return?"

"They will return, Susmo, unless you consciously reject them every moment of your life. You might go back to Cusco and begin pulling in the filaments you used to share with your male friends. You have to be conscious of where you are and what you are doing every moment, waking and sleeping."

"*Madre de Dios*, Don Eduardo. It is a lot to ask."

"It is all that is asked of you at this moment, Susmo. It's not so much to ask. When you become conscious of your behavior, you will find yourself watching your ego. The ego must be tamed, My Friend, and yours is big, unrefined and like a fly that will not be still. You must work at self observation."

Susmo appeared humbled and repentant. "Yes, Don Eduardo," he said softly. "Is there any way I can make things right with the women I have used and with my dear wife, who has been good to me in spite of my behavior?"

Don Eduardo laughed at his humility. "Susmo, find yourself! Quit this drama. I am not impressed with your humility. It is not authentic and neither are you. Apologize to every woman you have ever diminished or hurt in any way." Susmo looked shocked as Don Eduardo continued. "I know it may take you the rest of your life to find them all, but do it and begin here with these gifted women. If any you have tormented have died, journey to them. Begin paying attention to your every moment from a place of contemplation without involvement. Become an observer, a witness to your life. This will teach you to be authentic and to know that what you have been is a disgrace to the Brotherhood and the Mission."

Susmo was burning up with embarrassment. Don Eduardo was showing him no mercy. The *ylloq'e* knew that the ego would stop at nothing to stay in power, so the best tactic was complete humiliation – and ruthlessness. He continued to assault Susmo until he was limp – beaten.

Throughout the session, which was painful for both of them, Don Eduardo held Susmo in a place of unconditional love. Breaking the ego was never pleasant. Like all of the mystery teachings, the guide would be an adept, one who had been through it years before. That made empathy an acceptable emotion, while sympathy was not.

Susmo returned to his tent like a whipped puppy. He lay for several hours on his sleeping bag weeping and contemplating the work he would have to complete to be authentic. His ego reared up a number of times, doubting the path, discrediting Don Eduardo, and reciting litanies of core beliefs belonging to an assemblage point he no longer held. Don Eduardo had done his job well.

After Susmo had left him, the *ylloq'e* walked by the little river that ran alongside the village. He climbed up into the rocks where the river tumbled down towards the village until he reached a more quiet pool. There he removed his poncho and the black traditional dress of his people and stood naked before the mountains, the water, and the unseen stars. He begged *Mamacocha*, Mother Water, to cleanse away the heavy energy from his encounter with Susmo, which was his sworn and preordained duty. He drank one handful of water and vomited into the brush behind him then he submerged himself in the icy water.

When he felt clean and light again, Don Eduardo climbed out of the pool and sat by its edge drying himself in the Sun. He knew Susmo would be fine. In fact, he knew Susmo would fulfill his destiny and would always be his friend. He loved him as a son.

In his heart, he thanked Leah's Higher Self for seeing a way, through the condor, to initiate Susmo's work, and Chris for orchestrating the whole affair.

•

After lunch, Leah and Brian spread out on a big rock to talk. Being together triggered memory of the dream for Brian, bringing insights into his consciousness very rapidly. Within a few minutes he had identified the source of his fears and the many forms those fears had taken. His desire to commit was offset by his fear of being smothered, controlled or manipulated. His excuse was often the possibility of an untimely death, like his father's. Each failed partnership was a reenactment of his reaction to his father's sudden death. All Brian needed were the tools to shift his reality.

"Brian, you know the core beliefs that are holding you back," Leah said. "I could have you write them down, but why make them more concrete than they already are? Why don't we take a little journey into your unconscious to break them once and for all?"

"I'm ready to let them go, Leah."

"Do you know what you will put in their place?"

"Yes. I am open to commitment, willing to risk my heart to find my destiny. I am courageous, authentic and impeccable, a true member of the Brotherhood. I have no need for control in my life, either exercising it or experiencing it from another. I have forgiveness in my heart for my parents. I am grateful to them for my life, but I am not their genetics," he said. "How does that sound, Leah?"

"Those are great, Brian. You may want to look at them in a year or so to see if they need uplifting further, or you might find yourself revising them tomorrow. It seems as though we are all on an accelerated course right now."

Brian laughed and asked Leah how she had done this work for herself.

"I was gifted this little journey that I am about to gift to you. It helped me, then my students, move through the work quickly. At the time, I didn't know that we were traveling into our assemblage points, but it didn't matter. We were there whether we knew it or not. In addition to this journey, I had a little help from my dearest friend."

"Who was that and how did your friend help you?" he asked.

"My friend was a wonderful wolf-dog who came into my life to absorb my fear and manifest all the disease that would have killed me. She gave me a gift of consciousness. I understand that I manifested her as an aspect of myself to perform that service. We sometimes do that when the genetics and toxins are too much for us to clear on our own. I found myself free of the things she was taking on for me.

"At the time of her illness and death, she taught me true strength and the nature of compassion and grief, which opened my heart. You don't have time to duplicate that one, Brian," she sighed.

"Nor the want," he replied, stroking her hand.

"I appreciated her every day she was alive. We had an agreement that she could be *salk'a* (undomesticated) if she would pay attention to what I was saying to her. We became completely telepathic. I never wanted to hurt her or to put her into service for me. It was orchestrated at a higher level in accordance with the Divine Plan – all of it. Don't think for a minute that you can worm your way out of what is facing you, Brian."

"Testing?" he asked, hesitantly.

"Of course you'll be tested. Do you think the Brotherhood wants to be full of half-baked magicians? This is pretty serious stuff," she said, passionately.

"I am ready to make a commitment," Brian replied with determination.

Then you will be tested, My Friend."

"So be it."

Leah took Brian on a short journey to a place in the Fourth Dimension, which represented his assemblage point. In that place, Brian had the freedom to withdraw filaments that supported detrimental core beliefs, and draw in filaments of higher frequency to take their place. This immediately shifted his assemblage point into higher frequency or consciousness and it shifted his reality accordingly. When they were finished, she asked him to spend a little time on the rock integrating the new filaments then she slipped off to find Chris.

At lunch, Chris had told her to bring a towel, water and some concentrated calories, so she stopped by her tent and loaded her backpack. She took all her layers of clothing, since the return trip could be cold. A flashlight and her knife were thrown in as standard procedure. Chris would have packed them as well.

About half an hour early, she found him near the community hut, sitting in a circle with the children. They were teaching him to play one of their flutes, an instrument that imitated the sounds of birds. Leah practiced a little invisibility, hanging back a bit to watch them. The giggling children adored him and weren't the least bit shy about crawling all over him, pulling his hair and stroking his beard.

Since she was unable to suppress her joyful heart for long, Chris spotted Leah leaning against the community building and motioned for her to join them as he rose to his feet. Then all the children ran to Leah, who knelt to receive them into her heart. Hoisting his pack over his shoulders, Chris spoke a few words of Quechua to the children, who ran off to some new game.

"Ready, Mate?" he asked Leah.

"Quite," she replied with a grin. "It will be good to get into hiking mode again. I'm getting far too much sleep and not enough exercise."

"My sentiments exactly," Chris agreed. "Do you mind if we hike in silence? The path is narrow and I like to merge with the surroundings as I'm walking."

"That's fine with me. I have plenty of meditative work to keep me occupied," she replied. "Lead the way."

They hiked up along the river, just as Don Eduardo had that morning. The climb was gradual until they reached the base of the mountains, where they began to climb a twisting path through the rocks along a smaller stream that fed the river.

Leah tried to collect her thoughts about all that was happening. Recollecting her dream, she decided that Brian had not been aware of their work on the Dreaming Paths when they talked after lunch, but his Higher Self prompted him from the realm of his subconscious mind. She felt it was likely that all of our insights and inspirations were bleeding through from the higher dimensions - dimensions we could access through the dreaming paths. Similar to shamanic journeys, these were not the mundane dreams of the unconscious, but power dreams in the superconscious.

Chris walked ahead in complete attunement with nature. Every sound filtered through his awareness. He took counsel from the wind about the weather and all the news it brought from as far away as the jungle. His step was soundless, non-aggressive and secure. He was not a human climbing up the mountain; he was part of the landscape. Soon Leah abandoned her efforts at understanding what was happening to the group and merged herself with the experience as well. Chris knew it immediately, and there was bliss between them.

Shortly thereafter, she heard the sound of falling water and picked up her pace to get right behind Chris. They were walking towards a rock wall that opened up like a bowl to greet them. A crystalline waterfall fell a good forty feet into this tiny canyon to become the stream at their feet. As they walked into the canyon, the rock wall sheltered them from the wind. Warmth, a strange sensation at this altitude, moved out to greet them. The canyon was full of green plants, ferns and little critters.

Leah continued to walk silently behind Chris as they came to a narrow passage through the rock. When she emerged beyond the passage, he was standing to the side, waiting to see her expression. There before her was a crystal-clear steaming hot pool. Those who used it had artfully edged its circumference with rocks, some of which offered inviting steps deep into the pool.

"Mother of God!" Leah breathed, lowering her backpack to the ground. "Chris, how did you find this place?"

"An explorative nature and a few good tips from Don Eduardo," he laughed. "I checked this place out after I arrived greatly in need of washing up. I have wanted to share this with you. I have wanted to give you something completely luxurious and renewing, Leah."

"Bless you, Chris. This is quite exquisite. It will be hard to have had a bath and keep it a secret," she grinned, " but I will be most discreet."

"I'll just step outside for a minute, Leah, to allow you your privacy. Call to me when you are in the pool and I'll join you."

"Chris, you are the most amazing man I have ever met," she said, gesturing towards him. "I feel like royalty, as if my ladies in waiting are just around the corner here at fifteen thousand feet," she laughed.

Chris smiled. "You are royalty, Leah. You are high priestess of Annu and your lineage is the House of David. I know who you are, Beloved. Just call me when you are ready," he added.

Leah sat on a rock for a few minutes to compose herself. She didn't know whether to feel embarrassed, amazed or grateful. She had never openly admitted her identity to anyone, though Chris seemed to know more about her than she did.

"Well," she thought, "I am not going to let all that keep me from a hot soak." Leaving her clothing carefully folded on the rock, Leah clipped her straight blonde hair on top of her head and eased herself into the pool. Arranged to accommodate people of different heights, the flat rocks on the pool floor made comfortable seating. She quickly found her niche in the steamy hot water. It was a slice of heaven.

"Okay, Chris, I am in," she called.

Chris slipped through the rocks again, already stripped to his jocks. He was lean, but not too lean, muscular but not too muscular, and decidedly good-looking, Leah thought. He surely did not look like a man in his late fifties. As he was laying his clothing on a neighboring rock, Leah told him her eyes were shut until he was in the water.

He slipped soundlessly into the pool and sat studying Leah, who was no more than four feet from him across the steaming water. How many years had he waited to be with her? He didn't want to count them. How many lessons had he needed to learn to be able to be with her in integrity? There was no sense counting those either. What he counted was his lucky stars and the fact that dreams could manifest into this reality. Despite four days in the wilderness, she looked every bit the Goddess of his dreams. "I'm in," he whispered.

"I know," she replied. She opened her deep blue eyes and their hearts locked together in bliss. "Chris, this is a good time to confess that I adore you," she said dreamily. "When I was given your flyer as I was leaving Perth, I folded it into my little traveling book and vowed to meet you the next time I came to Australia."

"The Divine Plan saved you the trouble," he said.

"It feels very right to be here with you, just like this."

"You know it's such a simple thing to please you, Leah," he replied. "Would it offend you if I came close to kiss you?"

"You've already kissed me today," she laughed with false indignation. "Do you *need* two kisses in one day?"

"It is a bit piggish of me, I admit," he replied with a serious expression, "but maybe one for each reality would be nice."

Leah closed her eyes and raised her arms to the surface of the water to beckon to him. Chris came to her without touching her body and kissed her softly on the mouth. Drawing away, he whispered, "How long I have waited to be worthy of you, Leah." Then he kissed her again, more deeply.

When he drew away again, he saw that she was weeping softly. He brushed the tears from her cheeks. "Can I help you, Leah?" he asked.

Releasing a great sigh, she opened her eyes to look into his. "I have denied an aching deep inside of me for most of my life, Chris. I find it now being filled with your tender presence. It feels good to let the tears flow into this water."

"Our lives have not been easy, My Love. Our callings have isolated us and tested us unmercifully. I am sure there are greater tests ahead, but I consider it quite hopeful that we have found each other," he said, stroking her face and hair. "I will love and protect you as best I can."

"I feel that, Chris, and at the same time, I know that I must complete my own initiations. I have learned to be detached. That is the only way I know to survive this Mission."

"I know, Leah. I have detached from everything except my heart's longing for you. Perhaps I will have to face that as well, but I believe when two can be one, truly one, there is no need for detachment."

"What is the secret of being one?" she asked, touching his heart.

"Frequency," he answered. "It is for those who have balanced their inner masculine and feminine. When a man is no longer looking for his own feminine in every woman he is with, and a woman is no longer searching for her masculine in every man she encounters, then the two can be one. Only in wholeness can we experience oneness, and with it bliss – ecstasy – God. You somehow complete me. I feel expanded in your presence, Leah. I think you are smart, though, to include detachment in the criteria."

"It's autonomy, Chris – what you are saying. It allows an individual to remain sovereign in partnership. The source of my soul's aching was the experience of just the opposite. It feels good to have released it."

"Are you all right with the heat, Leah?" he asked.

"For a little while longer, then I will have to sit out for a bit," she replied.

"May I tell you how deeply I love you?" he asked.

Tears sprang from Leah's eyes again. She was silent for a few moments then told him of her feelings. "For some strange reason, Chris, I fear the perfection of this moment. I have never felt love from someone as I feel it now for you. It is true love from deep in the heart and soul. I long to return it to you. Perhaps it is the danger of attachment I fear. Most people think I am fearless, but here is this fear."

"I don't think it is a fear," he said. "I believe it is a discernment of the Higher Self to protect you from the entrapment of attachment - that loss of sovereignty. It may not apply in this case."

"Why wouldn't it apply? Are there exemptions to the Universal Laws?" she asked.

"There are," he whispered in her ear. "Some other time we can discuss them. Right now I would like to serve you in what ever way I can."

Leah was ready to melt. She could not contain her passion with her intellect too much longer, and Chris knew it. He took her hands and drew her out to the center of the pool where the water was a little deeper.

"How can I serve you?" he breathed into her ear. Leah wrapped her arms around him and received his touch. His hands were in appreciation of her slender, curved body. Leah had the relaxed breasts of one who had mothered her young and Chris honored that service with tender kisses. They loved each other without physical intercourse, for to do so would have jeopardized their joint Mission on the present journey.

When the water became too hot for her, they splashed in the cold creek under the waterfall then sat at the pool's edge, she in his arms.

"You have liberated something deep within me, Beloved," she told him.

"That is called 'firing codes', Mate," Chris laughed. "The gift of the ruby light has been activated."

"Ah, so this was a plan, was it?" she teased.

"The Divine Plan," he replied, taking notice of the fading light. "One more dip before we go?"

"A short one."

They hiked back to the village in silence. How easy it had been to forget the group, the journey and the greater Mission. Luxury was a mild description of the afternoon for both of them.

•

As Leah was walking from her tent to the dining hall for dinner, Sonia popped out of nowhere to walk beside her. "Second time that has happened," Leah thought to herself, startled. "I had better stay focused in the moment."

"Hi Leah," Sonia said, "want to hear something astounding?"

"I'm all ears, Sonia," Leah replied, sensing the excitement in her voice.

"Okay. Get this. I am sitting on my rock writing in my journal this afternoon, and who should appear but Susmo. As you well know, Susmo and I have quite a history together. I have moved enough beyond my need to feel special by being with him, so he quit soliciting me a few years ago and I got to work through jealousy watching him with other women. He's sure been a great teacher for my lessons of learning to love other women. So I don't know what I was expecting from him this afternoon, except the usual amount of charisma. Do you know what he did?" she asked excitedly.

"I couldn't begin to guess," Leah replied. "You'll have to tell me, Sonia."

"He apologized – for everything – every little thing he had ever done to me. He even recognized the subtle manipulation, a game we both played, and asked me to forgive him. What could I do but ask his forgiveness as well."

"Sounds like a shiny new assemblage point to me," she said, turning to hug Sonia. "Doesn't it feel good to get things all cleaned up with someone?"

"I feel like a new woman, Leah. I'm ready for anything. Now I am free to show my love and support for Susmo. I'd like him to speak to every man in my family, every man in my neighborhood and the whole city of Albuquerque."

"It could be a great career for our dear Susmo," Leah laughed, as they entered the dining hall. "Wow!" she thought, "energy is really moving in this group today. Blessed Be."

•

When the circle met with Don Eduardo that night, he passed the first *kint'u* to Leah. As he watched Leah take the gift from the *ylloq'e* and blow her power and intent into it, Chris saw the new light in her field. It was a delicate pink glow around her White Heart, the activation of "The Beloved". Jesus had spoken of this mystery with the words "when the two shall be one". It was one of the great mysteries of the Brotherhood. Leah felt it as a firing of the heart, giving her greater capacity to love. It was not lost to the sight of Don Eduardo, who, while honoring her with the first gift, subtly raised his eyebrows at Chris.

No one else could see the ruby light, though Susmo might have if he had been paying attention. He was quite lost in his remorse. It wasn't surprising then, after the weaving of the assemblage point for the evening was complete, that Don Eduardo called Susmo to stand before him for a cleansing. Once again, the room reeked of *Agua Florida* as the filaments of Susmo's luminous body were rehabilitated for service to the Mission. When he had finished, Don Eduardo gave a small pouch to Susmo and asked him to set a grid around the skull with the emeralds of the Incas.

Susmo allowed the fabulous stones to fall into his hand, then set the six-pointed star around the skull. The first Merkaba formed and began to spin. Then he asked Brian to set the outer grid with amethyst to honor the Amethystine Order. Again the second Merkaba went into a counter-spin, moving the group into higher dimensions. Brian and Susmo had definitely stepped up their frequency in the past twenty-four hours. To Leah, the difference in their luminous fields was inspiring.

Don Eduardo filled up his baby alpaca-skin pouch with coca leaves and cleared his throat. "Everyone is looking good tonight," he began, staring right at Leah. Practiced in the art of energetic fencing, she did not draw attention to herself by reacting outwardly, but inwardly she accepted the compliment from her teacher, and he knew it. "I promised to complete our oral history tonight with the Incas, Lord Muru, and the invasion and conquest of our adopted land by the Spaniards. As I said last night, Lord Muru brought my people and our Lemurian records from Tibet to Titicaca Lake in his flying ships under the guardianship of the Brotherhood of the Red Hand. There we found the offspring of *Wiracocha* and *Mamacocha*, who looked similar to the Elder Race, but who were of normal stature.

"My people understood the Mission and consented to the mixing of the blood. The frequency of consciousness encoded in their genetics uplifted our people and gave new life to the Mission. Our dominant characteristics masked their genetics in bodies of the race of Mu.

"Every once in a while a blue-eyed child would be born. These children were given to the priests and priestesses for training after they were weaned from their mothers. The only notable characteristic of the *Akhus* carried down in our physical appearance was the Inca nose, which is still with many us," he chuckled, rubbing his long, narrow hooked nose.

"We were discouraged, but not forbidden, to mate with the remnant peoples of Titicaca Lake. We had brought our own language, the pure Quechua with us, which had been the language of Lemuria. It is not as old as the Aymara language of the altiplano, the remnant Elders' earlier language, but our tribe has kept it in its original form. We were welcomed into the Temple of the Sun on Sun Island and our women into the Temple of the Moon on Moon Island.

"As the blood mixed, certain of the offspring were trained in the ancient mysteries until their luminous bodies were fully activated. These were the ancestors who held within their luminous bodies the teachings of both wisdoms. Later in our culture, the Inca was the Inca because his luminous body shone like the Sun. He was temple-trained – a fully initiated and realized man who embodied the ancient wisdom. At his side was a fully realized woman who ruled with him.

"Our people spread out from Titicaca Lake in all directions. Lord Muru was building citadels throughout the Andes, using sound to move the huge stones that you now find in the Inca ruins. The smaller stones, set with less precision, are the work of later Atlantean immigrants and then our descendants. A dedicated group of priests and priestesses stayed on at the island temples in Titicaca Lake. My own ancestors came to establish our village where Paucartambo is right now. We were close to the jungle on the river whose waters begin at *Apu* Ausangate, and we were sheltered in a valley with tillable mountains around us. The settlement grew rapidly, for it was an ideal location. We kept our ties with Lord Muru, who sent his emissaries to enrich our lives.

"Then there came a very special time in our history. We believe it corresponds to a time six thousand years ago by your counting. Into our village came a soul of the Elder Race. Her spirit took over the body of a dying girl, so she was raised as one of us, but she was gifted beyond our skills and knowledge. When she was a young woman, her partner and brother, another Elder Soul, manifested on a mountaintop above the village.

"He was Inkari, a ray of the Sun, and she was Qoyari, the Rising Star. They did not come to enrich our blood, but to enrich our lives and reawaken our purpose. Our people had developed the woes of a community with much unhappiness and turmoil. When Inkari and Qoyari came to us, they healed the wounds among us and redirected our energies towards the *Hanaqpacha* (Higher Consciousness). They revitalized all aspects of our culture, from farming to weaving, and brought love into our hearts.

"Qoyari was the Divine Mother, the embodiment of love and compassion. Inkari was the first Inca, the Lord of the Sun and a great *ylloq'e*. He taught us the ritual of *kint'u*, the value of offering our food and coca first to *Pachamama* and *Pachakamak*, then to each other, then to ourselves. He reordered our world. He was a great *ylloq'e* of the Ruby.

"Inkari traveled to Titicaca Lake to be received by Lord Muru and to integrate his Divine Feminine at the site of the Feminine Aspect of the Permanent Ray. He brought with him our village *paqos*, who were descendants of those trained on the Sun Island.

"Lord Muru took Inkari to his secret monastery in the mountains north of Titicaca Lake. There in a warm lush valley, Inkari was shown the records from Lemuria, which included the scrolls of the Elder Race. He looked at the glyphs of the star beings and began to read them to Lord Muru. Because he understood the language of the stars, Lord Muru took him into the most sacred vault of the monastery containing the written records of the Elder Race. These records had come with them from *Chaska*. His relationship with Lord Muru was bonded and he went back to the monastery many times to work with the translation of the ancient documents - the esoteric teachings of the Shining Ones from *Chaska*.

"Using the techniques of masonry that were the legacy of Mak-Ma, *Wiracocha* and Lord Muru, Inkari built the city of Cusco to be the head of the Inca Empire. Understand that Inkari was, like *Wiracocha*, more of a king, and that Lord Muru was more of a priest. Inkari founded an empire, while Lord Muru headed the brotherhoods.

"Inkari and Qoyari co-created Machu Picchu and many other citadels in the valleys of the Incas. At Machu Picchu they established the first city of the *Hanaqpacha*, a Golden City. Here they trained a select group of people to live in the higher worlds. Many of these people came from our village; some came from Titicaca Lake and others from those of us who had settled elsewhere. Here they worked with the *paqos*, or the priests and priestesses, to hold an ideal that was Inca. Machu Picchu was not a political city, but more of a monastery similar to Lord Muru's hidden valley. *Paqos* were initiated through the stages of consciousness that were the priesthood. They were tested in many ways to prove their worthiness. Inkari gifted our people with a way to talk to the stars. When a *paqo* reached the level of *alto mesayoq*, he was put in charge of a mountain, which had a mountain spirit, an *Apu*.

"At first, it was a small mountain with small things to say. As the *paqo* increased his abilities to communicate with the mountain, he was given bigger and bigger mountains to guard. The *kuraq akulleq's*, the most esteemed elders, were given the very big mountains, like Salkanti, Yananti, Veronica and Ausangate. Our Priesthood has passed that tradition on to the present time.

"Inkari taught the *paqos* how to bring the messages of the stars from the mountains and how to interpret them. This information was continually integrated into our culture. Before he left us, he established the tradition of calling forth prophecy from the stars through the *Apus* once every five hundred years. This prophecy was an integration of the messages from all the *Apus* of our land."

Don Eduardo stopped to fill his baby alpaca-skin pouch with coca leaves and drink some tea that the young boys brought to him from the fire. The group took a deep, collective breath, as if swallowing a large dose of Truth and preparing for the next giant spoonful. Don Eduardo finished his tea, filled his cheek with coca leaves and continued. "Inkari and Qoyari did not stay long on *Pachamama* compared to *Wiracocha* and *Mamacocha*. It was not part of their Mission to be long-lived, but they did not die. They walked off into the jungle to find their way back to *Chaska*. They said they would be back one day – we have awaited them.

"Led by the *alto mesayoqs*, our *paqos* were a powerful group of priests who carried on the teachings of Inkari in their priesthood and brotherhoods. Above all other aspects of their Mission, they were of service to the people. Machu Picchu blossomed as a spiritual center even as Cusco became the head of a vast and powerful empire, the Empire of the Sun. Lord Muru gradually abandoned the Islands of Titicaca Lake, moving all of his work to the hidden valley. He gave the great Disc of the Sun to the first emperor to hang in the *Qorikancha* in Cusco, where it stayed until just before the conquest.

"A little over five-hundred years ago, the *paqos* of our people read the prophecies of the *Apus*, the communications from the stars. All of the *paqos* who guarded the *Apus* came to Machu Picchu with their message. The *ylloq'e cuna* guided the compilation of the wisdom, and the prophecies were announced to the people at *Inti Raymi*, the festival of the Sun's return.

"At that time, the empire was already divided – corrupt, and power was being misused. Past prophecies had clearly stated that this would bring the demise of the empire. It was announced that a dreaded power would come from across the sea to end the empire forever. When these white men came, we were not to confuse them with returning *wiracochas*. On the contrary, we were to take our few treasures and wisdom and hide all of it, for they would be as vultures preying on our wealth and as crusaders for a lesser Truth.

"We were to abandon our beautiful cities and move into the high places, where we remain still. To offset our grief, the *Apus* told us that this invasion was inevitable - that material wealth had nothing to do with our Mission. Spiritual wealth was our Mission, and we were to hold it for the next five hundred years, until the true *Wiracochas* were reborn on *Pachamama* to continue it for us. Then our long, long Mission on *Pachamama* would end.

"Many years passed between the reading of the prophecies and the complete evacuation of the city and many more before the false *wiracochas* arrived on our shores. By that time Machu Picchu was consumed by the *salk'a* of the jungle. The Spaniards did not fool those of us who held the greater Truth; however, the empire fell easily as the people knelt down before those false and deceitful *wiracochas*. Millions of our people were slaughtered, our material wealth was lost, and they tried to force the loss of the spiritual wealth as well.

"Long before the arrival of the Spaniards, the Order of the Red Hand took the golden Disc of the Sun from the *Qorikancha* in Cusco to Lord Muru's hidden valley. It now resides in the *Hanaqpacha* in the vicinity of Titicaca Lake. What the Spanish found was an illusion, a replica of the great Disc of *Inti*. Those who cannot hold the frequency of the *Hanaqpacha* will not see the true Disc of the Sun again.

"Our tribe went unnoticed here in the mountains. The Spaniards had no interest in this environment - sure that nothing could survive here. We sent our people to the jungle through a safe route to bring back food for our winters to compliment our meager potatoes and corn. The *paqos* had trusted communications with some lower villages, where certain of our people were living. We heard of the tortures and deaths of those who would not accept Christianity. The burning flesh came to us on the wind and spoke of these atrocities committed in the name of God – in the name of Jesus. Our *paqos* met many times to discuss these things and to pray for all of the people in the Andes.

"We knew Jesus. He had appeared to us many times. We knew him as a Shining One, a star being, from *Chaska*, a Ray of the Sun and brother to Inkari. What was happening in our land was not the work of Jesus. It was the work of greedy kings who never listened to anything Jesus said.

"Jesus carried the Codes of Kingly Service – to honor and uphold the ways of those you have conquered. He would not have destroyed us. He would have honored us and improved what was already in place.

"Now, most of the people of this land have a dual relationship with God – one side false and one side true. However, we of our villages have not deviated from the Truth and we have forgiven the Spaniards. The High Council of *Chaska* would not allow the Mission to fail, and so we were spared.

"Several years ago, we read our prophecies again. I was privileged to help guide the compilation of the messages from the *Apus*. Some of you were able to be there with us on our beloved *Apu* Sinaq'ara.

"We were told that now is the time – the time of completion of our Mission, the time of the return of Qoyari and Inkari, and the new *wiracochas*. Thirty thousand years is a long time to focus intent. We are grateful, but we are tired, and there are few of us remaining.

"It is your story now, for we have passed our wisdom to you, Shining Ones. Take care with *Pachamama*, take care with each other, and do not lose sight of your Mission as you have in the past. Your culture will have to cure their lust for materialism and devote their lives to loving service – love and service to *Pachamama* and each other. You in this room must remember who you are and learn to speak to the *Apus*. Otherwise, where is your future, and where is your past?

"*Listo*," he said, wiping tears from his cheeks with his coca pouch. Leah had been on Sinaq'ara for the reading of the prophecies, but it always brought tears to her eyes to hear Don Eduardo talk of it. It was not so much the passing of the Mission as the fact that these gentle people might be leaving the planet or that their tribe would lose its purity through assimilation. Their culture and that of the Tibetans were among the last remnants of the Motherland.

She was not alone in her tears, for all the women had become emotionally involved in the story. It was difficult to sit through any explanation of the conquest - the Inquisition brought over the sea - without becoming dreadfully angry. But that anger was offset by their love for these people who had given their lives to the greater Truth. It was a tumultuous evening.

Don Eduardo announced that, with the completion of the oral history, their group would be leaving in the morning to begin the next segment of the journey together. They were to rise early, have breakfast at eight o'clock and leave on horseback by nine. He, Doña Felicia, the *alto mesayoqs,* and a few of the women would be walking with them. Typically, he gave no indication of their destination.

Brian and Susmo removed the grids from the room, returning the stones to Don Eduardo. The *ylloq'e* insisted that they take responsibility for them on the journey and refused to take them back. Susmo was deeply moved and assured Don Eduardo of their safety.

Brian looked to Leah for an explanation. "What can I tell you, Brian? When he's done with a Mission, he's done!" she announced. "You wanted commitment, My Friend. Start with the stones."

"I have a lot of guilt about the conquest, Leah," he said, hesitantly.

"We have all had to let go of that, Brian. Take our journey again tonight before you sleep. Break the beliefs that hold you to that guilt. Okay?"

"Good idea, Leah. See you in the morning," he added, slipping the pouch of stones into his pocket.

"You may want to soak those stones in some water from the river tonight, Brian, otherwise you may not sleep at all. They've been on active duty."

"Thanks for the warning," he said, kissing her on the cheek. "Good night."

Gradually the group filtered out of the community hut, while Don Eduardo kept a steady grip on Leah's arm, holding her back. When they were alone, he drew a soft mesa cloth out from under his poncho. It was a natural *tejido* of *vicuña*, the smallest and most *salk'a* member of the llama family.

"The *ylloq'e* unfolded the cloth to reveal a heavy golden pendant and chain. A crescent Moon was superimposed on a replica of the Disc of the Sun that was about four inches in diameter. An exquisite ruby was set along the perimeter of the Sun and an equally perfect sapphire alongside the moon.

Pointing to the Sun, Don Eduardo said *"Inti."* Leah nodded that she understood. Pointing to the Moon he said *"Mamaq'illa."*

"Ah si, Mamaq'illa," she replied, smiling.

Then he slipped the chain over her head, positioning the pendant in front of her heart chakra. Holding his hand over the pendant and her heart, he continued in halting Spanish. *"Es para ti, Wiracocha* - It is for you, Shining One. *Es de Qoyari* - It is from Qoyari."

Leah protested. *"Oh, Papacito, no. Es para los Incas* - Oh, Little Father, no. It is for the Incas."

"Si. Es para ti. - Yes, it is for you.," he repeated folding the mesa into her hands.

"Gracias, Papacito. Es muy preciosa, - Thank you, Little Father. It is very precious," Leah said softly, her heart pounding from the energies of the pendant.

"Buena."

Don Eduardo zipped Leah's jacket up to hide the pendant, then knelt down to wrap the golden skull in its cloths. She followed him out under the moonlight and walked with him to his house. There he kissed her on both cheeks, tasting the salt of her tears. The *ylloq'e* had shown her how much he loved and supported her by connecting her filaments with Qoyari, the Rising Star, the Goddess from *Chaska.*

"Her soul is one with Qoyari," he thought to himself. "Like Qoyari's golden pendant, she bears the rubies and the sapphires. I cannot see the whole of her destiny, but I know she is more than she seems."

Three Wise Men

Just before nine o'clock the next morning, Lobo and his group of young warriors secured the group's gear onto the pack horses. All of the horses would meet them at the far end of the village, giving them an opportunity to say good-bye to the good people who had hosted them. Don Eduardo and the *alto mesayoqs* joined them as they came through the village. The priests were accompanying the *ylloq'e* to protect him from physical harm and to assist the Mission.

Chris and Leah walked in the center of a throng of children who wanted one last chance to be playful with him. He engaged them in their games, the object of which was to bring him and Leah closer together. One game was a great snake that took little steps on an inward spiral until they were all smashed together. He and Leah, who played the head of the snake, towered over the little ones in the center of the spiral, face to face. As the children pressed closer and closer, Chris gave Leah a kiss on the cheek, commenting on how wise the children were in their matchmaking. Leah could not contain her laughter, which made the children clap and crush them tighter.

"Have you ever had children, Chris?" She asked, sobering up as the snake unwound.

"Not that I know of, Mate," he teased. "Why do you ask?"

"You have a way with them."

"The Maori kids taught me how to play. You just get into their group assemblage point and have fun. The rules are not to be in a hurry, not to be stuffy, and to be open to learning from them. Kids are my favorite people," he added, tossing a tiny boy in the air.

Leah stopped to embrace Doña Felicia and the women shamans who were gathered near the end of the village. Her gratitude for the women was shown with small gifts of beaded necklaces, colorful hair ties and pictures of Lord Sananda that they greatly loved. Natalie, Ellia and Sonia, who had been guests of the villagers on previous journeys, had also brought gifts to share. They, in turn, received little mesa cloths and beaded hat ties. Doña Felicia presented Leah with a ceremonial neck scarf woven of the finest *vicuña*. Leah discreetly slipped one hundred soles into Felicia's hand and kissed her on each cheek. In hesitant Spanish, Felicia told Leah to make an offering to *Pachamama* when they came to Mistipukara in order to ground her luminous body for what lay ahead on their journey.

Soon the eleven women and three men were mounting horses and waving farewell, as the entourage set off towards the east. Don Eduardo and his priests led the way on foot, followed by three of the women - Doña Felicia, Doña Lucia and Margarita. They would be winding their way through four additional villages of their tribes, crossing mountain passes and camping between Chua Chua and ChaCha Bamba, the last village, before beginning a descent to the valley floor near the edge of the high jungle. The little town of Paucartambo would be part of their journey. There they would restock supplies and continue to some unknown destination.

Many of the group rode side by side, visiting with each other on the easiest parts of their journey. Snow-capped mountain peaks rose up around them as they traveled with the Sun and the wind.

Men and women from the neighboring villages dotted the hillsides, harvesting the small potatoes of the high mountains. Passing through the villages became a good time to dismount and walk the horses since each village contributed *alto mesayoqs* to the band of *paqos*. The Indians could not pass through the villages without numerous greetings and sharing of news. Chris fell back a number of times to connect with Leah and the women, and the three men had a wonderful time riding with each other. Doubts and worries were put aside for the sake of brotherhood.

The strangely discordant melodies of the Indians' flutes drifted back through the group to enchant Leah, who rode between her women and the young warriors. The young men had a bit of fun galloping back and forth across the infrequent *pampas*. Softly, she began to sing some of the chanting songs of the village women that were meant to accompany the music. She felt very much at home in these mountains – much as she did at Titicaca Lake and the mountains of Bolivia. It was easy to be at peace there.

When they began their descent on the second day, the jungle loomed before them with the billowing rain clouds of mid-afternoon hanging over its canopy. They were headed towards a campsite that was sheltered from the wind in a valley below Mistipukara. From Mistipukara, a power place of the *paqos*, they would be able to see the town of Paucartambo nestled in the river valley near the edge of the high jungle.

Leah hoped, with all her heart, to see some of the children she had adopted who were attending school in Paucartambo. "Surely," she thought, "the spectacle of our arrival would bring them all from their homes and schools." She was *madrina* (godmother) to many children in this district from the years she had come to these mountains with her friend, Don Carlos. Beyond that spiritual duty, she and her students had sent many bright children from Don Carlos' mountain community of Pakulmaka to school in Paucartambo. Some of those children were the sons and daughters of Angelica, the young woman shaman of Pakulmaka, who, with her mother, Francesca, had reawakened Leah to the sisterhood.

One of Francesca's sons was a very special child who connected his heart with Leah the very first time she had come to visit. He was fifteen now and had survived the death of his mother when he was thirteen. Leah remembered the fierce and selfish way in which he had loved her that year, and how she had opened her heart to receive his grief. Her own grief was enormous, for Francesca was a true and beloved sister. Memories flooded Leah's awareness as she rode.

Camp was set up before dusk, leaving time for the group to sit with the mountains at the Hour of Power – the time before and after sunset. Her groups had always joked about it being cocktail hour – a time for drinking the intoxicating elixir of the Andes. Joining Leah, Chris sat back to back with her - adding the energy of their combined fields to the magic of *Pachamama* at dusk. When the darkness gathered force, they began walking back to camp for dinner, he with a warm arm around her shoulders.

"That feels good, Chris," she sighed.

"I'm more than happy to oblige, Leah," he replied. "Tell me of your dreams last night. We really haven't had a quiet moment together today."

"My dreams – well, I was very focused in a dream with Master Mukda. You were nowhere in sight all night, by the way. Mukda was teaching me to project the power of my entire field further and further out until I could hold an entire city in my consciousness.

"It was a rather wild experience, since I began filtering through all the garbage of the collective consciousness – people's malicious or negative thoughts, for instance. I was frantically trying to transmute all of this for what seemed like the whole night and exhausting myself in the process. Near the end of the dream, he tapped me on the shoulder and said, 'watch what you could be doing'. He projected his field around the city, including the mountainsides surrounding it, and flooded it with this astounding light force. This he did simply by filling his field with that force. It was *munay*, of course. The rest of the dream had me exercising the power of my Sacred Heart in that way," she concluded.

"Quite a night, Leah. I was focused as well, but elsewhere. After becoming conscious of each Dreaming Path and all the aspects of self, which we engage in them, the next exercise is to pull all the aspects together into a single focus. I've been at these exercises on and off for a few years now. These dreams don't necessarily have a point or lesson, since the lesson is contained in the nature of the Dreaming Path."

Leah agreed with Chris and added, "When I journey with my students to other dimensions, we exercise our consciousness by pulling all of the aspects of Self together in one focal point above the heart. To apply that to the Dreaming Paths sounds like a similar but infinitely more difficult lesson."

"I've certainly had my struggles with it," he said, thoughtfully. "They are usually isolated exercises, so perhaps we will meet on the Dreaming Paths tonight."

"I will look forward to it, Chris."

They had lagged behind the group to remain in the fading light alone. "You asked me about children today. I am guessing correctly that you are a mother, Leah?" Chris asked.

"Yes I am a mother, and I have two bright and lively grandsons. It took me a lot of years to learn to appreciate that time in my life when I raised my children."

"Did you go it alone?"

"I did. I have a lot of compassion for single parents, especially when they are young. I was young."

"Purposely, Leah – because you are still young now," he said, pulling her into his arms, "and your essence has the immortal beauty of a Goddess." He kissed her forehead as she rested her head against his chest. "Did you ever think of remarrying in all those years?" he asked.

Leah laughed, drawing away to look at him. "All the time in the beginning, a little bit in the middle and not at all of late. Of course, I wanted a white knight to ride in and save me from having to be so independent and responsible, even though it was my choice to divorce. Eventually I understood it as the path I had chosen, both for the children and myself. We are all self-sufficient. I confess that in all those years I never tried to live with a man again."

"Now, I expect you are a little far out for most of my gender."

"To say the least," she laughed. "I would not expect anyone to deal with my schedule, either. Do you know I was home for only eight weeks last year?"

"Ouch! How does that feel?"

"I love being home – whenever I can be, but I feel at home anywhere on Mother Earth. I had to stop needing form to ground me a long time ago."

"Speaking of grounding, would you mind if I ride behind you tomorrow – just to guard your back, Leah?"

"Do you expect danger?" she asked, her face showing concern.

"Always – in these situations. It's the surest way to avoid it. I find it's too easy for people to slip into altered states where they lose their focus on the outer world."

"I did that plenty today, but I know these mountains. There is no harm here, other than the weather and an occasional bold puma. Thank you, Chris. It would be nice to have you back there."

He kissed her lightly on the lips before they continued towards the stone hut of the way station, looking for dinner.

In the morning, the expedition proceeded to Mistipukara, the sacred place of the shamans. At around thirteen thousand feet, Mistipukara overlooked the jungle and the valley of the Paucartambo River. Gale-force winds blew over the rounded surface, continually deterring all but the dedicated. Dotted with pre-Incan ruins, the landscape was anything but hospitable – a natural place for shamans to leave their power before their passages to the other side. Those seeking that power came to sit upon the land, hoping to be gifted with it.

Chris had ridden behind Leah, moving into the role of guardian. She did not object, but wondered at his motivation. At Mistipukara, he followed her at a distance out among the scattered rocks until she had found the spot where her offering to *Pachamama* was to be made. They had been told to meditate and take whatever power was offered to them. Chris had come through Mistipukara on his way up to the villages, and Leah had been there many times with her groups. They were less than four hours by horse from the village of Pakulmaka and the hacienda of Don Carlos.

After she had made an offering of coca leaves, white sage and tobacco, Leah reached into her blouse and pulled out a necklace she had worn since her first visit to Peru. It was a golden pendant of an Inca idol that had been given to her by Don Ricardo, a jungle shaman who had worked with Don Carlos. He seemed a good *wayki*, but he had had a sexual agenda with Leah.

She had seen or experienced this with every shaman she knew who had contacted the outside world, and every *mestizo* who promoted himself as a famous shaman. When Westerners held them in a place of honor and respect as teachers, boundaries seemed to crumble, especially sexually, but also with money. It was no different than the questionable behavior of many gurus in this age of spiritual voyeurism. Leah saw it all as a wonderful way for women to get clear about their power and support each other, but the dramas were sometimes messy. For this reason, her heart thrilled to every step of Susmo's ascension to mastery.

Leah took the idol off the chain and set it in a little hole she had dug in the Earth. "It is time for you to rest, My Little Friend," she said, smoothing the dirt over the idol. "It feels that I am walking into a new place, and you cannot go with me. I let go of you and of all that you have signified, Little One. I hope that someone sits upon you and receives a blessing from my detachment."

Leah sat cross-legged on the Earth and thought about her dreams the night before. There had been another training dream, this time with the physical body, not unlike Kung Fu. Chris had come to her in a separate dream as a white knight.

"What a sense of humor he has," she thought, chuckling to herself. Carrying a jewel-studded sword at his side, he had worn the red cross of the Templar crusaders. He did not see her in the dream, but appeared to be focused on his Mission.

In yet another dream, they made love on a beautiful ocean beach. It reminded her of Costa Rica, with the beach backing up to the jungle, a place where the energy shifted from water to Earth in pure *salk'a*.

She worried about the depth of the love she felt for Chris. Attachments had always come with big lessons – lessons she did not want to experience again. A part of her longed to be with him and a part of her was vigilantly watching her ego for the red flags of attachment.

In fact, her ego was under continual surveillance by her Higher Self to guard against the pitfalls of an important Mission. It was all too easy to sacrifice aspects of the Mission to personal gratification. The Siriun High Council had made it abundantly clear to her that such behavior was unacceptable. "Perhaps the Mission has just become more interesting," she thought. "I could handle that, and I welcome the support of a spiritual warrior."

Chris held Leah in his second attention while he had his own thoughts. He did not wonder if Leah was attainable or even compatible with him. He knew who she was, her importance to the Mission, and the need to guard her. She was unaware of her true power because she had subdued her ego considerably – to the point, he felt, that it could jeopardize the Mission.

Leah would be called on to confront the status quo, to meet them face to face and shift their consciousness in the wink of an eye, but along with her ego she had subdued her warrior, and that warrior was going to be needed too. The Dreaming Paths were one way to reawaken her warrior and activate her White Heart; experience would be the other. He knew that she operated primarily out of her heart space - riding the frequency of love, from which space she was fearless. However, even that power would be tested – was it not for Jesus? Leah would be best off operating from energy – Sixth Dimension. Obviously Master Mukda agreed on this point.

Thinking back over his own training, Chris laughed to remember surviving it. The physical challenges regularly put him in life-or-death situations, but they forced him to awaken all of his powers of perception to anticipate everything before it occurred. He could, in the split-second before something happened, see all possible outcomes and choose his action accordingly.

That gift had not come to him easily. He learned to value his life by continually seeing the possibility of his death before him. A cushy tenure at the university had been abandoned because he had been challenged – no, forced - into Higher Consciousness. Finding his awareness meant losing his mind. He had left his envied faculty position to become an aikido master, a meditator and an Outback survivalist and tour guide.

Suddenly, his second attention flooded his consciousness with a kind of etheric adrenaline. His entire focus came to bear on Leah, who had just let go of a powerfully charged attachment. He saw corded filaments fly out of her field into the Universal Matrix.

When they were back at the horses, he observed a number of elementals hanging around her – powerful thought forms that were trying to penetrate her field. His perception had been accurate, for he had sensed trouble coming towards her last night, perhaps attracted by the intent of that detachment. Luckily she had agreed to let him follow her, providing him a vantage point from which to watch her field. Since his perception was aligned with the Mission, the violation of her boundaries was worth the effort to protect her.

On the last leg of the descent to Paucartambo, Leah was leaning forward in her saddle on a fairly steep incline when he saw the energy coming. It was shaped like a small black hurricane flying through the clear blue sky right towards her. In his experience, complete invisibility would be needed to fend off such an attack of evil energy.

Leah was not conscious of the energy, had no reason to be invisible while riding a horse into Paucartambo, and would never have expected or deserved an attack of that nature. His perception opened wide, stretching time to observe outcomes and interventions. Clearly he needed to get her off the horse, but to do so invisibly to protect his own field.

Invoking a cloak of invisibility, energetically turning his electromagnetic field inside out, Chris pushed his horse hard to overtake hers on the mountainside of the path. As the energy hit the edge of her field, the horse sensed it, as if someone had waved a flag in front of his eyes. He reared up on his hind legs, whinnying loudly enough to get everyone's attention.

Chris grabbed Leah as she went flying backwards and literally tossed her over his horse onto the gravel on the side of the mountain. Her horse slipped over the edge and slid nearly thirty feet down the switchback to a lower path while struggling to get his footing. Dismounting quickly to restrain his own horse, Chris made his way back to Leah, who had landed sitting up facing the path. She looked stunned, dusty, but physically unharmed. Chris tossed his reins to Susmo, who had been right behind him, and came down on one knee in front of Leah.

"Are you okay, Leah?" he asked, brushing loose hair from her face.

"How did I get here?" she asked in shock. "One minute I am riding a horse and the next I am sitting in the dirt. I don't know what happened."

"Leah, I had to throw you about eight feet. Are you sure you are all right?" he asked incredulously.

"Never felt a thing," she answered with a smile. "It was just like fencing with you in the ashram, Chris."

"Well, that's good news, Mate. Tell me who would send you energy so evil it might have killed you?"

"No one! Who would want to do a thing like that?" she demanded, in disbelief.

"Someone. I saw it as clearly as I see you right now. It may have something to do with your time at Mistipukara. I observed a number of elementals around you there."

"Thanks for telling me," she said, not at all happy with his observations of her. "Were you watching me the entire time?"

"I was. Leah, understand that it's partly why I am here. I had a clear perception that something would befall you today. I saw a huge cord leave your field at Mistipukara. What was it?"

Leah thought back to her time there, her offering and meditation while resisting the urge to smack him for being so snoopy. "Chris, I buried something that a shaman had given me years ago. I wanted to be done with that part of my life."

"Who was it?" he demanded.

"You don't know him. His name was Don Ricardo – a jungle shaman. I may have angered him by rejecting his advances," she added reluctantly.

"Whatever you buried was a kind of leash that he has had around you all that time."

"Oh, how appropriate. It was a pendant, and I have worn it most every day since he gave it to me."

"Why?"

"Why do women wear things, Chris? It was gold, it was fascinating and it was a piece of Peru," she said, a bit irritated.

"The bloke's a black magician, Mate," he said firmly, trying to bring her back to her senses. "Your horse is lamed and you could have flown God knows where. The energy he sent has entered your field. We will have to remove it tonight or risk losing you to illness or insanity. Am I impressing you with the seriousness of this?"

"Well, Darling, to tell you the truth, I haven't been this intimate with anger in a long time. Everything about this is making me angry. Don't take it personally, but I feel like strangling someone right now."

"Not surprising! I wouldn't expect an energy like that to be filled with joy and angel's harps," he laughed, trying to ease the mounting tension.

"Help me up, Chris. I think I will walk the rest of the way to town."

Chris helped her up and dusted her off, using a little more force than she was used to. Walking to the edge of the path, she saw Lobo and one of the warriors leading her horse along the bottom path. The horse was nicked up and bloody on all four legs from the sharp rocks and prickly bushes he had slid through. Susmo, who had dismounted to manage Chris' horse, held Leah close for a few minutes, giving his support and love. She kissed him on the cheek and started up the hill on foot, feeling regret at having injured an innocent animal. Susmo turned to Chris and shrugged his shoulders, indicating his inability to understand the situation. Chris thanked him, grabbed his shoulder for a second, then mounted his horse and continued behind Leah, watching the fluctuations in her field.

Knowing he was watching her did not ease her emotion. Anger was turning to fury – all of which he was observing in her field. When the group rode into Paucartambo, Leah was still on foot, happy to be grounded and anxious to be alone. The warriors and the men spread out from the plaza to round up supplies, while the women popped into the little stores, wandered over the arched bridge to the market, or stood around talking to each other in the plaza. Leah walked up a cobblestone street lined with shops to the church and slipped inside. It was deserted. She walked up the center aisle to look at the statues in the sanctuary.

"I come here to find solace," she said aloud, "and find instead bleeding statues, pain and suffering. I'm angry, Jesus – angry that anyone would try to harm me, angry that I need to be watched like a child in order to be safe. Perhaps I have trusted too much the power of love," she concluded. Then, sitting down in the front pew, she wept. "Perhaps my love has not been pure enough to be worthy of this Mission, whatever it is."

Chris moved out of the shadows in the rear of the church. "Perhaps it is simply that you have been too innocent," he said, loud enough for her to hear. "This self-pity, on the other hand, is coming from ego, and is not aligned with the Mission."

She jumped up, wiping her tears away with her shirtsleeve. "You!" she cried. "Am I not to find solitude, even within a church?"

He walked forward to stand before her. "More likely, you will find the ghosts of the Inquisition in this church, Leah."

Something snapped inside Leah and she threw a punch at Chris. He deflected it with ease and she threw another. They might have been walking the Dreaming Paths as all of her martial arts training came back into a body suddenly supple and incredibly strong. A magus and a priestess sparring up and down the aisles of the village church was a rare sight indeed. Chris was a master and Leah, he concluded, was not bad at all. She was angry, powerful and persistent. Her kicks needed a little work, but she had great potential.

Leah saw no humor in the situation, her anger reaching the level of rage. Chris knew that Leah could not see how her emotions had been commandeered by the black energy, or that the incident had brought her warrior fully to the front from a place of denial. She could not stop reacting until, exhausted, she began beating aimlessly against his chest.

"Who are you and what are you doing in my life?" she wailed.

Gripping her by the shoulders while staring into her eyes, he shouted, "Listen to me. I am Mana Sanar Kumara, Lord of the Ruby, and I command that you, Evil Energy, leave this woman and return to he who sent you, gathering strength one hundred fold as you return. Please deliver this Truth to him from the Ruby Order - whatsoever you soweth in this life, that shall you also reap." With that he blew into each of Leah's chakras from the base of her spine to the top of her head, and the black energy left her field, flying out through an open window of the church.

He had a grip on Leah's shoulders when she began collapsing as the energy left her. Chris grabbed her under her arms as she sank and laid her down gently on the smooth stones of the floor. Rolling her to face down on the floor, he began to channel energy into the base of her spine while watching the chakras reactivate themselves. When her nervous system had recovered, she began to stir, but he asked her to wait a few minutes, to take more energy and breathe deeply.

When she was replenished, he helped Leah slowly rise to her feet. Chris walked her over to a church pew, where he sat down with Leah next to him and wrapped his arms around her like a father. The last of her tears flowed unabated as she sank into the security of his embrace.

Feeling balanced, and in her body again, she whispered. "Forgive me, Chris. I doubted you, your motives and your actions. Will you accept my apology? I am so ashamed of my childish projection."

"Beloved, I would gladly lay down my life for you, but I'd rather avoid that extreme at the moment. There is no need to apologize for the Divine Plan. There is no need to be ashamed of behavior resulting from an attack of black magic. I will share with you that I am secretly pleased that your warrior came out to play with me, and I admit that I provoked her."

"You reactivated a lot of old training, Chris. It's interesting that it doesn't leave you – like riding a bicycle. Of course, I wasn't very effective, was I?" she laughed.

"You weren't bad at all, Leah. We'll keep training on the Dreaming Paths and spar a little bit when we get the chance in this reality – every church we come upon if you like, Darling," he laughed.

She looked around the church again. "There is something quite appropriate about getting dark energy exorcised in a Catholic church," she mused.

"Are you ready to walk back to the plaza now?"

"I am. Thank you, Chris – for saving my life."

"You are welcome, My Love," he replied kissing her softly on the mouth. "I am glad to be of service," he added helping her to her feet. "You're sure you're all right?"

"I'm fine now," she said, as they began walking to the doors of the church. "Chris, were you trying to intimidate the energy when you called on the lineage of the Kumara's?" she asked.

"It has been a curse and a blessing to know who I am, Leah. I was using a power to pierce through defensive layers of the energy."

"So, you are a Kumara? What did you say, Mana Sanar Kumara?" she asked, stopping before the doors to look at him.

"It was necessary to reveal myself on your behalf, Leah. I know this day will stay between us and that you will understand as more is revealed to you," he replied, turning to face her.

"You are Lord of the Ruby as well?" she asked, quietly.

"That is correct, Leah."

"Well I don't doubt that. I have never met anyone with your perceptions. Is it appropriate that I love you?" she whispered, her eyes widening slightly.

"It is all that I have dreamed of, Beloved," he whispered back, taking her in his arms. A passion unleashed within each of them that clearly had a life of its own. However, the Divine Plan saved the integrity of the Mission by sending the parish priest from the sacristy into the sanctuary of the church. Clearing his throat as loudly as he could, the priest turned toward the altar, no doubt praying for the salvation of their immortal souls. Leah and Chris burst out the doors onto the church steps, flushed with sexual excitement and laughing freely.

Back in the plaza, the group was loosely gathering together again. Leah was greeted by a horde of children - all of her godsons and goddaughters, their siblings and friends. She introduced them to Chris, who became an instant hit again. "How about ice cream?" he suggested, and like a swarm of bees, all of them were off looking for the ice cream cart.

After having cleaned out the ice cream boy's inventory midway across the arched stone bridge, her children stood clustered around Leah, sharing with her all that had happened in their lives since they had seen her last. She was their spiritual guardian and took the job very seriously. When everyone's ice cream was finished, they turned to walk back to the plaza. At the end of the bridge, an older boy stood with a pack hitched up over one shoulder, watching them. He was cleaned up, obviously very bright, with soulful dark eyes as big as the Moon. He wore a blue-violet fleece jacket to honor his *madrina* who had given it to him the year before.

"My Julio," she whispered to Chris. "He is so precious to me that I grieved the retirement of Don Carlos from teaching, thinking I would not be coming here again. Ridiculous of course, because here I am! Come meet him."

Leah pressed coins into the hands of all her little ones, who fled off to see what they could buy. She and Chris had walked halfway to Julio when Chris stopped Leah.

"Leah, look at his field. Do you see the White Heart?"

"My God, Chris, I have never noticed it before."

"Perhaps he was growing into it," he mused.

"His light has always been intoxicating to me. I wonder if the death of his mother has moved him into his calling?"

"Quite possibly. He will be coming with us, of course."

"He will?"

"He is a member of the Ruby Order, Leah. He must come with us."

"No objections from this quarter," she said, smiling.

Julio greeted Leah formally, with a handshake and kisses on each cheek. At his age, to show affection in public would bring him nothing but grief from his friends, and Leah knew it. Chris knew exactly how to handle the situation and showed Julio a great deal of honor and respect. "Such a small thing for Chris to do, but how meaningful to Julio, how sensitive to his needs," Leah thought.

Chris was able to bring others into their spiritual power because he knew who he was. He had no need to joust with another man, impress all the women, or be a big winner. Those were character traits of a man who measured himself through the opinions of others. Chris had no use for such behavior. Instead, he measured himself in terms of his own integrity and the purity of his intent. She saw his potential as a strong, positive role model for young men.

On their way to the plaza, Julio asked them to step into a small shop with him. A few words in Quechua sent the old merchant woman bustling into her back room. Julio asked Chris to stand in the doorway then he released all of his emotion, loving Leah, his head resting against her heart. It was a great outpouring of the heart for each of them and when it was finished, it was finished. Julio thanked Chris, picked up his pack and led the way to the plaza.

Chris threw his arm around Leah, laughing. "Well, Mate, you two go back a long way together on this planet. Do you think he will share you with me?"

"Perhaps with supervision," she teased. "I know he loves me in a lot of different ways, but he will sort it out, Chris. He is a fierce warrior of the spirit – a *ylloq'e* in the making."

"He's magnificent, Leah. Thank you for finding him."

"He found me, Darling. All I did was show up at Pakulmaka. Thanks goes to Don Carlos."

"Why did Carlos quit the work?" Chris asked.

"Many reasons, Chris. His Mission was complete, he was tired, and he wanted to begin writing his memoirs. I think that his health might have been a factor as well, but that is a guess."

They had crossed the street to join the gathering group in the plaza. Julio knew a number of Leah's women and was busy giving them the news from Pakulmaka in his version of English. Leah embraced Brit and Genevieve, who were watching the joy-filled scene before them. Soon everyone's attention was directed to the narrow street they had taken into the town.

"Get a muffler!" Sonia shouted in Spanish, but her words were lost to the noise of the approaching truck. At least twenty-five men, women and children from the mountains piled out of the back of the decrepit blue pickup and hurried off to do their shopping. The windshield was too dirty to see who was inside, but Leah recognized the truck and jumped in the passenger side of the cab.

"*Papacito*, what a surprise!" she sang, giving Don Carlos a great hug and kiss. "How lucky that you have come to town just now," she added.

"*Aye Chihuahua*, My Leah," he replied. "I had a vision this morning that you were in danger – like arrows shot at you from afar. I have heard that you were in the villages, but my vision told me Mistipukara. So I am here. How can I help you, My Great Love?"

"You are too late, Carlos," she laughed. "A great *ylloq'e* has already rescued me, but your vision was correct. Do you remember Don Ricardo?"

"Slime of the Earth," he muttered.

"Slimy black magician is more like it," she said with fervor. "There was some energy of control and lots of anger connected to the gold idol that he gave me. I have worn it for years, Carlos. At Mistipukara, I freed myself of the idol and provoked an energetic attack."

"Not surprising. Leah, I did not know about Ricardo when you and I went to Iquitos. I am sorry to have caused you this grief."

"Forget it, Carlos - no regrets. I have never felt controlled by him, so never suspected anything."

"Things happen in other dimensions, Leah."

"What are his connections?"

"Drugs, rare medicinal plants, you name it. Wherever the money lies, there you will find Ricardo."

Don Carlos sat against the door and looked at Leah. He was a handsome man of obvious status. Silvering wavy hair framed a weathered countenance and radiant brown eyes. His engaging smile caused Leah to abruptly change the subject.

"Enough of Ricardo," she said, cutting the energy. "Tell me about Angelica. I saw her son, Favio, just a few minutes ago. I do miss Angelica."

"She is riding back with me, Leah. I am sure she will be here soon. You can ask her yourself."

"Oh, how lucky I am today. How are you coming with your memoirs, *papacito*?" she asked.

"My memoirs are my pretext, as you well know," he replied winking. "My passion is to free every mountain village in the Andes from the yoke of Christian suffering.

This will easily take me several lifetimes. I was sure you were going to help me," he smiled.

"I know you were, but my Mission is elsewhere. However, I hold each one of these dear people in the center of my heart, *Wayki*."

"You look wonderful, Leah. Whatever you are doing, it certainly agrees with you."

"A door has opened, Carlos. I am very lucky."

"You've always been lucky. Now you feel enchanted, like an awakened queen." Leah blushed. "Well, I am just very lucky."

Chris popped his head through the truck window and thrust his hand across to greet Don Carlos. Soon Carlos was out in the plaza hugging Natalie, Sonia and Ellia, who knew him well. Leah saw Angelica come around the corner from the market. Julio ran to meet his sister taking her bundles to Carlos' truck.

Like all the women of Pakulmaka, Angelica wore the traditional dress of the region – layers of black, wrapped woven skirt with colorful edging, a white blouse and layers of sweaters in deep pink, yellow and aqua. On her head was the saucer-shaped traditional black wool hat edged in yellow wool fringe and embroidered with flowers. White beaded ties, like those presented to Leah by the women of the high mountains, secured the hat under her chin. Angelica was a beautiful woman, with dark, almond-shaped eyes and long shiny black braids. Her family had descended from the original Lemurian colonists. They were very old upon the land.

She saw Leah as well and the two women came together to embrace in the middle of the street. Angelica was a true Priestess of the Sun, the descendant of the lineage of light in the Andes. She and her mother, Francesca, had opened Leah's codes of light, when they recognized the Solar Disc in her heart and Third Eye chakras. Leah's love for Angelica and her deceased mother was profound. Language did not keep them from communicating that love, sisterhood, and joy to each other as they sat together on a park bench until the men returned to the group.

Carlos and Don Eduardo embraced as old friends then wandered away from the group together to speak to each other. Leah knew that Don Eduardo would be asking Carlos to come with the group, out of courtesy and respect, but that Carlos would refuse. He had a pretext – and it was not his calling. She admired him for seeing his own path so clearly, and she admired Don Eduardo for his finesse.

Brian and Susmo appeared on the scene, carrying a box full of icy water and fresh trout. It was not long before Julio dashed over to say good-bye to Angelica, who spoke to him in Quechua.

"Angelica has asked me to take good care of you, *Madrina* Leah."

"Then I am sure to be safe. Tell Angelica that I will take good care of you as well, Julio."

Julio translated Leah's message for Angelica, who rewarded her with a broad grin. They touched each other's hearts and put their heads together before hugging good bye. Leah hugged and kissed Don Carlos as well, then, taking Julio's offered hand, began the winding walk through the village streets down towards the river.

She remembered a time when he was eight – a walk above the village of Pakulmaka. His eyes had continually scanned the hills and mountains above them looking for pumas and other signs of danger. Carlos had confided to her later that Julio had been told by Francesca to protect Leah as he would a baby llama.

Since that time, he had laid claim to the role of her guardian when they were both at Pakulmaka. Leah had offered to send him to school in Paucartambo that year because he was so bright. He had done well, managing to learn the western way without losing his connection to *Pachamama*. Now they were hand in hand again, one step further along on the Mission.

Attending to the cooking supplies, Lobo and the young warriors had gone directly to the horses, where many bundles were being tied on the pack animals. Leah had a hunch where they were headed, but could not fathom why they needed all those supplies, unless they were not coming back for some time. Though many of the group may have shared her wonder at the supplies, not a single eyebrow was raised. They had all learned fluidity and trust through the blessings of the path.

Led on foot by the Indians - now over thirty men by hasty count - the group rode along the dusty dirt road towards the jungle. Julio walked at Leah's side, while Chris rode behind her, continuing to scan her field.

Depending upon the skills of the sender, evil energy could be returned. He was not certain that Don Ricardo was a black magician or if the idol had been passed on to Leah without the intention of harm or control. The idol itself may have been the vehicle for the evil. Chris began to relax his attention as they neared their campsite, for not only had Leah stayed free of the energy, her aura had increased in brilliance as the journey progressed. A suitable campsite was not found until just before dusk, which sent everyone scrambling to get camp set up in the last light of day.

The group was exhausted and thankful for a night in the valley where staying warm was not the primary concern. Lingering out among the stars with her guardians, Leah rededicated herself to the Mission. Don Eduardo had called her to the Indians' makeshift dwelling thrown up from stones and heavy plastic tarp. She had stood before the *ylloq'e* to receive a *limpia*, a cleansing, to insure that sinister energies were not in her field. Out under the stars along the river, she was strengthening her connection to the greater Truth, *Chaska* and her Mission, as she understood it at that point in time. Chris and Julio were strengthening their connection to each other a short distance away.

"Do you love my *madrina*?" Julio asked him, getting right to his point of concern.

"With heart and soul, *Wayki*," Chris replied. "Do you think its possible that we could both love her?" he added, sensitive to Julio's feelings.

"Maybe. In my dreams I have made love with her many times. I know that is not acceptable in this reality, so I have not told anyone until now," Julio said, unashamed.

"I understand, Julio. In dreams, it is good – it breaks no codes of integrity. In this reality, it will harm the Mission. I believe, for all of the brothers, that Leah represents the Goddess - the feminine. If we can honor her in that way on the Dreaming Paths, we honor and nurture our own feminine."

"Does it break your codes of integrity to make love to her in this reality, *Wayki*?" he asked, not willing to give up the topic.

Chris chuckled to himself. "At this time, it is not appropriate. It would interfere with the Mission. However, in the future, it would do no harm for me to make love to Leah. Does that answer your question, *Wayki*?" he asked.

"In part, it does. Why is this so – that you can love her in that way?"

"It is so because Leah and I have written it into our soul work together. You and she wrote a different but beautiful story together - the story of a kind and loving *madrina* who would nurture you through the loss of your own mother, then set you free to find your destiny. In turn, you would protect her from all harm and do well educating yourself for the fulfillment of your own soul's purpose."

"That sounds true, and worthy. How do you know this?" Julio asked.

"Sometimes I can see this written in the records of people I love or wish to assist."

"Can I do that someday?"

"Perhaps, if you hold those gifts in your luminous body. However, you may have unique gifts of your own, My Young Friend."

"May I interrupt?" Leah asked, coming to sit on their rock with them.

She leaned back into Chris' sheltering arms while reaching her hand out to Julio, in respect for the younger man's feelings. Leah had felt Julio's love for her transit through his awakening manhood. She thought it beautiful, but had wisely moved into the full role of a *madrina*.

"It seems that most of the *waykis* have gone to bed," she said.

"Not everyone has your energetic resources, Beloved," Chris replied, squeezing her.

"Even I am winding down, My *Waykis*. Anyone care to walk me to my tent?" she asked.

Looking up at Chris, Julio excused himself to go find a sleeping space with Don Eduardo's men. Leah hugged him good night, then stood up to go. As she and Chris walked along the river back to the tents, they saw Brian with Natalie at the river's edge.

"*Almost* everyone's exhausted," she whispered, slipping her arm through Chris'.

"Is this something new?" he inquired.

"They have struggled in relationship in the past. If they were reuniting, it would be nice to see Brian hang in there this time. Natalie's a powerful woman. He just needs to hold his own and not let her become his mother again."

"I had a powerful mother." Chris offered.

"What was she like?" Leah asked, curious to know more about him.

"She was a professor, which is why I was a professor. She saw to it that I was exhaustively educated, that I had every advantage imaginable intellectually, and all it cost me was my emotional freedom.

"She had an expectation that I would solve her problems, bring her love and grow up to be exactly what she had in mind. It was a bit incestuous, though not in the physical. By the time I was eight I was on to her, but caught in her prison. I acquiesced to the education, but tuned a deaf ear to her problems."

"Where was your father, Chris?" Leah asked.

"Dad was emotionally absent and rarely around in the physical. He couldn't stand up to her, so he ignored both of us and finally left when I was eleven. I was trapped. He was not. I find it remarkable that any adult would burden a child with problems, their fears, and their grief, but it happens all too often."

"Did you find a way out while you were still a kid?" she asked.

"Emotionally, yes. I think Mother helped me develop more skills than anyone else and for that, I am grateful. I took my life back when I was thirteen, designing and conducting a mystical initiation ceremony for myself. Being an avid reader of unapproved books, I accessed all manner of magic.

"There was, in the ceremony, some kind of galactic intervention because I came out of it a man, and not only a man - a warrior. That was the day I started making decisions for myself and began a long study of martial arts.

"I was lucky. I have worked with a lot of uninitiated men who took their mother work into adulthood. So now I work with kids and their parents back home. Young boys need that ritual of separation from the mother, the honoring of their own soul's purpose and plan, to be balanced and happy. Boys need a strong father figure in their lives. I like it to be their own dad and not me, and I like Mom to be ready and willing to let go."

"It makes me think of Julio – his ritual of separation was so severe."

"He's done really well, Leah - with your help."

Arriving at her tent, Leah turned to Chris to say good night. "I am grateful for today, Chris – all of it. Thank you for being my shadow."

"I will be there again tomorrow, along with Julio," he replied, taking her in his arms.

"Chris, I support you on this journey as well. Whatever I can do for you, let me know about it, will you?"

"I don't think I am going to come out of this journey unscathed, Leah. If I cannot rely on my own resources and you can help me, I will ask you."

"Fair enough," she replied, looking up at the stars again. "There's magic in the air and it is written in the stars, Chris. Can you feel it?"

"It is high magic, Leah. We are heading into something unspeakably holy. Please share your dreams with me tomorrow. They may be quite important," he added, kissing her lightly on the lips.

His kiss reawakened the passion within each of them. Leah wondered where the bliss had hidden itself, for all she felt now was an aching to be united with Chris. It felt to her like a desire to merge on a cellular level – a longing to be part of him. Chris was fighting off an urgency to consummate their relationship and all of the rationalizing that accompanied his desire. "How could a man be more challenged than this?" he thought. "I have found my deepest love and am not permitted to use the instinctive human means to acknowledge and claim her."

For a long time, they stood before her tent holding each other, catching their breath, and allowing their hearts to still. Then Chris whispered in her ear, "For some reason we are called upon to be heroic, to step beyond our humanity in all ways at this time, Darling. It's the nature of the Mission."

"It is contrary to my life-style, which advocates being in the now moment, but if we are being tested, I can rally to the cause," she laughed. "Good night, My Love – and thank you once again for returning that energy to whoever created it."

"See you on the Dreaming Paths," he replied, tipping his hat slightly as he walked away.

Leah's dreams were vivid that night. Her time in the ashram with Master Mukda touched, as usual, on the art of focusing energy. She surprised herself by asking Mukda about the nature of her relationship with Chris. Mukda laughed. "At this time, it is to build the energies of transformation using sexual attraction," he began. "That is to say, disciplining those energies that they might be used for a powerful step in your ascension. You are human but also Divine. Move those energies into the Divine and you will recover your bliss."

"How did you know I was concerned about my bliss?" Leah asked him.

"When you ask a question, Daughter, you reveal the totality of your mind to me. If I can assist you I will read the writing in your mind and answer your questions – all of them."

"Because I have shown my openness by asking you, it is a form of permission to read my mind?" she struggled.

"It is so, though not with everyone. At the soul level you have asked me to prepare you for your Mission."

Leah was grateful for Master Mukda's wisdom and his skill. Obviously she had been working with him before she had become aware of it. He confirmed as much and moved her through another level of energy training.

Dreaming with Chris was not on the schedule for that night, but an ending dream left her breathless. She was meditating in a cave, somewhere in the Andes she thought, when three men appeared at the door of the cave. The first man looked like a swami, but his apparel was too ornate. He was young and extraordinarily beautiful, with eyes deeply wise. Kneeling, he set before her a sword with a golden handle that was studded with diamonds and rubies.

The second man was much older than the first. He had unruly graying, black hair, olive skin and a fierceness or intensity that startled her. He lay before her a simple golden chalice filled with a luminescent liquid.

The third man was unmistakably a sheik – a sufi master. A long gray beard framed a kind and beautiful face. "A truly holy man," she thought. He knelt before her, his turbaned head lowered in respect, and placed a single pearl within her hand.

The three men bowed to Leah and disappeared. She looked at the beautiful gifts asking to know their deepest meaning.

The sword was the Sword of Truth. It was to be wielded by one worthy – a spiritual warrior. The chalice symbolized service to mankind and it held an elixir of immortality – the nectar of the Bodhisattva who comes in service to humanity.

Leah knew well the story of the pearl, a parable of Jesus from the Gospel of Thomas. It was the story of a young prince who was sent from the stars to Earth to steal the pearl away from the dragon. He became lost in the density of the Earth world and forgot who he was and why he had been sent. His Father sent an eagle bearing a message – a reminder of his origins – and the young man remembered, recovered the pearl and brought glory to his Father's kingdom. Leah knew the meaning of the pearl. It symbolized the Mission.

Picking up the chalice, she drank every drop of the elixir then energetically moved the chalice into her heart space. The drink was effervescent, deeply refreshing and filled with light energy. She asked Master Saint Germain to help her fashion a golden chain for the pearl that she might position it over her Third Eye. Then she would never lose sight of the Mission and the pathway back to the stars. When this was completed and the pearl was in place, Leah picked up the sword. Placing it in a shimmering sheath that magically appeared around her waist, she left the cave to complete her Mission.

Leah awoke at dawn. While excitedly writing the dreams in her journal, she experienced a growing awareness at her Third Eye and within her heart. Several times she reached up to her Third Eye to brush something away before she realized that the pearl had been placed there in some reality and that it's presence was bleeding through to Third Dimension. In her awareness, the chalice was clearly lodged within her heart. "It will be a challenge to go through life without getting twisted up in the sword sheath," she chuckled.

Out of her tent before the young warriors had the tea water ready, Leah was off to find Chris. He had most of his gear packed away already and was organizing his backpack for the day when she arrived at his tent. A look of amazement on her face, she stood there for a few moments before he noticed her.

"My you're up early, Mate, and you look like you've seen an apparition? What's up?"

"Sorry, Chris," she laughed. "I'm simply amazed and impressed. You know, I don't think we're at all compatible. My tent looks like a small tornado swept through it – and in only one night."

"Exactly the point, Beloved. We are yin and yang, so you are obliged to have the opposite traits and yet there is a seed of tidiness within you somewhere."

"You may be right, Chris. What do you do with a toothpaste tube?" she asked, grinning.

"Get in here, Crazy Woman," he laughed. "What have you brought me – your dreams?"

"Big dream, Darling, big dream. Listen to this." Removing her boots to crawl in beside him on his sleeping bag.

Leah repeated the dream to Chris, who asked for details of the men's dress, their attitudes, everything. He stretched her well beyond her normal memory to bring through the frequency of the dream itself. When she had finished, she felt exhausted, as if she had just sparred with him for several hours.

"Chris," she protested, "don't you think we might have overanalyzed a bit?"

"Not at all, Leah. That was just another reality. It should be as clear to you as this one. Great dream, by the way."

"And you?" she inquired. "What of your dreams?"

A deep light filled his eyes as he looked at Leah. "I was with the same three men, Beloved. However, the circumstances were different."

"You're kidding?" she said in disbelief. "Who are they?"

"Brothers of the Ruby."

"I didn't see their White Hearts."

"You were looking at their faces and their gifts, not at their hearts, Leah."

"Right you are, Chris. Can you share your dream?"

"Are you sure you want to hear?"

"Of course," she replied. "Well, I don't know, do I?"

"It won't hurt you to know, though it might embarrass you," he offered, smiling.

"Tell me," she demanded.

"We were all making love to you, Leah."

Her face flushed slightly, but she recovered her composure quickly. "All at once?" she asked, her eyes wide.

Chris laughed loud enough to wake up the entire camp, then shut the tent flap and wrestled her down on the sleeping bag.

"All at once," he said, "and there were more than four of us."

"Oh, My God," she gasped. "I am not surprised that my consciousness was blocked on that dream. Are you serious?"

"Yes. You need to understand that you are, for all of us, the embodiment of the Goddess. I find that curious because you are also one of us, but I am suspicious that one of us volunteers for that duty on behalf of the Mission – balancing the Divine Feminine."

"So how did it feel to share me?" she asked as he kissed her.

"I don't mind if you don't mind, Darling," he replied roguishly, while lavishing kisses on her neck, down her throat and in her ears.

"You are a terrible tease, Chris."

"I am a lot of things, Leah, including your willing servant. In the esoteric sense, I don't think I fear the possibility that you might consume me. However, you represent more than the Goddess to me – and that I will share with no one."

"What is that, Chris?" she asked, suddenly serious.

"I suggest to you that we are in the process of discovering it together. It would be unwise for me to intellectualize something more powerful than the highest magic. Visualize it as the return to God, My Love." Leah was suddenly chilled to the bone. A chord of Truth had been struck deep within her.

"Chris, would you just hold me for a few minutes?" she asked, her eyes brimming with tears.

He held her until the heat came back into her body then let her go pack up for the day's journey.

By ten o'clock that morning, they started uphill on a horse trail that spurred off from the dirt road along the river. The river would eventually join the Madre de Dios as it snaked through the high jungle into the Amazon. Climbing steadily, the group was rising above the level of the jungle canopy riding towards Kañacway Mountain. The trail was not especially steep, but steadily uphill with one welcomed rest for lunch.

After crossing a high pass, they came to a fork in the road. Don Eduardo led them along the left-hand path towards Tres Cruces de Oro. The right-hand path led down into the jungle. They arrived at their campsite before three that afternoon and found a modern shelter where the group could sleep and eat together. Tres Cruces was very cold, with a harsh wind blowing all of the time. A good fire in the building would take the chill out of the air and allow everyone to sleep comfortably.

Camping gear was piled at one end of the building where they would all be sleeping, while the cooking gear and food were piled at the other end next to a neat stack of wood that seemed to have come with the building. In the midst of the organizing, Don Eduardo asked Julio to bring Brian and Susmo to speak with him. When the three men met with the *ylloq'e* he seemed concerned.

"It is planned that we will meet other people here today, *Waykis*," Don Eduardo said. "A part of me is worried that they are lost, perhaps taking the road to the jungle by mistake. It is also possible that they have taken another hiking trail coming up from Paucartambo. The three of you have until sunset to find them. Julio, you take the jungle trail, and run quickly to make it back in time. Susmo and Brian take the walking trails to the west. Hurry now."

Julio was off running immediately, since everything he owned was strapped on his back most of the time. Susmo warned Brian to bring his pack with water, snacks, matches and warm clothing. There were never any guarantees in these mountains. Brian was continually overriding anxiety as he prepared to leave.

The two men trekked off to the west without so much as a clue about whom they were trying to find or where they might be. Susmo walked towards the mountain, while Brian veered off in the opposite direction. After an hour of downhill trekking,

Brian began to worry that he might not make it back before dark. He had a flashlight, but lacked the perspective that daylight would provide. On the other hand, he did not want to fail Don Eduardo or his commitment to the Mission so he walked further shouting *"Hermanos, Hermanos."*

Susmo happened on the small group of *waykis* near the mountain. Leading them back to the camp as the night came upon Tres Cruces de Oro, Susmo called out to Brian to return. Brian was well beyond the range of Susmo's voice, though he was already heading back towards camp.

As night fell upon the mountain, Brian realized that he was lost. He knew he would not find a magical stack of firewood, for there were no trees. However, he remembered the Indians burning dried plants at night because the smell reminded him of marijuana.

Searching with his flashlight, Brian began gathering dried plants from the mountainside. In addition to water and protein bars, he had a lightweight blanket, a parka, gloves and a hat in his pack. He felt reasonably secure after the fire was started. Then the noises of the night began to surround him, and true anxiety set in.

Brian had never been a Boy Scout and had no solo camping experience. Even if he had, imagination runs wild when the night animals come from their dens to hunt. He went out to gather more weeds, knowing that fire would keep away the pumas. At least he thought that it would.

Julio was first to arrive back at the campsite, out of breath and empty-handed. The group was preparing the space to sit in circle that night when Susmo arrived at the door with the lost *waykis*. Chris and Leah were stacking duffel bags against the wall when the small group entered the building.

"Pretend I didn't tell you about my dream, Darling," Chris said wryly.

Leah was flushed - her heart pounding and Third Eye on fire as the three men from her dream turned to look at her. "This is beyond bleed-through, Chris," she whispered. "I find this hard to believe."

"I admit to being a little surprised myself," he replied as he tossed a heavy duffel against the wall. "I never expected them to arrive as we saw them in the dream."

"Then you knew they were coming?"

"The Order of the Ruby is meeting for the first time since the great exodus of Elder Race from the Earth. We've been really slow getting our act together," he chuckled.

"Are all of you Elder Race?" she asked.

"You mean, are all of *us*, Elder Race? No. It has just been difficult to meet in this reality, though small groups have convened. We meet regularly on the inner planes."

It was all the confirmation she needed to know that Chris was the sole Kumara.

The sufi sheik was the first of the brothers to approach them. "I am Leah, Beloved Master," she said offering her hand. "I am grateful to you for a message sent in the form of a pearl."

He smiled and replied in perfect English. "It suits you well, Leah. I like what you have done with it," he said, touching her Third Eye. "I am Sheik Yebra Fakoum. It is a pleasure to meet you at last." He bowed to kiss the sapphire ring on her left hand as Leah stared at the intricate wrapping of his turban.

Leah flushed slightly, thankful that he was kissing her ring and not her filthy hands. The room fell silent as the three men greeted Leah, then Chris.

Scarcely noticed, three porters set the men's bags inside the door and left, while their guide waited outside the door to be compensated. The women gathered around, enclosing Leah, Chris, Susmo and the three men in a circle of light, pleased to be part of a momentous occasion.

When Sheik Fakoum moved next to embrace Chris, the wild-looking brother bowed before Leah. "I am Demetri Malkodina, Beloved Leah. I see that you have drunk the elixir from the chalice within your heart. Now your true work begins," he added with a sparkle in his eyes.

Leah was speechless as he bent to kiss her ring and moved on to Chris. She tried to brush the dust from her blouse and pants as the Indian man came towards her. As beautiful as he had been in her dream, he was dressed in the richly woven fabrics of the royal palaces of India with a turban of several vibrantly colored cloths wound together. He had the eyes of an adept and the gentle manner of a monk.

Bowing to Leah, he presented her with a small replica of the diamond and ruby-studded golden sword from her dream with an attached golden chain. "Maharajah Ramandi, here to serve you, Dearest Lady," he said, as she extended her hand to him. His White Heart was fully opened and glowing with a ruby light.

"Welcome, My Prince," she said bowing slightly. "Tell me, were you three alone on your journey up to Tres Cruces?" she asked.

"No, Beloved One. We had with us a guide who did not know where he was going," he reported, smiling.

"Bless beloved Susmo who has found you," she replied. Leah was radiant, but humble, in the role of high priestess, a role she had never played outside of Dreamtime. The three men had a more accurate idea of Leah's identity and destiny than she did, so honored her in ways she did not understand.

Soon all the women were being greeted as priestesses, and then the *paqos*, with Susmo making the introductions. "Susmo looks radiant," Leah thought to herself. "I believe we are all beginning to understand the greater Truth of our Mission." It warmed her heart. She searched the room for Don Eduardo and found both him and Julio to be missing. She laid her hand on Chris' back to get his attention and he bent to listen to her.

"Chris, Brian has not returned and Don Eduardo and Julio are not here either," she whispered.

Chris scanned the room then closed his eyes to connect with the filaments of Don Eduardo. He saw him separated from his body and immediately retracted his filaments to protect the *ylloq'e*. "Don Eduardo is fragmented at the moment. I can't pursue him mentally in that state," he told her.

"What is the state of fragmentation, if I might ask?"

"He has separated his etheric double from his body and he's flying. I imagine his body to be close by, likely guarded by Julio, and his double to be searching the mountainside for Brian. He sent him off knowing he would be challenged, but does not wish to lose him."

"Don Eduardo will find him. He's quite handy with his double," she assured him, returning to the social scene.

Chris looked at her, shook his head at her mysterious response and left the building. He found Julio sitting beside the supine *ylloq'e* against one end of the building. Nodding to the young man, he lay down next to Don Eduardo. Within a few minutes, Julio had the bodies of two flying *waykis* to look after. Chris followed the filaments of Don Eduardo's intent and soon found the *ylloq'e* seated at Brian's fire. He and the *ylloq'e* chose to be invisible to Brian, who was making a valiant attempt to get centered. Don Eduardo acknowledged Chris with the wave of his hand, motioning for Chris to stand in the bushes behind Brian to hold space for whatever happened next. Brian kept his eyes closed for the most part, but occasionally opened them to glance around.

When Brian next opened his eyes, the *ylloq'e* became visible as a serpent – a cobra with head erect, sitting up quite calmly to study Brian. Brian rubbed his eyes to see if he were imagining the serpent. He concluded that the cobra was real, just on the wrong continent. Taking a deep breath, he closed his eyes again for a few moments, his ears alert for the slightest movement. Opening his eyes after a few moments, he saw a jaguar sitting where the serpent had been. The spotted cat sat perfectly still, and stared at him. Brian kept closing his eyes and breathing and the *ylloq'e* kept shape shifting. He became a condor, an eagle, a dragon and a hummingbird. Brian held steady through all of it, acknowledging to himself that he was being tested.

Chris realized that Leah was right. Don Eduardo was a master of the double and a master shapeshifter. He fully enjoyed watching the *ylloq'e* reweave Brian's filaments into an assemblage point worthy of the magi. When he had finished, he became visible as Don Eduardo, which really gave Brian a start. Don Eduardo couldn't help slapping his knees and laughing like a fool. Brian was stunned but not fearful when the *ylloq'e* stood, taking a mesa from his poncho. He walked over to Brian and thrust the mesa into Brian's heart. That gift of wisdom lodged in his heart appearing as a developing star.

Brian raised his hands to his chest, trying to hold onto the master's energetic gift while looking at Don Eduardo in disbelief.

Don Eduardo walked towards the path and yelled to Brian. "Are you coming or not, *Wayki?*" Brian jumped up, stuffing everything he had in his pack, and ran after the *ylloq'e*. Chris materialized at the fire and covered it with loose rocks. He made it back to his body well ahead of Don Eduardo, who had to move at Brian's human pace. Nodding to Julio as he arose, Chris stood up and reentered the building.

Nonchalantly rejoining Leah, he received her inquiring look. "Everything all right?" she asked.

"You were right. Don Eduardo is magnificent. Brian should be back soon, and with a new assemblage point."

"Isn't it interesting that no one has really missed him yet? These brothers have provided Brian with an opportunity to transcend his little boy and his ego all at once."

Brian returned an hour later, led by the fading image of Don Eduardo. The *ylloq'e* slipped back into his body unnoticed by all but Julio, then the two of them joined the group for dinner. Brian had assessed the situation in the building and had immediately refocused the emotional energies of his experience on his three newly found brothers. He did manage to thank and embrace Don Eduardo, who claimed to have been in camp the entire time.

After the cooks had cleaned up the kitchen, Don Eduardo asked everyone to sit in circle to hear from the new *waykis*. With a good fire blazing, the building was quite comfortable for the group as they settled on top of sleeping mats while leaning against the duffels. Don Eduardo organized the circle, and seated the three new men in front of a makeshift altar, where many beautiful stones had been placed around burning candles.

Sheik Fakoum sat in the center, with the Maharajah to his right and Demetri to his left. Chris and Leah were asked to sit across from the men, with Julio, then Brian, on Leah's left and Susmo on Chris' right. Don Eduardo sat next to Demetri with the Indian women, while the *paqos* sat to the right of the Maharajah. The sisterhood filled in the circle with the young warriors.

Lobo was burning sandalwood on hot coals, and circled the group to cleanse the energies in the room. The *ylloq'e* brought out the golden skull, and placed it in the center of the circle on a tribal weaving. The three new men were quite taken with the skull as Don Eduardo positioned it to face them.

After a brief hushed discussion among the three men, Don Eduardo and the *paqos* began to chew the coca, signaling their readiness to receive wisdom. Sonia sat at attention to provide translation from English to Spanish, while one of the *alto mesayoqs* sat behind Don Eduardo and the other *paqos* to simultaneously translate the Spanish to Quechua.

Sheik Fakoum opened the circle with a moving meditation that set the tone for the evening – reverence. "We are deeply grateful to all our brothers and sisters for supporting the efforts of the Brotherhood of Magi. We have gladly traveled to the Andes, because a portal exists here within the Feminine Light Ray. Through this portal we will access and activate the next phase of our Mission.

"I am told that you have already heard the story of the brotherhood as it evolved from the Elder Race through Lemuria. Now you will hear how it evolved in our part of the world. When I have exhausted my esoteric resources, Ramandi will continue. Demetri will add essential parts missing from our stories.

"Twelve brotherhoods emerged from ancient Egypt during the reign of Aman-Ra many thousands of years ago. Aman-Ra and his Twin Ray, Mir-An-Da, those whom you call Osiris and Isis, came from the star Ak-An, Sirius. They were of the Elder Race, true Bodhisattvas, who came many times to serve the Earth's ascension.

"They were *Akhus*, star beings, Shining Ones. They appeared in human bodies and bore children who were also *Akhus*. The offspring eventually forgot who they were, coming into the darkness of separation, and their bodies were no longer worthy of the true *Akhu* soul. Thus began the incarnation of opposites amongst the gods made men.

"Aman-Ra and Mir-An-Da lived for thousands of years and their children were long-lived as well. It was a Golden Age that did not end until the leaders experienced 'the Fall'. 'The Fall' is to forget your identity – to fall asleep. Most people now are asleep. Partly, that is because those kings of long ago forgot the greatest gift they had been given – the Grail Codes.

"These are the Codes of Kingly Service. When those descendants of Aman-Ra and Mir-An-Da turned from the Grail Codes to personal power, they lost their true power and fell into humanity's deep sleep. You will see that the *Akhus* have come since that time to reactivate the Grail Codes, but few have been awake enough to benefit from that gift. Still, it is there in the collective for all of us to garner.

"The First Times, Zep Tepi, are a reference to the reign of Aman-Ra and Mir-An-Da. It was the seeding of Higher Consciousness and new genetics in Egypt. With the exception of their heirs, Amen-Se and Mai-An, the children of Aman-Ra and Mir-

An-Da were free to intermarry with the remnant tribes found in Egypt at that time, thus seeding the new genetics into the human genome.

"Within those new genes were light codes of ascension. Obviously these codes have spread into the genetics of many in this world. Thus it was and still is the Mission of that starseeding to elevate the consciousness of the Earth. Other starseedings have their own Missions.

"Zep Tepi was a time long before the Great Flood that sank Atlantis and changed the face of the Earth. At that time, Egypt was not a desert, but a fertile paradise. It was the paradise of our myths where God and man were together. In other words, where men knew their Divine origins and the wise *Akhus* lived side by side with them.

"When that was forgotten, man moved into duality and the myths of good and evil. As above so below – for this was just a reflection of the duality made manifest in the galaxy and beyond. To know that you are Divine is to embrace the duality within yourself and with the 'Other', the reflection of yourself.

"Aman-Ra and Mir-An-Da had twelve boys in addition to their kingly heir, Amen-Se. Each of these twelve sons became the head of a sacred brotherhood. There were the astronomers who mapped the heavens, the stone masons who cut and moved stone with light and sound, the architects who used sacred geometry in form, and many more, including the magi. Of course these orders were not new to the Earth, for the Elder Race had originally instituted them in this area. These brotherhoods were entrusted with the knowledge of the stars. Much like the kingly lineage, the wisdom was lost in time. Is it any wonder that we seek out the sacred sites that they built to reawaken memory within us?

"The magi moved into secrecy, and retained the wisdom of alchemy until this day, primarily through the Order of the Ruby. These brotherhoods belonged to a greater brotherhood, that of Annu, the Sun, as represented by Aman-Ra, the Son of the Sun, the one divinely united. At one time, Aman-Ra sent a number of his sons on expeditions to discover the world and spread the Truth of one God.

"Like Aman-Ra and Mir-An-Da, these sons were golden-haired tall men of great intelligence. They traveled to Atlantis and the Americas, to the British Isles and Scandinavia, around the Black Sea, to India and to Mesopotamia. Eventually they returned home with information about the spiritual and physical climate of each place and its people. Aman-Ra made the decision to colonize the most important places, and sent his sons and daughters with volunteers from the young men and women of mixed blood.

"Many people went to Atlantis, where they established a large colony of stone masons who eventually returned to Egypt to build the pyramids, a construction learned from the Atlanteans. In India, a large colony formed around the wisdom of astronomy and astrology. The Maharajah can share more of that with us.

"The final major colonization was in the valley of the Tigris and Euphrates rivers. The brother establishing this colony was head of the artisans. The remainder of the brotherhoods stayed in Egypt until the kings fell into separation. However, each brotherhood had at least one representative in every colony.

"Aman-Ra and the High Council of the Great Lodge of Light from Ak-An saw this as a safeguard of the Sacred Truth. The Siriun High Council has always been the guidance for this Mission on Earth. The magi and the prophets were as essential to the Mission as the builders and artisans.

"In the Mesopotamian colony, the Hebrew lineage, an unrelated remnant starseed that had mixed with the *Akhu* descendants of Aman-Ra, emerged within an established monarchy. Adam was one of their kings, but in no way comparable to Aman-Ra. Adam was in separation, as our myth reminds us. There was in this settlement, a strong group of magi, as there were in India as well as the homeland of Egypt.

"When the kings of Egypt went into separation, well before the flood, the magi left Egypt to live at the Red Sea. Of all the brotherhoods, they have been able to withstand corruption and deterioration. I believe this is due to the nature of their mastery – it defies corruption.

"Everything changed with the flood – so much was lost, it was pitiful. Yet it was the Divine Plan, because the integrity of the *Akhus* had already disappeared. Civilizations had to begin again, but without the golden glory of enlightenment. The ancient king-making rituals were lost to the new monarchies, but kept safe within the Order of the Ruby. The magi never lost their power, just their visibility."

Sheik Fakoum placed his hands together as if in prayer, and bowed his head to the group. "Prince Ramandi will continue now with a story of great importance," he concluded. Everyone in the group returned his act of humble reverence, then looked to the Maharajah, whose serene countenance touched everyone's hearts.

"Thank you, Brother Yebra," he began. "I do not need to detail to this group the wonders of Vedic Astrology or the great tradition of the masters in India which sprang from the colonies of that most ancient Egyptian origin. We were also deeply touched by the spiritual values of immigrating Lemurians and the neighboring Tibetan colonies of Lemuria. The Himalayas have been the anchoring point of the Masculine Light Ray on the Earth and that is reflected in the essence of our religious heritage. Now we have spent our resources and look for the Feminine Aspect of God here in the Andes. When the two become one, we shall know God within us. I am, for that reason, your humble servant, for I acknowledge the God within each of you. I am grateful for the openness of your hearts in receiving us this day.

"I have chosen to tell you a remarkable story that is appropriate to our journey together. We have been fortunate to have strong brotherhoods in India, especially the magi, the prophets and the astronomers. Some of them descended from Aman-Ra and others came from Lemuria. Like the descendants of Lemuria in the Andes we have, in secrecy, brought forth the prophecies periodically in our history. We have just completed this five hundred year cycle once again."

Chris' eyes met Don Eduardo's. Both men were stunned at the synchronicity and periodicity of the prophetic events occurring at the Masculine and Feminine Poles of the Permanent Ray. Perhaps it had been a Lemurian tradition continued in the two cultures.

"Over two thousand years ago, our prophets spoke of the coming of a King, an *Akhu* of the Elder Race. This King would know that he was God, for he would not be born in separation. He would bring to the Earth once again the Grail Codes of Kingly Service and the light-encoded genetics of Higher Consciousness just as Aman-Ra and Mir-An-Da had thousands of years before him. A coded message hidden within those prophecies required the combined efforts of the brotherhoods of astronomy, mathematics, symbols and prophecy to decipher it.

"Within the code it was foretold that a most auspicious celestial occasion would mark the birth of the God-man. Our astronomers charted the heavens through the coming years until they arrived at a most auspicious event. In the spring of the year that you call 7 BC, eight planets of our solar system would align.

"That phenomenon of the heavens is occurring again within a few days, except that it will now include the Sun and Earth. We will not be able to see it. In 7 BC this astrological event did not include the Sun, making it visible in the night sky as the brightest star imaginable – many times brighter than our greatest planet.

"It took these men most of one year to determine the birthplace of this new King. He was not to be born in India, but in a land west of Mesopotamia and east of Egypt - Palestine. These brilliant brothers sought the counsel of the magi who had themselves been expecting the birth of a God-man for many years. If anyone were to survive an expedition into that land of tyrants to greet this God-man, the magi would, for they were true spiritual warriors.

"Word was sent out to the enclaves of the brotherhood who were affiliated with our brothers in India. Our magi assumed that the Egyptian Therapeutae in Heliopolis would have similar evidence of the God-man and neglected to inform those brothers. However, the Divine Plan would bring the God-man to them.

"Four men were chosen, a magus from each of three colonies and one astronomer, to make the journey of homage to the *Akhu* child. Each was a prince or king among his people as well as a magician of the Order of the Ruby.

"I am a descendant of Maharajah Ram, Melchior, who led the expedition, if we might call it such. He traveled with an astronomer named Tsekinata, who charted their course upon the Earth. They journeyed within the protection of invisibility to Damascus where they met the second Brother of the Ruby, Valtasassour (Balthazar), a king from the Arabian branch of the Brotherhood, who had traveled far from his Mission with a small group of brothers in Gaul. These two magi waited in Damascus to rendezvous with the third Brother of the Ruby, Gaspar, a dark-skinned magus and king from Armenia. Gaspar was said to be of Nubian descent.

"Tsekinata followed the planets until they were in alignment and calculated the place on the Earth where the brilliance of that convergence pointed to the God-man. He took the magi beyond Jerusalem, the bastion of the Roman tyrants, to a small village eight kilometers or so from Jerusalem. In this village of Bethlehem, within a cave, the enlightened princes and kings of the ancient Order of the Ruby bowed down before the God-man child, our beloved Jeshua.

"They brought him gifts of gold, frankincense and myrrh, the gifts of kings to a King. Our dearest Melchior knelt before the child, Jeshua, in his golden robes and drew his magi's sword. The child's parents did not flinch, for they could read the impeccability of his intent within his aura.

"Maharajah Ram broke the sword over his knee and lay it before the child, announcing that all authority rested at the feet of the child, Jeshua. He lay prostrate before the child in complete recognition of the Divine Union within the babe.

"These three men told the parents of the child's destiny as well has his origins, advising them to raise Jeshua in that consciousness – that he would always know who he was. This story has been retold in my family since that time.

"The parents took the child to Heliopolis in Egypt when the magi warned them that, in a jealous rage, Herod, the petty tyrant of Judaea, had commanded that all boy babies be slaughtered. Word of the new King had kindled in him a monstrous paranoia. In Heliopolis, the God-man was recognized and honored by the priests of the Therapeutae.

"When it was once again safe, the parents returned to Judah from Egypt to raise the child among the Essenes, a lineage of the Bird Tribes. The child's guardian, Joseph, was, in that order, the living King in the lineage of King David. Jeshua, his firstborn male, was a prince of the remnant blood of Aman-Ra. He had been sent to reawaken and reorganize that blood.

"When the child was a young man, he journeyed to our land to complete a series of initiations. These gateways of consciousness were necessary to fully activate his Mission on Earth. We do not refer to Jeshua simply as a magus, for he was a high master of all the brotherhoods, including those that did and do not exist in this reality. I now yield to Demetri, who will continue the story using resources of his people."

The circle received the humble blessing of the Maharajah and returned his reverent gesture. Demetri closed his eyes before beginning to ask for the blessing of beloved Lord Sananda, the ascended Jeshua, before speaking of the Master's secret life. Given the nature of the gathering, the blessing was granted and he opened his eyes to the group.

"Beloveds," he began with a thick accent, "I am a Greek Cypriot, hailing from that island were the Gnostics eluded both the Romans and the Christians. I am a Gnostic, a follower of the True Way that Jeshua exemplified. Deep esoteric mysteries remain within the mortar of our buildings from those days when Master Jeshua walked the Earth.

"What I share with you tonight I have learned from the secret writings of the brotherhood and the Gnostics. These Truths have never been altered by those wishing to control and were never contained in the great library of Alexandria that the tyrants burned to the ground. The library of the Order of the Ruby is contained within the consciousness of its members, incarnate and disincarnate.

"When Jeshua completed his puberty rites with the Essenes, Joseph sent him to the Egyptian Therapeutae in Heliopolis. Heliopolis was the ancient center of the Golden Age and in the time of Jeshua, the center of the remnant brotherhoods. He went to Heliopolis with his beloved friend, Simon Zebedee. Together they began the initiatory journey of the adept - the ancient Egyptian Mystery School.

"As was the custom, the first initiation occurred within three months. During those three months, they had taken instructions in the rules of the Therapeutae and the basic philosophy of the brotherhoods. Jeshua, Simon, and the other young men were brought, individually, before a panel of elders who questioned them rigorously about this knowledge. They were required to formulate their highest intent with respect to their training and lay it before the panel. This initiation eliminated those boys who were there to fulfill their parents' expectations and not their own, as well as those who were just not bright enough to pursue the studies.

"After this initiation, the boys were required to spend one month in each of the brotherhoods to know the totality of the Sun wisdom. Again, they were tested on their knowledge, more rigorously than the first initiation. Then they were expected to prepare an argument supporting their choice of a particular path of study.

"Simon had long been interested in the magi, so was relieved to be finished with the preliminaries at the Therapeutae. He was sent to the magi within Heliopolis to begin the study of alchemy.

"Jeshua showed a keen interest in all the brotherhoods but decided to pursue the Path of Healing, the specialty of the Therapeutae. One year was spent intensely exploring the fundamentals of healing with herbs, energy, and simple surgery. Jeshua had a natural ability to heal and was soon teaching the teachers. He saw healing from a totally new, but really very old, perspective – that all disease was a human perturbation of Divine perfection and harmony.

"Jeshua and Simon took the third initiation together at the end of their third year in Egypt, becoming Priests of Isis. Preparation for this ritual entailed the thorough cleansing of the temple – the human body. Having been raised by the Essenes made the preparation less difficult for Jeshua, but still, the organs and systems of the body were purged of impurities. At the same time, the emotional and mental bodies were purged of impurities as well.

"Ritual baths with sacred oils cleansed the exterior of the body and the aura, preparing them to meet the rising Sun between the paws of the great Sphinx. When the Sun hit Jeshua's field, he began to vibrate into the Sun's field – to match its frequency. In that state of bliss, a door opened which would have taken him back to God, had the high master of the Therapeutae not been there to stop him. He shouted a word of magic at Jeshua – a powerful word. Jeshua's body re-materialized to continue the Mission here on Earth. The high master knew then that he had found the one they had awaited.

"Simon went on to deeper studies of alchemy and magic after he and Jeshua completed the Fourth Degree of the brotherhood. In Hindu terminology this would be called *shaktipat* – illumination given through the powers of the high master. Connected to their Higher Self or I AM presence, they began bringing to Earth the ancient knowledge of their souls.

"Jeshua was introduced to the most secret of teachings as the remainder of his education continued in mystery. At that same time, Jeshua's brother James came to study at the Therapeutae.

"Jeshua was regularly teaching younger students and was invited to discussions with the faculty and the priests. Simon had reached his threshold of initiation and concentrated his energies on magic. Jeshua continued to work in the healing center of the Therapeutae where spontaneous cures began to occur. Before long, people came from all of Egypt to receive his healings. His explanation for the healing was the simple act of aligning the individual's energies with their innate God-Force.

"Throughout his education in Egypt, Jeshua trained his physical body to be the vehicle of a spiritual warrior. Higher degrees of initiation required the man to be fully realized, whereas lower degrees could be acquired by intellect alone.

"When Jeshua received the Fourth Degree, he moved out of the normal world of mind and into the higher world of wisdom and knowingness. This is the first step beyond intellect. Its center is in the heart – in the Now Moment. From the center in the heart, he moved into the mastery of energy – moving energy with intent.

"With this mastery, his physical training became one with the training of the spirit, the mind and the heart. He knew no separation of the three. At that time he regained the power of Union that Melchior had seen in him as a newborn babe - for even Jeshua experienced a thin veil of illusion. With that awakening, illusion vanished.

"He was put to many tests of physical strength, purity of emotion, absence of fear, and abilities to use energy impeccably before coming to the fifth initiation. The only fifth-degree initiate in the Therapeutae at that time was the high master who trained Jeshua in secrecy as his superior had trained him many years before.

"The trial was severe. To pass the Fifth Degree, the initiate was lowered into a large stone pit filled with poisonous snakes of all kinds. When the rope was removed, the only exit was a pool of water where several hungry crocodiles lived. Of course we know that Jeshua survived this trial because his life beyond is known, but for the initiate it is a death – a death to all but the Union of Essence and Divinity. To achieve that place one must have mastered energy and truly believe that the snakes and crocodiles are our brothers and sisters, as much a part of God as we.

"So it was with pure and impeccable essence that his love subdued the serpents and crocodiles and he emerged a high master. He was entering his sixth year of study at the Therapeutae when he equaled the training of his teacher.

"Because this level of initiation brought dissolution of the ego, Jeshua did not threaten the high master. On the contrary, the high master knew his destiny and guided him towards it. From that point forward, the high master could not teach from his own experience for it had not been his calling to go further, but he had access to the written legacy of Aman-Ra. He began preparing Jeshua for the ancient king-making ritual, the final initiation of the ancient brotherhood. Mastery at the level of the sixth initiation was interdimensional and cosmic.

"We could say that the fourth initiation, the Flowering of the Heart, was the birth within of Christ Consciousness and therefore the initiation of the Christ body. The third was comparable to light-body – initiated by the Sun. Mastery of energy brought forth the body of the magus and the final initiation activated the cosmic body and the possibility of Divine Oneness. Forgive me for referencing this as an archaic ritual – the initiations have not changed to the present and they are not, nor ever have been, limited to men.

"For beloved Jeshua, the Sixth Degree, which opens the portal to the seventh or cosmic dimension, was to pass through the doorway of death and survive. Similar to the near-death experiences reported throughout the ages, the initiate was taken to the light in the Heart of God. The difference between the two was that for the true initiate, the death was intended. It was a ritual death – passing through the doorway of immortality.

"It is exactly the way in which kings were made within the lineage of Aman-Ra. Like the true Incas of this land, the king was a cosmic God-man. To successfully prepare for and complete this initiation, the high master required the assistance of the magi, for it was within the alchemy of the magi that the formula of death was known. The magi prepared the potion from the venom of a certain snake, the holy keeper of wisdom. If the formula were not correct, death was certain. Even so, it was a terrible risk to be taken only by one fully prepared.

"In truth, the magi of that time had never used the potion but prepared it as part of their esoteric tradition. A true King had not come along for a very long time.

"The ritual took place in the King's Chamber of the Great Pyramid accessed through secret underground passageways. Jeshua lay within the sarcophagus after drinking the poison given to him by the high master. The initiate was to be left alone in the chamber and to emerge into daylight without assistance.

"I shudder to think how a modern twenty-year old might approach this ritual, but I like to imagine that Jeshua, a realized man, would have been perfectly content to rejoin God or to bring God back with him – that being the general idea. A true *Akhu* does not come to the Earth for himself or herself. They have no need to engage the dharma or the karma, for they are here only to serve. Jeshua was on a Mission. He had no attachment to life other than the completion of that Mission.

"The king-making ritual was one of death and resurrection – a theme important to all of the mystery schools. Jeshua rose from that death and walked out into the light of day passing through the thick stone walls of the pyramid. He had *seen* God and knew that he *was* God. He had had an experience during that death with the Siriun High Council that clarified his Mission, and he knew he had no more need to train at the Therapeutae. The high master had hoped that Jeshua would stay, for the mere stimulation of being around him, but that was not to be.

"By that time, Jeshua's brother James had finished the Third Degree, which marked the end of his studies. James' path would be one of merchant and philosopher. Jeshua, James and Simon left Heliopolis and spent a year in Alexandria drinking in Greek philosophy at the same time they researched the ancient archives in Alexandria's great library. Jeshua and Simon poured over the maps of the known world and plotted an expedition to the British Isles. The three men set out on a journey that taught them all about life outside the monastery. It was another kind of initiation, requiring that they use the skills they had acquired or perish. You and I know that all initiation undergoes validation in the world of men. Would we need initiation if the world were not as it is?" Demetri asked with a curious look on his face.

"Were it not for Jeshua's healing skills, the three young men would have suffered a dreadful fate at sea. They were robbed by the ship's crew almost immediately and put to work in the galley, despite the fact that they had paid well for the passage. By an extraordinary stroke of the Divine, their crusty captain became terribly ill and Jeshua was able to cure him. Given the skills of these men, one wonders at the nature of his illness and its relationship to their work in the galleys," he added, raising his eyebrows slightly. Don Eduardo slapped his knees laughing while Chris' crooked grin betrayed his love for this new *wayki*.

"In the south of the British Isles the true identity of the men was immediately discerned by the Druids, who took them under their wings. The Druid teaching originated through the missionary work of the Elder Race and the Lemurians when they were still on the Earth.

"Jeshua had two things in mind when he planned the expedition to Britain, and both were accomplished. The three received the full initiations of the Druid Priesthood, and they prepared the land for the future. Until the fall of Camelot, the energetic portal which Jeshua and Simon put in place there allowed the merging of realities, from the Kingdom of Fairie to the Fifth Dimension. It was large-scale Sacred Geometry – establishing energy fields of the Golden Cities. At some level, they still exist there.

"As for the initiations, they were quite different from those in Egypt, for they bound one to all things in nature. Jeshua wanted this shamanic sort of experience to balance all of the knowledge and magical power he had acquired in Egypt. Simon felt deeply connected to the Druid teaching, the warrior archetypes they embodied, and their unity with nature. James was there to connect with the land, for he would return as Joseph of Arimathea to plant his staff and bring the church of *The Way* to the Isles merging it with the Celtic traditions.

"Jeshua experienced the temptations of the flesh with seductive women, lessened the limited vision of the scholar by discovering the glory of God in every living thing, and faced death once again. Both he and Simon passed their initiations and the three men moved on to Gaul, where they worked again with the geometry and the land.

"In Gaul, the energies were created to protect the sisterhood, the secret teachings and the bloodline of the *Akhus*. Jeshua saw that it would be a refuge for his future family as well as those who embraced his teachings. There had been a small group of magi in Gaul from the time the southern shores had been settled by the tribe of Benjamin.

"Jeshua could clearly see that southern Gaul would become a place of persecution in the future but that the truth would survive through secret societies, the bloodline, the sisterhood and brotherhood.

"When they returned to Judaea, Simon was taken into the West Manasseh Magi and Jeshua returned to Qumran for a short while. His beloved Mary Magdalen had grown from child to a beautiful young woman, but it was not yet time for marriage. He saw even more clearly the power struggles and dysfunction existing within the different groups in the community, and spent time with Joseph, who was failing in health. Joseph was the father of the community, king of the House of David and Jeshua the heir to that service.

"However, his training was not complete for the greater task that lay before him. He joined his uncle's caravan and traveled to India. I would be a fool to discuss that aspect of his training in the presence of Ramandi. If you would not mind, Maharajah, I should be most pleased to hear of Jeshua's time in India."

The Maharajah acquiesced. "I am truly honored, Demetri," he began. "I believe it can be said that we are not trying to repeat history with this story, but to reveal the unknown history. I know that you women have heard this story from the perspective of Mary Magdalen and now hear it with a different emphasis," he continued, nodding to Leah. "It is all good Truth. Jeshua spent eight years in India, embracing Buddhism, Hinduism and Taoist philosophies, working miracles, walking with princes and lepers, curing disease, and teaching love on all levels.

"It was not until the last two years that he felt the call to the Himalayas. There he cleansed himself continually, fasted and sat in meditation by himself, until one day a yogi came to him. He had been asked to bring Jeshua to the region now bordering Tibet to study there.

"He went through the ritual initiations of the great yogis before being taken to a high mountain cave, where he was asked to sit with a very holy man. This man had initially called him to India with his intent. Jeshua sat with that holy man for many months before the man so much as blinked at him. Jeshua traveled out with him in his meditations, experiencing God energy and light.

"Then on a momentous day, the holy man lifted his finger, directing Jeshua to kneel before him. He received the highest level of *shaktipat* from that ancient ageless being, completing his quest in the east.

"We have always revered Jeshua in my country. We were fortunate to experience his essence without the politics that plagued him in his homeland. Many people feel that he died a very old man in Kashmir and is buried there, while many others believe that he ascended with his body. His ashram on the inner planes dwells over the

s near Darjeeling, but he is everywhere. Demetri, you can continue with your story now," he concluded, bowing his head.

"Thank you, Brother Ramandi. When Jeshua returned to Judaea, he found that Joseph had died and he was made King to the people at Qumran. However, he found it beneficial to protect his expanded state of awareness from the lower frequencies of the compound, so spent more time at Mird, the monastery referred to as the Wilderness. Before going to Mird, he was betrothed to Mary Magdalen, whom he later married.

"Now I shift to Simon's story, for he was a magus and a Brother of the Ruby. He had returned to Qumran with Jeshua and James after their initiatory journeys to Egypt and Britain. Simon did not stay long at Qumran either, though long enough to make the acquaintance of Helena-Solome, one of Mary Magdalen's dear friends. They were to become lifelong friends and lovers, for neither had the inclination to marry and Simon was something of a rogue.

"Simon's training took him to Arabia, where the brothers who had trained Balthazar took him deeper into the alchemy and instilled a great warrior spirit within him. When he returned to Judaea he joined the Zealots, warriors for independence from Rome. Politically radical and completely devoted to the philosophy that Jeshua began developing in Egypt, Simon had to swallow hard when his dearest friend came back from India a Mystic.

"Still, he never left Jeshua's side through his trials, and used his high magic to move Jeshua into the death ritual on the cross and revive him in the cave of his Resurrection.

"Simon believed in Jeshua completely. He assisted a pregnant Mary and their two young children in their escape to Gaul prior to the destruction of Jerusalem. He aided Jeshua who remained in hiding until it was safe for him to travel to Rome and then the east.

"Simon was the truest of magi, for he protected the sisterhood and the royal blood in ways unimaginable to the ordinary mind. He led the Nazarenes from Jerusalem to Mesopotamia, saving them from the scourge of Rome, poisoned Herod-Agrippa to instigate the revolution, then joined Mary and Helena-Solome in France, where they formed the early Gnostic sect.

"Simon was not one to write gospels or reveal much of anything about himself. He was a warrior for the Truth and a high initiate in the Brotherhoods of the Sun.

"While in Gaul, he became a substitute father to Jeshua and Mary's children, Tamar, Jesus Justus, and Josephes. Jesus Justus became the crown prince, traveling to Britain with his Uncle James for further studies.

"In Jerusalem, James had been bishop of the Nazarene church of *The Way*, until his life was threatened and he escaped to Gaul. There he assumed the family title of Joseph of Arimathea and brought the new church to Britain.

"The Gnostics grew in southern France, and even at the early stage were persecuted by the Church of Rome. The Gnostics were as well guided by women as men and held no restrictions on them. Quite the contrary, they were honored in every way and Mary was regarded as the embodiment of Sophia, the Holy Spirit. This fostered the devotion to the Black Madonna, which continues to this day. Peter and Paul had a tremendous fear of women and the feminine, so they designed the church of Rome to exclude them as unworthy and unclean.

"Because the Gnostics held equality of men and women within their sect, the women were privy to esoteric teachings reserved for the men in the Judeo-Christian traditions. They wrote gospels of their own and were respected teachers in that region. Mary's ministry was widespread in both France and Italy.

"The culture was rich in many ways, but Simon heard the call to go to Britain himself and took young Josephes for initiatory training with the Druids, just as he and Jeshua had experienced years before. Josephes would be the Grail Child, the male seed of the lineage, for Jesus Justus' only son, Galains, chose to become a celibate Mystic.

"The firstborn child of Jeshua and Mary, Tamar, was a mysteriously transparent and lovely young woman who died in service to the lepers of southern Gaul. Tamar's daughter, Gabriella carried on the female royal line and the magic of her secret father, Simon the Magus.

"Simon returned to France after Tamar's death to help Mary with her own passage. Jeshua came also from Rome, where he had felt her readiness to leave the Earth. Simon saw to her burial in an alabaster tomb near St. Baume, then returned to Britain, where he was supposedly persecuted and crucified for his beliefs.

"Personally, I have a hard time believing that," he concluded, "as I believe he had higher magic than history would ever acknowledge."

Demetri folded his hands together in a blessing of Simon's courage. "There are certain points to be made from all of this tradition. One is the Mission of the Brotherhood of Magi, which was twofold. It was to protect the sisterhood who carried the planetary codes of consciousness that would bring the Christ Mission to its fulfillment. As you can see from the story, it was also to protect the bloodline of Christ – both duties were more important than their lives.

"Another point to be made is about initiation. These men experienced awe-inspiring initiation in a number of so-called mystery schools. These exhausting trials were transformations of body, mind and spirit. At each of these levels they faced fear until they became fearless, ego until they became ego-less, and death until they transcended their mortality."

Codes of the Holy Grail

Firelight danced on the walls of the cement building as the assemblage of brothers, sisters and friends laid down their sleeping mats and bags for the night. Chris met with no objections as he positioned himself next to Leah. Their love was obvious and considered a blessing in the heart of each participant. After Chris returned from a check of the camp periphery with Julio, he settled down into his sleeping bag, facing Leah.

"Good night, Darling," she whispered as he stroked her cheek.

"I love you, Leah,'" he replied softly, leaning towards her to kiss her lips.

"Thank you, Chris," she sighed. "I love you too, and I do understand why you are protecting me."

"You understand part of it, Beloved, the codes and the blood. Soon you will understand it all. How do you like Demetri?" he asked.

"I adore him, Chris," she whispered passionately. "Demetri is just how I pictured Simon Magus – a wild and crazy, totally dedicated and authentic man."

"He is that, Leah."

"Hearing about the initiations of Jeshua jogged my memory of past incarnations, making me even more grateful for this life as a woman."

"Speaking purely for myself, I am glad you're a woman too," he whispered, kissing her again. "You know though, there is something about the way in which men get settled into things with their mothers, with their wives, with their jobs, with their spirituality and on and on that calls forth these initiations. Perhaps it makes the task of manifestation somewhat simpler."

"I have always thrived on change," she replied, "but I do understand how it scares people – especially men."

"I'll keep that in mind," he said, pulling her closer. "Why don't you roll over now so that we can curl up together all night?"

"I might decide to change position in the middle of the night," she teased, rolling over to nestle against him.

Chris kissed Leah's ear and whispered, "you'll find I can roll with the punches. Sweet dreams, My Love."

Leah was asleep within a few minutes, warm and secure next to Chris and comfortable with the presence of such a paradox in her life. Chris drifted off feeling mystery engulf him – the enchantment of "the Beloved".

The group was awakened well before sunrise to meet a short distance from the building, where the Sun would be seen rising over the jungle canopy. Sunrise was the main event at Tres Cruces, the reason that people protected by mountains or jungle forest journeyed to this less hospitable place, where *Tayta Inti* rose unobstructed. Bathed in the light of God, the group held hands facing the east while gently stepping their feet on the Earth to announce their intent for the day.

That intent, as stated by Don Eduardo, was the manifestation of a considerably higher frequency in all the group's activities - in every thought, word and action of the day. He revealed to the group that there existed an interdimensional portal at Tres Cruces, a portal made manifest to those whose frequency matched it. As a short-term goal of the group, matching that frequency would be a formidable task, for it was fully Fourth Dimension. Don Eduardo pulled Leah aside and gave her instructions for the women's training that needed to begin that morning in circle.

After breakfast, the men went off towards Kañacway Mountain, leaving the women in the camp. Ramandi and Sheik Fakoum had fortuitously brought some rugged clothing. However it was an interesting sight to see the eight brothers of such diverse backgrounds trekking out of camp behind the *alto mesayoqs*. Clearly they were cosmic guests of the Indians, for not a single brother felt the need to assert himself to take over Don Eduardo's leadership role – Chris least of all, though he was the Lord of the Ruby. His humility greatly impressed Leah and would have impressed all of the women, had they known his true identity.

Leah brought her women together in circle on the sunny side of the building. Doña Felicia, Doña Lucia and Margarita sat beside Leah, holding the space for all of the women. The wind whipped about occasionally and the Sun felt deeply healing to the entire circle.

Leah opened the session with a meditation on the light of the Sun grounded through each of them to Mother Earth. Then she asked each of the women to share her thoughts and feelings, especially any that needed to be released to move forward with the work at hand.

Natalie was right there with the first question. "What exactly is the work at hand, Leah? It feels to me that we are incubating some kind of cosmic egg – trouble is, it's pretty elusive. Do you know what's in store?"

"Well, you do get to the point, Natalie," Leah laughed. "We are moving closer to our dreaming work. Apparently we will have today to clear out anything standing in the way, which means emotions, ego, mental clutter, physical problems, anything that isn't high frequency. We have spent time in the higher dimensions before. We do know what Fifth Dimension feels like, so I suggest that we clear everything, holding Fourth Dimension fully then go to Fifth Dimension to be able to capture the dream. Obviously you are all here because you will be able to do this, and we have had plenty of practice clearing."

"Any idea what this dream looks like?" Liu asked.

"I have always thought of the Fifth Dimension as the ashrams of the Ascended and the Golden Cities, for example. We will see what it looks like when we get there, Liu. In the Hindu teaching it is the causal plane. What I know for sure is that it is heart space – Christ Consciousness."

"Are we expected to transcend our egos in one day?" Brit asked, feigning a worried look. "I may need more than one day to complete the job." Everyone laughed and the group loosened up a bit. The task at hand was enormous and the path uncharted. Leah knew it.

"Well Brit, the ego will have to be tricked. We have all had those moments when it was transcended, allowing us to connect directly to the Divine. Our job is to create that kind of dream, through the weaving of its assemblage point, then step outside of time with it. We have worked on all of this before."

"Just a walk in the park," Sonia laughed. "Let's get to work."

"Would you like to start, Beloved?" Leah asked, opening her mesa - a finely woven bundle containing stones and sacred items. She laid it out upon the Earth before her. "We will use the power of the mesa and *Huascar Inca* to shift some energy here. *Huascar* guards the *Ukhupacha*, the unconscious, and he loves to clean house," she added, laughing.

"Sure, I'll start," Sonia offered. "I've just had this tremendous breakthrough with Susmo, because he's had some kind of breakthrough himself. It's like a door has opened and I am flooded with memories of men I have known, including those in my family. I am hearing their words and mine, the womanizing, and the seduction, and my own manipulation of them. Everything I have participated in is in my face whether I was conscious of it or not.

"I would like this flood of criticism, self and otherwise, to wash into the Ocean of Forgiveness. I want *Mamacocha* (Mother Water) to swallow it all and make me whole again. It is definitely time," she concluded passionately.

"Has anyone else noticed that it has become difficult to be in denial on this journey?" Ellia asked. "What Sonia is experiencing has been a little catchy, like a virus from the *Ukhupacha*." The women laughed at her reference to the unconscious, the dark interior world of shadows.

"I would like to turn off the voices of the past myself. The shame-based stuff I have within the core of my being that has been too painful to clear, but I find it's in my face. I lived a pretty normal life when I was young, but was shamed into thinking I was a slut and a failure in my family. I understand all of the psychology and the core beliefs and I'm ready to part with it. I don't want it dragging down our efforts to weave this new assemblage point. I'm laying it out on the mesa right now so *Pachamama* can eat it up."

"Way to go, Ellia," Carolyn chimed in. "While *Pachamama* is at it, she can devour my deep-seated need to be special. I like coming on trips with you, Leah, because you are so incredibly special and you don't appear to care. Maybe the piece I'm missing is to surrender to my Mission so I can just walk away from the identity issues. It's a big one for me."

"For me, too," added Genevieve and Bridget at once.

"Let's face it, we are all in that boat, Sisters," Natalie added. "I am sure that each of us has a poignant story of how we overcame all manner of obstacles as women to finally become somebody. The idea of letting all of that go is a little disconcerting. How does it make us feel? Or think? Or look to the world? I guess the trick is to not care. Is that right, Leah? Do you just not care that the man of all of our dreams is knockdown in love with you?"

Leah laughed, blushing. "I love you, Natalie. You are so up front with your feelings. I think it's obvious that I care enormously about Chris, and yet it feels like the Divine Plan unfolding – no plan of mine, I assure you. That somehow simplifies it, because my expectations are fairly minimal. It's an unfoldment."

"If I knew something like that would happen to me, I'd let go of all my dreams and expectations," Marie Louise said, "but then I guess that's an expectation, isn't it?" Everyone laughed.

Leah sensed the group moving into a slightly higher frequency. "It is, Marie Louise," Leah replied, "but it's the right idea. One little expectation can detour the Divine Plan, because your ego had to fulfill a need that the real you didn't need at all. It's an absolute surrender to the Divine Plan that opens the door.

"Everything you are saying this morning, all of you, speaks of detachment. Changing core beliefs is as much a detachment as letting go of an agenda, a plan for your life. Detachment opens doors - doors of the Divine Plan. I suspect that we are experiencing some benevolent help with our work here. It seems a perfect time to let go of all kinds of things that are stopping us and it is really coming up, so why don't we put more out on the mesa for *Pachamama* to eat?"

The group continued to bare their souls to each other and to the spirits of the Earth and sky that hovered around them. As they did, they began to feel lighter, freer and more connected. It wasn't new work for any of them, though deep issues were emerging from the unconscious that had not been addressed before. In addition, this combination of women had not worked together before this journey.

As their fields cleared of old thought forms and emotional baggage, their assemblage points shifted into higher frequency. Following on the heels of this shift was a predictable arousal of the women's egos. Fearing its own demise, the ego consistently reared its enormous head whenever the Higher Self emerged. However, at this level of the work, the ego was subtle in its game of survival. Leah tracked ego as the women continued to communicate.

The higher aspects of the Fourth Dimension offered other subtleties as well. Wisdom, Truth and imagination came only with detachment from knowledge, opinion and rationality. Detachment proved always to be a doorway to higher dimensions.

Listening to the discussion, Leah would hear wisdom one minute and knowledge the next, sometimes accompanied by opinion or rational thought. They were clearly traveling companions in the mind. With her intent, she began pulling more of the higher frequency filaments like wisdom and Truth into the group assemblage point, at the same time asking particular women to let go of lower-frequency core beliefs that were holding the group back. Sensitivity and finesse were the only tools necessary to accomplish this purpose.

Near the end of their session, Georgia put forth a dilemma that she had encountered recently. She had attended a seminar given by a well-known woman in the field of self-help. Though superbly presented, the words of this woman were in obvious contradiction to her actions. Part of Georgia wanted to set the record straight for the other participants, another part of her wanted to take the good ideas and leave the rest behind, and another part of her longed to transcend it all – but how? She asked Leah.

"What a perfect example, Beloved, thank you," Leah began. "Your initial reaction came to you through the formation of opinion. Opinion is a way in which we have been trained to make choices about things. Its foundation happens to be knowledge. Without knowledge there can be no opinion. Opinion relies on comparison for its power – 'she's not walking her talk like I am'. The part of you that wanted to take the good and leave the rest behind used discernment. Maybe you were able to see and honor the contribution she was making to the world. Discernment requires a little heart, since what might appear to be correct based on knowledge may not work for you. When you discern, you follow your heart while referencing your knowledge. It may not make sense, but it feels right, and the outcome supports your purpose.

"Now, your third idea strongly supports the Fifth Dimension, which is to honor this woman for her innate Godliness. This we can do by accepting paradox in our lives. Our lives are paradox. Opinion does not support paradox. Even discernment does not support paradox. Paradox means embracing both her inspired ideas and her actions, which appear to contradict them. Either/or doesn't work in paradox. Paradox is the landscape of both/and.

"Paradox says it is all to be loved and embraced. How can we love life if we cannot accept paradox? Life is paradox. That is why most people suffer here on Earth. Paradox is beyond the illusion. Paradox finds God in the expression of all things.

"Opinion is the domain of the ego. Discernment is the domain of the initiate, and paradox lifts the veil of illusion to reveal the Higher Self- the adept. The initiate struggles with the ego, while the adept transcends it.

"I have watched what happens to ego on this spiritual path. We begin in a place of ego gratification – getting our wants, needs and desires met. We are in lower-body and lower-mind. This is the domain of opinion as well. We progress to that place of discernment where ego is challenged and assemblage points are shifted radically to accommodate new views of reality outside of wants, needs and desires.

"Finally, accepting the paradox that arises in that stage of discernment, the door opens to attainment – the ego is the servant of those who truly serve God. Do you all see this?" she asked.

"I understand what you are saying about the evolution of the ego, but I always get messed up with paradox," said Bridget. "Are you saying it is possible to accept violence, wars, killings?"

"Do you accept life?" Leah asked.

"Of course, I accept life. Here I am," she answered, throwing her hands in the air, with a grin.

"Wars, violence and killing are part of life, Bridget. In addition, there is an innate violence in nature and within our bodies. If we are to be fully alive, without illusion, then we accept that these things exist, somehow belong, in the landscape of the Third-Dimensional human experience. Fifth Dimension is another story.

"Do we become violent with others? Of course, not. However, if we have dedicated our lives to Higher Consciousness, we must accept that we, as human beings, share a template with all other human beings that gives us the potential to be violent. If we cannot accept this, we will have great difficulty seeing the God in others."

"What do you mean, the violence within our bodies?" Carolyn asked. "Are you talking about anger and frustration?"

"That would be too obvious," Leah laughed. "What do you think your immune system and all of the pathogens you host are doing in your body night and day? It's a war, Beloved, and you are a participant - in fact you, much like the Earth, provide the landscape for this violence. Of course, this is all our perception of it but we have chosen that particular perception of immunity. It leaves no space for an alternative concept.

"As long as we remain in separation from that which truly is life, we will experience this violence. When we are in the Oneness, there is no violence, but there is no fitting definition of life either, only consciousness. Accepting paradox baffles the ego, opening the door to Higher Self.

"By far the greatest paradox we have to accept is that, in the grand scheme of things, we are nothing, and yet we are everything – God incarnate."

There followed a reflective pause before Ellia spoke up. "What if people are getting hurt by the woman in Georgia's example?" Ellia asked.

Leah spoke passionately, thankful that Ellia was anticipating where she was going with the teaching. "Well, if any of you think the participants are getting hurt, look at your own ego and its opinions. The other people are not in ego pain. You are in ego pain.

"You have an agenda. It is your ego up in arms because you know better; you are wiser, more astute and impeccable. It is with missionary zeal that the ego dives into a situation to save the ill-informed peasants of the world.

"But wait a minute, those peasants have souls too, and they are all on their own journey back to God. What they are hearing from that woman may start them on their spiritual paths – shift their assemblage points enormously. In time, they will arrive at discernment too, and make those choices for themselves - and so will she. Like you, they will struggle with their own egos over a similar situation.

"Here is the great work of enlightenment, Beloved! If you think there will be no paradox in the Fifth Dimension, think again. It will be Fifth Dimensional paradox. If you think that ego does not exist in Fifth Dimension, think again. Ego is everywhere outside the Heart of God. If you think that Fifth Dimension will be somewhere in the clouds, remember the words of Jesus in the Gospel of Thomas -

" *'The kingdom of heaven is spread before you on the Earth, but men do not see it.'*

"Third, Fourth and Fifth Dimensions, like all dimensions, exist simultaneously, and we are presented with numerous opportunities to rise and fall through them every day. All of the dimensions are right here, right now. Your awareness of them is a function of your frequency.

"From the perspective of the assemblage point, ego feels most comfortable when others share its view of reality. That is the missionary credo. It's also manipulation.

"Living in Higher Self presumes acknowledgment of the fact that no two people have the same view of reality, though they can share aspects of it. Higher Self honors that sovereignty. Higher Self delights in it.

"These blocks will need to be removed if we are to stabilize assemblage points for the higher dimensions. Any questions?" she concluded.

"What is the purpose of war?" asked Genevieve.

"What is the purpose of peace, Beloved?" she responded.

"Is it all just the nature of the Earth experience?" Genevieve asked again, a little frustrated.

"You may have something there, Genevieve," Leah answered, smiling. "I will let you consider that until we meet again tomorrow. What I will say now is that as the Earth experience changes - as Earth moves towards Fifth Dimension - human behavior will shift from war to peace. Where does it start? Within each of us. When we change our individual templates, the collective template shifts. As we move through this day and evening, let us consider the ego. We will bring what we can of it to the mesa tomorrow morning and feed it to *Pachamama*.

"I would ask you to look at the manifestations of ego; defensiveness, territoriality, competition, intellect, possessiveness, greediness, power and its abuse, special-ness, desire and ego-centered thought. At the root of it all is fear.

"The ego fears loss of control. It is the ego that fears the unknown. Death is an unknown to the ego. Higher Consciousness is an unknown to the Third Dimensional ego. Ego is invested in this life. Find out how that appears in your life. Are you invested in success, in wealth, in getting your needs met, or in service?" A few eyebrows were raised with her last words. "Yes, Beloveds, I said service. If we are invested in service, it is the ego. If we serve from compassion and unconditional love, it is Higher Self. Ask yourself if you could die tomorrow without a single regret – without a single attachment?

"What has happened to our playfulness?" she added with deep feeling. "We are children of God who have become so invested in this life that we have forgotten how to be free. We have lost our freedom to our investments.

"Find out what your investments look like and bring them to *Huascar's* mesa tomorrow. How do we identify ourselves? Who and what are we?

"Understand that to do our work in the world, we wear the clothing of the world. Our True Self lies within, visible to all those with eyes to see. In this way we don't sublimate the ego, but we use it to fulfill our soul's purpose. What we break is the ego's dominion over us. We will need to be in our God-presence to begin our dream work, Beloveds. The dream must be impeccable."

Lunch was almost ready and the Sun as warm as it was going to get. The women's circle broke into small groups gathering the sunlight as they discussed their work.

It wasn't long before the men came back into camp. Dusty and disheveled, the brothers entered camp as spirited comrades. Brian was limping, but seemed to be filled with a fierceness previously lacking. Chris gave Leah a gentle kiss on the cheek, asking her about the morning session.

"We are making headway, Chris. Might I ask what you dusty warriors were doing?"

"We were jousting, of course, but without the horses," he teased, massaging her shoulders and neck.

"An initiation for dear Brian, by any chance?" she asked, smiling.

"Very insightful, Mate," he replied, kissing the nape of her neck before letting her go. "Birthing the spiritual warrior is risky at best."

Engaged in spirited sparring, the men had tapped into deep remembrance of their lineage as warrior knights. Simon Magus had been a Zealot, a warrior on behalf of freedom and justice. The Zealots were radical – some of them would be called terrorists in this age.

However, the magi were motivated by duty, loyalty, compassion and honor, and not by the lust for power or need to be right. Those ideals were supported by the qualities of Truth, wisdom, love and integrity. These were essential Grail Codes. Simon did not strive for personal power, but used the powers that he had to overthrow tyrants. Jeshua had not always agreed with him or endorsed his actions, but respected him for following the magi's codes. The magi embraced the paradox and used it to move energy.

As Chris recounted the story, Brian had taken an unexpected tumble over the edge of a sudden drop off while sparring with Don Eduardo. Unexpected it may have been. Unforeseen it was not. Brian's memory opened as he flew through the air, powerless to stop the fall. He instinctively went limp and landed ten feet below, with no more than a slightly pulled Achilles. His compassionate brothers were all around him within seconds, Julio having leapt from the drop off unharmed. The incident had brought Brian into sudden alignment with the brothers and the Mission.

"A pulled tendon is a small price to pay for illumination, don't you think?" Chris asked Leah.

"A small price, indeed," she replied. "I have felt the Mission approaching, so the timing is right."

"How are the women preparing?" he asked, leaning against the sunny side of the building.

"We have to create the Dreamscape, Chris. To do that we have to be free of ego and everything that accompanies it. Clarity is the key word right now.

"We did great work this morning dropping density. Now we are thinking about who we are and who we really are. It feels like we need to make that jump tomorrow then engage the dream in the form of rehearsal. How have the men been preparing?"

"What I know is that an inauthentic brother cannot complete this Mission. It would be a disservice, perhaps even a disgrace, to the Order. What we are doing is called "getting real", finding our authenticity at every level of awareness, physical, emotional and so forth. Basically it is the same thing you are doing with the women. You are right; it doesn't feel like we have a lot of time. The last of our brothers should be arriving today, then we will really dig in and clear out the *Ukhupacha.*"

"You are a most interesting collection of men at this point. Do you know who will arrive today?"

"I expect I will, though I am not aware in this reality yet."

Hot soup arrived in the hands of a young warrior. Leah and Chris sat against the warm wall with their lunch while the rest of the group spread out around the site eating in small groups.

"You know, Chris," Leah continued, "I have known you for ten days in this reality and I am realizing that I am invested in you. We women are contemplating our investments this afternoon.

"I realize that I am invested in the idea that we might have at least one night together when this journey ends. I am invested in a notion of spending time with you in the Outback. These are little things, but I am clinging to them. This is fair warning that I have to let it go to the Divine Plan."

"What if it is the Divine Plan?" he said, grinning in that way she found irresistible.

"I have no way of knowing that, Darling." she replied cautiously.

"Yes you do, Leah. It's written in your heart. What does your heart tell you?"

"My heart tells me that we are blessed somehow to have found each other. My ego wants me to fail the Mission, so it will rationalize desire however it can. That is why I cannot trust my desire. My vision tells me that there is something very sacred, fragile and mysterious about all of this. It is an unfoldment to be honored."

"Right on all counts. Full expression of our love does not require that we consummate the relationship. However, through the consummation there can be a portal to the Divine. There's nothing wrong with it at the appropriate moment. Still, you have a point about investment. We might both try to detach from the investment without losing the essence of our love. I do share your investment, by the way. I have the hotel all picked out in Lima."

Leah smiled somewhat sheepishly. "I wonder if it is the same hotel I have picked out?" she laughed, grabbing his knee.

Chris reached over to shake her lightly by the neck. "Walk with me down the jungle path after lunch, Leah. The jungle is such a sumptuous contrast to the mountain energy."

"I think I could manage that," she replied, touching his arm. "It might balance our energies. What were your dreams last night, Chris?" she asked.

"Darling, I was making love to you on at least three Dreaming Paths, with and without company. Having you right next to me intensified all of them. I distinctly remember kissing the curve of your neck. I was also involved in a dream with Mukda and Sananda. We were chanting before the Disc of the Sun in the ashram."

"I was with Mukda as well – moving energy again. Every time it is a little more exacting, but I understand more and more this art of moving energy. I remember the kiss on the neck as well, but I think it was in this reality."

"Quite likely to be a recurring event, I would think," he replied, with a twinkle in his eyes.

After lunch they wandered down the jungle path that Julio had taken searching for Sheik Fakoum, Ramandi, and Demetri. Julio was attending to Brian's tendon, making it easy for Leah and Chris to slip away alone. As they walked down through the high jungle, the strong vibration of Mother Earth began to surround them. Awareness of the cycles of life in the jungle intensified the eroticism in Nature. Subtler than the low jungle, the sexual energy was nonetheless palpable.

After an hour of hiking into increased warmth and moisture, Chris veered off the path towards the sound of water. Rushing water from a mountain stream pooled out amidst inviting foliage. Footprints in the mud indicated the presence of nearby jungle animals, while the birds kept up a continual chorus of cries, caws, and whistles.

"You have done it again, Chris," Leah laughed, leaning over to test the water temperature. "It's cool and clear, just right for bathing."

Leah produced a washcloth and ecological camp soap from her waist pack, setting them down on a rock. Chris grinned, shaking his head. "Of course, you would be prepared," he laughed.

"It's a funny thing, Chris, but when I am tromping around with you I somehow expect to get my needs met no matter where we are. I expect you would find a hot pool at the South Pole and a cool pool in the Outback."

"I am happy to manifest whatever you need, Beloved. Would you like me to leave?"

"On the contrary, I'd like you to help," she replied with a mischievous light in her eyes. "Then I will help you. Can we do this impeccably?"

"The perils of sexual love shall not befall you, Luminous One," he replied. "Thank you for the privilege."

She stood before him while Chris slowly undressed her, one layer at a time. He did not try to hold her or kiss her, knowing that the Universe was testing him. In this regard, she was a Goddess. She was one with the jungle and all of life.

Though the air was warm, the water, cascading down from the mountains, was fairly cool. Therefore, Leah sat at the pool's edge with her feet in the water. She bent forward into the pool to wet her hair. After stripping to the waist, Chris lathered the soap into her thick blonde hair. He massaged her scalp, noticing the wise gray hairs that were numerous but difficult to see among the blonde. She dipped her head again to rinse her hair while Chris soaped the cloth. As if bathing a newborn baby, he gently washed and rinsed her body. Touched by the exquisite beauty around her and the impeccability present in Chris' touch, Leah allowed the tears to roll down her cheeks. She felt renewed and nurtured in every way.

Chris finished undressing as Leah squeezed the water from her hair and combed it out. Then unbinding his long hair, he dipped his head into the pool as well. Chris sat at the pool edge while Leah rose to wash his silvery dark hair, returning the gentle massage. After he rinsed his hair, she bathed his body as he had bathed hers - as if he were a God. Overwhelmed by her attention, he shed tears of gratitude as well then submerged himself in the pool to rinse off.

Both refreshed, they sat back to back on a great flat rock, sharing the vibrant energies of *Pachamama* within a combined luminous field. Warm surges of energy charged up their linked spines. Resisting the urge to allow the energy to bloom sexually, they moved it higher through all of the chakras and out their heads like a fountain of light. Feeling the merging of their flesh, they lost all sense of individuality to the Beloved. Passion had been transformed into the most profound experience of love.

When the light began to dim, they dressed slowly in silence, so as not to break the enchantment of the moment. Following Chris out to the main path, Leah wondered if it were possible to be invested in the perfection of that Oneness. There had been no desire or ego in the experience. Integrity could bypass those snags entirely. They had hiked into the jungle feeling a building human passion, but the Divine Plan had provided them with an alternative. Subtle misgivings about their relationship vanished.

Like childhood playmates, they hiked hand in hand, laughing and singing, up the trail towards the camp. When a little over half the way back, they came upon a man sitting on a tree stump looking up the trail. He wore the simple traveling robes of a monk with a shoulder cape and matching cap of Oriental brocade. A long, thin gray braid hung down his back. Leah grasped Chris' arm.

"A brother?" She whispered to Chris who had stopped on the trail.

"A most revered elder brother," he whispered back, sensing the man's energetic field.

Aware of the intrusion, the man turned around and Leah gasped. "Master Mukda," she whispered incredulously, "here in the jungle?"

"It certainly looks that way - unless we have entered the Dreaming Paths."

"I've never been certain that Third Dimension isn't a Dreaming Path, but this is not Lord Sananda's ashram."

"Lord Sananda is a Kumara, Leah. His ashram is everywhere," Chris replied, pulling her along on the path.

When they reached the smiling master, Chris knelt before him to receive his blessing. To Leah, Chris seemed a knight kneeling before Merlin. Images flashed before her eyes - courtly scenes of Arthur and his Grail Knights. She was carried into that vision until Chris touched her arm, bringing her from the trance-state. She walked up to greet Master Mukda, who rose from the rock as she neared him. Expecting to kneel before him, she was stunned when he took her hand and knelt to kiss her sapphire ring.

"I did not wish to break the enchantment of your Divine loving energies below," he said in perfect English while nodding down the trail, "therefore I chose to await you here."

"Master Mukda," Leah replied, "why do you honor me so? I should be kneeling before you."

"Humor an old immortal, My Dear Woman. I have had little opportunity to behold the Goddess in this reality."

"I must represent the Goddess of Outdoor Adventure," she mused to herself. "Do you really live in this reality?" she asked as Master Mukda stood.

"As a brother, this is the dimension of my current Mission," he responded. "It isn't necessarily where I am comfortable."

Chris picked up Mukda's pack, thinking it amazing that Mukda had come from the jungle floor to Tres Cruces. The Madre de Dios River was not the easiest way to arrive. The weight of the pack made it clear to him that Mukda had manifested himself on the trail, knowing that they were nearby. Cleverly he had decided to walk into camp with two people who knew him well.

Arriving in camp, they saw the horses and packs of the remaining brothers. Surrounded by *waykis*, they had been introducing themselves to the group. The circle parted as Leah and Chris arrived with Master Mukda. Brian and Julio looked startled, having remembered Mukda from their Dreamtime. Everyone else bowed slightly out of respect for the Tibetan Master, who went immediately to greet Don Eduardo, his brother from across the sea. Leah and Chris approached the newly arrived brothers, giving them hugs and kisses on the cheek.

Tall and slender, Peter Wilshire was an amiable, gray-haired Welshman. He had an easy smile, soft brown eyes, and radiant heart energy. He knew of Leah through a mutual friend in Glastonbury, but never expected to see her in the middle of Peru with ten other women. The second brother, Jacques de Villey, had been born, and still lived in a French village near the border of Italy. Jacques was agile yet strong, having the enduring kind of tensile strength of a gymnast or skier. Wavy dark hair framed a narrow face with aquiline features and amazing blue-violet eyes.

Until the Hour of Power, the group mingled with each other in the easy acceptance of the new arrivals. They watched the Sun sink in the west, creating glorious colors in the sky. The entire gathering was silenced by the depth of their gratitude for all the magic that was life.

With the addition of the three brothers, the group was complete. That night a circle formed to hear the stories of the brotherhood that Peter and Jacques had to offer. It was decided that Master Mukda would conclude the storytelling the following night. Peter and Jacques sat in front of the altar facing the gold skull, while the rest of the group sat in an informal circle around them.

Chris and Leah sat across the circle facing the two men, while Master Mukda perched on a duffel bag next to Chris. The scent of *Agua Florida* filled the room as Peter and Jacques came before Don Eduardo for a *limpia*.

Producing six pieces of amber, said to have paved the roads of Avalon, Peter set the six-pointed star grid in the room, lifting the frequency towards the Golden Cities. The golden skull began emanating a warm ruby-red light. Chris' eyes met those of Don Eduardo, acknowledging with deep gratitude the *ylloq'e's* part in manifesting the first gathering of the incarnate Order of the Ruby since ancient times. The skull was completely activated.

Peter's storytelling task was immense, beginning with what he knew of the bloodlines of Jeshua and his brother James as they came into early Britain and France. Not a blood lineage, but a soul lineage of warriors dedicated to Higher Consciousness, the magi incarnated to be near the bloodlines carrying the Grail Codes, the sisterhood, and anyone serving the Truth. Peter extended his gratitude to Don Eduardo for initiating the gathering and to all present for the warmth of brotherhood and sisterhood.

"Brothers and Sisters," he began, his deep, thickly accented voice rolling out into the circle, "The importance of this gathering has not yet saturated my consciousness, since I am still integrating the odyssey of managing to get here. My gratitude goes out to Don Eduardo for focusing the energies, which have allowed this gathering to manifest.

"To do justice to the exquisite plan of the Siriun High Council, we must reach back in time to 586 BC with my part of the story. At that time, a young woman of the House of David, Tamar Tephi, the daughter of King Zedekiah of Judah, was brought to Ireland by the prophet Jeremiah to marry King Eochaid I. Queen Tamar was an *Akhu* and a priestess of the beloved sisterhood. She brought priestesses with her to establish a temple of the Sun in old Ireland. She held codes of consciousness which were to enrich the Gaelic people of the Western Isles on behalf of the planetary ascension Mission.

"Tamar's guardian, Jeremiah, was a magus. He brought with him the Stone of Destiny, an engraved smooth granite stone that was held to be the stone upon which Jacob rested his head when he dreamed of the ladder reaching up to heaven. The stone symbolizes the succession of Grail kings and is now hidden somewhere in Scotland.

"Jeremiah died soon after completing that last part of his Earth Mission, but not before he had touched the hearts and beliefs of the Druids, whom he knew to be keepers of the Lemurian wisdom.

"In Judah, Jeremiah's unheeded prophecies had foretold the loss of the throne of Judah by the House of David; thus he was just as happy to be elsewhere through the darkness that overtook Judah. Jeremiah had been offered status in the Babylonian court by the conquering king, Nebuchadnezzar, who greatly respected his gift of prophecy. However, Jeremiah chose the magi's path as guardian of the sisterhood assisting the new light on its journey to Ireland. As an aside, it is interesting that Nebuchadnezzar, in capturing the Hebrews, established a place in Babylon where they could practice their rituals and teach their beliefs. In fact, that is where the Torah was birthed. It seems to me that, unlike the kings of Judah, Nebuchadnezzar actually practiced the Grail Codes of Kingly Service, at least with respect to the Hebrews.

"Nearly a millennium after the *Akhu* bloodline came to Ireland, the descendants of Eochaid and Tamar Tephi were spread throughout the Isles, with strong branches in Wales and Dalriada which is part of present-day Scotland. From these lineages came Emrys Ambrosius – The Merlin, Saint Columba, and the Pendragons of Dalraida. The Pendragons also had the blood of the House of David through Joseph of Arimathea.

"In Britain and France, the blood of the offspring of Jeshua and Mary Magdalen and Jeshua's brother, James, who became Joseph of Arimathea, brought forth a number of royal lines. Of importance to our story, these lineages included Viviane del Acqs, Queen of Avalon and keeper of the Celtic wisdom, her husband, Taliesin, the Great Bard, and the descendants of their offspring, Morgaine, Arthur, Lancelot, Galahad and Gawain.

"Camelot was not a metaphorical tale of medieval England, but a historic kingdom of the Grail – the bloodline of Jesus. The House of Acqs originated from a later Tamar, the daughter of Mary and Jeshua, in Provence where Mary Magdalen raised her children, spread the gospel, and died consciously at the age of sixty. Her ascension was in death.

"Joseph of Arimathea traveled to Britain with twelve missionaries. Later, with the grandson of Jeshua and Mary, Galains, he founded the Brothers of Alains; twelve knights dedicated to the service of the bloodline. This was the Grail Table. So it is not surprising to find twelve Knights of the Round Table, most of them with the sacred blood in their lineage, who were dedicated to very high ideals. Galains and his brothers were vowed to celibacy and thus the kingly succession of David transferred to his Uncle Josephes, the second son of Mary and Jeshua. Josephes, already the high priest of the bloodline, carried forth the lineage of Priest Kings, the Fisher Kings.

"Morgaine was the high priestess of Avalon and the keeper of the Celtic wisdom upon the passing of her aunt Viviane and her mother, Ygerne. It was Morgaine who steered Avalon into the mists when the kingdom fell, and it was she who dragged her beloved half-brother Arthur and their son Mordred from the battlefield to guide their passage from the Earth.

"Morgaine was a priestess of the sisterhood, but she was also a magus of the brotherhood. Surprised?" he asked the group, though he was looking directly at Leah. "Don't be. I have learned that it is possible for the magi to incarnate in female bodies to complete difficult joint Missions of the sisterhood and brotherhood. I will continue with the story of Morgaine and the great magus, Merlin."

Chris held his hand lightly behind Leah's heart as she absorbed the truth about her own White Heart and the complexity of her Mission. He felt a constriction around her heart in his own heart as she held back emotions that could not be expressed under the circumstances. Later, he would try to support their release – either out under the stars or on the dreaming paths.

As Peter was preparing to speak, Master Mukda grasped his staff from its resting place against his shoulder and began tapping it on the floor. When he had everyone's attention, he smiled mischievously and began to speak. "For a variety of reasons, there are those in this room who are having a difficult time accepting the magi-priestess role of Morgaine. Why don't we step outside of time for a few moments to clarify a Mission that has been greatly misunderstood?"

Gratefully, Peter gave the floor to Master Mukda. Master Mukda leaned towards Chris, asking him to hold the space for the group, and nodded toward Don Eduardo, indicating the need for his support with what he intended. Don Eduardo's eyes shimmered as he focused his power to assist his brother, Mukda. A glowing light began emitting from the top of Mukda's staff. It quickly grew into a force, which he directed towards his right, at the wall of the building, behind the circle of *waykis*. As faint images began to appear on the wall, those sitting in that area moved to face an increasingly clear picture projected as a hologram from Mukda's staff:

Shrouded in billowing, dusky robes with ample hoods, a gray-bearded man and slight, graceful woman walked in silence through the mist of the gathering night. Their path took them alongside the dark waters of a placid lake, which was the source of the mist. An owl could be heard, calling from the forest towards which they walked. Leaving the lake, they entered the forest on a narrow path, the woman following the man. Dense foliage seemed to create a tunnel through which they moved, until the two emerged into a clearing to stand before an enchanted dwelling.

Smoke spiraled upwards through the thatched roof of the dwelling. Its walls were made of tightly woven sticks that formed geometric patterns of magical protection on the windowless hut. The roof thatch had also been placed with the intent of protection and invisibility, giving one the impression that an ordinary person could walk along this forest path and never notice the small dwelling. Hanging under the eaves, circling the dwelling, were little bells that had begun to ring as the two had approached.

Responding to the bells, an old crone opened the door of the dwelling to cast a path of warm firelight towards the man and woman. As the two came forward, bending to enter the dwelling through the low door, the crone bowed to them then silently stole off through the woods, leaving them alone with the fire.

First shaking the dew from their robes, they hung them on pegs near the door and moved towards the fire in the center of the hut. He warmed his hands while she stirred the coals, put more wood in the fire, and hung a kettle of tea water from a tripod above the flames. Firelight danced in the old man's blue eyes and bounced off the gold brocade trim of his deep blue-violet robes. His gray hair and beard betrayed his true age while his skin, in color and tone, was as youthful as his companion's.

Clinging to her slender but shapely body, a moss-green gown embroidered with ivory roses offered an enchanting contrast to the shining head of red hair that fell in soft curls nearly to her waist. Her perturbed scowl cast a shadow of discontent on an otherwise beautiful face. When she settled herself by the fire opposite the old man, her piercing green eyes began to soften under his gaze. When laughter began to dance in her eyes, the old man spoke.

"My Darling Morgaine, I do believe you have been carrying a heavy load of judgment in your heart."

"How well you read me, Beloved Teacher," she replied with a smile. "How very well you read me."

"It might be best to speak your feelings and opinions to the fire before we work with our intent this night, Beloved. Our work together must be at the highest level of our capabilities," he offered seriously. Then, with a twinkle in his eye, he added. "Judgment will taint the brew."

"Indeed, it will, Wise One," she began. "You know the depth of the love I carry in my heart for Arthur, Dear Emrys. He is my brother and my only love. He is also capable of

provoking more anger within me than can be fathomed. Are we witnessing the way of God, Wise Teacher, or the way of man?"

"The two cannot be separated, Morgaine, for all men are part of God. Some of them behave as the beloved Master, while others carry on like asses. It is truly amusing to behold this contrast."

"Perhaps you can transform my reactions from disgust to amusement. Perhaps I am too much a participant and too little an observer."

"That, in itself, is a good observation, Dear One. I am more than willing to try. Why don't you continue? I want to know what is in your mind and your heart."

"Very well. My mind is mired by paradox. My heart is in reaction to what seems irresolvable contradiction. Birthed and growing within it are fear and pain.

"Prior to Arthur's king-making ritual, he was a great warrior for the Truth. Granted, he obeyed his father's commands to increase the lands of Dalriada, but his heart was pure. He carries the blood of the Master Jesus, Emrys. Codes of the Holy Grail beat in his heart. How could he forget the Truth of the Master and allow his kingdom to be split by that sorry excuse of a wife whose loyalty is not with the land but a church that grows powerful in its falsehood?" Morgaine's powerful voice cracked with the pain in her heart. "How could that be? You are the Merlin. You are his guardian. How could that be, I ask you?" she pleaded passionately.

"Morgaine, My Most Beloved Apprentice, there are powerful forces at work in these perilous times. You and Arthur are Twin Rays, two sparks from the same luminous aspect of God. All that you feel for him, including your rage and deep disappointment, is nothing more than the reflection of the deep unrest within yourself. You are also of the Master's blood. What are you doing to save the kingdom from the church?"

"I am a woman!" she hissed. "What can I do? I train priestesses to hold a Truth that cannot be free nor thrive within this world. We have moved into other realities because our power is a threat to this church. What else can I do, aside from black magic?"

"Do not forget who we are, Morgaine. The practice of black magic will cause certain death to those Magi of the Ruby."

"What is there to live for, My Teacher? Why must we maintain such integrity when these violators of Truth do not?" she pleaded.

"Morgaine!" he said forcefully, snapping her out of her negativity.

The energy he projected caused her luminous field to flare and shift dramatically. The keen observers watching the holographic projection saw filaments of light shoot out of her field like tiny rockets. Cupping her hands beneath her chin, she closed her eyes and allowed her heart to renew itself through an unabated stream of tears. The tiny pools of grief that collected in each of her palms were offered to the fire as the Merlin blotted her face with a piece of worn linen drawn from his robes.

"Beloved," he said, speaking softly, "the only thing standing between yourself and your highest potential is this little flaw of unrestrained empathy. That flaw is something you share with your brother, of course."

"How often have we discussed this, Emrys? Will I never become an accomplished wizard?" she moaned, her head leaning against the benevolent elder.

"You are an accomplished magus, Morgaine. You are holding an entire community in the higher dimensions at the same time you are intimately involved in the World of Faerie. You are a master of the dimensions, Beloved. Is it so much to ask that you learn to move in the reality of mankind as a master?"

She pulled her head away and looked him squarely in the eye. "*You know I despise this reality, dear Emrys, but I feel clear and ready to hear, one more time, this path I must walk.*" Then nodding towards the fire, she added, with a wink, "*let me steep our tea while you prepare my lesson.*"

The Merlin took his seat across the fire again while Morgaine removed the kettle of hot water from the tripod. She poured a portion of water through a woven strainer of herbs set into an awaiting pot. Soon the infusion of peppermint, red clover and a pinch of comfrey root filled the little hut with a soothing aroma. They were both smiling in anticipation of the warm drinks as Morgaine gazed across the fire, turning her attention to Emrys.

"*It is a mystery to me, Morgaine, how one of your skills falters at the very basic task of keeping your field of light protected. It is more understandable with Arthur, given that his was never the path of the magus, but you have spent most of your life under my tutelage. Perhaps it is that you are so much a reflection of each other. I am not certain that the why of this matters a great deal. It is what it is.*

"*Your challenge is to be both priestess and magus, maintaining the integrity of the portal established here by the Master. Those who do not share your Truth would offer you any number of ways to falter. It is a test of your strength and soul willingness to hold fast your Truth. It is not the only Truth, for their Truth has its validity as well.*

"*We play our roles on this Earth and humanity staggers between the dark and light of the whole. There is little precedent for the patriarchal lineage of the Master to uphold the Grail Codes – other than the Master himself. We are all learning and growing together. It is your duty to recognize the illusion without judging those who are blind to it. Do not walk about in this world offering your luminous field to the blind out of empathy or pity. Your service to the Mission is your own invisibility,*" he concluded, his stern words betrayed by the tenderness of his demeanor.

"*Oh Emrys, I am sorry to have fallen prey to their invasive ways again,*" she sighed. "*Why am I so susceptible to intrusion?*"

"*It is by virtue of your openness, Morgaine. Your soul sees the God in all things, including these vultures hovering around your brother at this time. That is good, but so is a bit of discernment. See the God, but be wary of the man, My Dear One.*"

"*Spoken like the true Archmage, my wise teacher,*" she replied, pouring their tea and passing a cup across to him. "*Would you care to elaborate about the vultures?*"

He drew a satisfying sip from his tea and laughed. "*As the drama unfolds, we find the very core of Arthur tearing him apart. He is his father's son, a warrior and king of this land with a legacy of dominion. He is also the child of your mother's lineage, which stretches back beyond the Master to the ancient Akhus - priests and kings from the stars. He was trained by the Druid priests to hold sacred the land, just as Master Jesus did upon this very soil.*

"*His father chose for him a wife believing she would bring strength to the kingdom through political alignment. This, as you well know, is more common than not. He was not wise enough to foresee her barrenness and the weakness she presented to the manipulative priests of the church. His Twin Ray and half-sister has more power than he, because she is authentic and of high integrity. She exerts a tremendous power over him by virtue of his longing for her – his only love. His son by this sister, Mordred, embodies the true Grail Codes at the same time he loathes his father and wishes to destroy his father's queen..*

"Do you see Arthur's torment? What a bed he has made for himself to sleep in! Do you see the fragility of the kingdom? The vultures are many. I would ask that you not be one of them, Morgaine. You must let him go."

There was no questioning the sternness in his voice at this point. She was, again, collecting her tears in the palms of her hands to offer them to the fire.

"Oh Emrys, how can you let go of your own reflection? It is like parting with half of your heart, the half where hope gushes forth time and time again with the vigor of springtime."

"Does she who is invisible cast a shadow or see her own reflection in a pool?" he queried.

"Am I simply to withdraw?" she asked, drying her eyes and drinking deeply of her tea.

"Indeed, Beloved. It does not mean that you do not love Arthur. It simply means that you choose not to live in the reality he has created. The circumstances of this world and your Mission will not allow the two of you to merge your essences in this reality. I would propose that there are realities that might find you in a more harmonious place with each other. I advise you to ponder what I say in the deepest part of your heart, Morgaine. You will never find peace with Arthur in this reality, but you do have an opportunity to fulfill your Mission.

"Meet him in the higher dimensions, Beloved Sister, and, in this world of men, let your well of hope nourish those who would receive it and return it in kind.

"You and I must now combine our skills to save what we can of Avalon and the priestesses and priests whose service to the Earth is well intended. If Arthur and Mordred are spared as well, we will consider it an act of destiny and not trouble ourselves with the right or wrong of it. Are you in agreement?"

She who would, in her power, detach from both lover and son nodded her bowed head. Morgaine was left gazing into her teacup, looking for both strength and solace as the holographic image projected from Mukda's staff began to turn in upon itself.

Master Mukda tapped his staff upon the cement floor of the shelter, quickly snapping everyone back into the reality of Tres Cruces while terminating the hologram. He nodded his thanks to Don Eduardo and Chris for holding the space during the powerfully realistic projection. Most of the women were wiping tears from their cheeks as Leah buried her own tear-stained face in Chris' shoulder, his arm firmly wrapped around her. Having felt the hologram on so many levels, she longed for the evening to end at that moment, allowing her the space to integrate its meaning. Since that was not to be, Chris wiped her tears away and charged energy into her spine to restore her presence.

He wondered just how much her heart was going to have to take that night. The message was not lost to him either, but his response was being filtered through the channels of his warrior training and, unlike Leah, as much distraction as possible was his fondest desire.

The group's attention turned once again to Peter, who ran a hand through his wavy graying dark hair as he began to speak. He voice is gratitude to Master Mukda for such a poignant vehicle of clarity.

"I am a Welshman and like many Welsh, am a descendant of Emrys Ambrosius, the Merlin of Camelot. I was not as fortunate as Morgaine who, as a child, spent hours at his feet but there is a legacy of magic in my family running through a lineage of magi.

"Emrys was a direct descendant of Tamar Tephi and Eochaid of Ireland, whose line immigrated to South Wales. Unlike Britain, Wales was not subject to Roman occupation, nor overrun by the Anglo-Saxons or Normans. We did not have the many overlays of conquering culture during that period, and to this day, have ancient links to the Druid teachings and the early Christian Truths spoken by Joseph, Simon and the many missionaries associated with them. Celtic Christianity was based on the teachings of Joseph of Arimathea, the sons of Jeshua, and Jeshua himself, who walked our land over five hundred years before Merlin.

"In the Celtic Christian Church, the Druids were the priests and the women of Avalon were the priestesses. Jeshua himself experienced initiation into the Druid priesthood. It is written in the records and well remembered. Viviane del Acqs, the grandmother of Morgaine, brought the feminine line of the messianic lineage from France to Britain to become the queen of Avalon. She was married to Taliesin, the Archdruid or head of the priesthood.

"Morgaine never met her grandfather for he was much older than Viviane and died well before Ygerne birthed Morgaine. "

"Taliesin had an illegitimate daughter who became the wife of Emrys, the Merlin. Taliesin was a magus and Emrys was his apprentice and successor as magus and Archdruid. With the heart of the Divine Mother, Viviane took both Emrys and his wife into her home at Taliesin's death and, in due time, the child Morgaine, who was sent to live with her grandmother when Ygerne became pregnant with Arthur.

"Viviane was of the dynastic House of Acqs, descended from Jeshua and Mary Magdalen, but she, like Mary, was also high priestess of the Sun, her soul aligned with the lineage of light – the sisterhood. We find Viviane, the high priestess, guarded first by Taliesin who was succeeded by Emrys, and in their presence the young Morgaine whose father, the Dux of Carlisle, was descended from Joseph of Arimathea.

"Simon Magus was the appointed guardian of Mary Magdalen and Emrys was the guardian of Morgaine – two very important women in the lineage, as I am sure you know. As an elder cousin of Arthur's father, the Pendragon King of Dalriada, Emrys also became the appointed guardian of Arthur when he became King.

"Let's dwell on all of this for a moment. Simon Magus co-created the Camelot-Avalon portal with Jeshua when they traveled to the Isles. At the inception of Camelot itself, we have Emrys guiding the two young ones, Arthur and Morgaine, who would attempt to bring forth an ideal worthy of higher dimensions. We have the sisterhood, the brotherhood and the bloodline.

"How long were the magi incarnating in Emrys' lineage? When Jeremiah brought Tamar Tephi to Ireland, he lived long enough to bequeath his power to Tamar and Eochaid's firstborn son, Irial Faidh. Thus the secret brotherhood of magicians was born in the Isles. The magi have always protected the sisters and the blood. This Mission is very old upon the Earth.

"Now, dear Brothers and Sisters, with the help of Brother Mukda, I have truly spent myself," he laughed. "I suggest a small break for tea and stretching, then we will ask Jacques to continue the history of the magi."

Grabbing her parka, Leah broke free of Chris' protective arm and made a dash for the door. Never hospitable, Tres Cruces at night was freezing cold and windy. It was just what she needed to calm her racing heart.

Taking short icy breaths, she moved out into the clearing to gaze at the stars. She knew that Venus and the other planets were tracking the Sun for the coming alignment, but the Dog Star, Sirius, was clearly visible in line with Orion's Belt. *Chaska*, the Eye of God, was the brightest star in the heavens and the closest to the Earth. "Just a stone's throw away," she mused, pacing back and forth to keep her legs warm, "but so unlike the Earth. I wonder how many hearts you have broken, High Council? For surely we have all fallen prey to our humanity."

"All too often, My Child," Master Mukda offered, coming up behind her.

"Ah, My Teacher," she replied, in a gentle voice, "you have read my thoughts. Have you found it difficult to be in the world of men?"

"Of course, Dear One. For the most part, I can be invisible within it, but you will not be. The world was not ready for Morgaine to be visible, but the world is ready for the Truth now. You and Chris will flounder, pick yourselves up and eventually grow into your Missions."

"Master Mukda, a million questions are springing to mind for me as you speak of this."

"Well they might, Child. I will answer only those that come from your heart," he added laughing.

"Quite right. My mind has not served me for a very long time. What comes from my heart is a longing not to repeat history, or what we think of as history. I fear attachment to Chris, then the necessary separation."

"Dispel your fear, Leah. It will not serve you either. In the ebb and flow of the Mission, you will know both attachment and separation – I should say on many levels. Yet neither of you will complete your Mission without the other. You will, of necessity, learn to balance the energies of attachment and separation."

"Will we ever know Oneness?"

"You have already experienced Oneness, have you not? I sensed this in the jungle as I waited for you on the path. Let me say that you will experience it on many levels as well.

"Yours is not an easy path, Leah. In many ways, Chris' is much easier, for he will be more invisible as the magi have been throughout time. Your work has not yet begun, My Dear One."

Mukda's eyes were as soft and doe-like as his demeanor yet he held a powerful humor that made them twinkle. Leah kissed him on the cheek, eliciting a broad smile. "How singularly lucky is our Chris," he chuckled. "He has drawn the most sought-after assignments a disproportionately greater number of times than the rest of us."

Leah laughed from deep within her. "Well, he certainly is good at fulfilling them," she offered. "Thank you, Master Mukda, for what you have just given me."

"I have done nothing more than read your heart, Leah. It is all written there. The Ruby Order does not require austerity, as you can see. It requires full participation in the Mission. You and Chris have more protection and energetic support from the other realms than any two of us have ever had. We have awaited this time on Earth for millennia. Make sure you have some fun! You've been too hard on yourself, my child."

"I feel like the weight of the world has been lifted from my shoulders," she sighed.

"Ask and you shall receive," he replied, nodding towards Sirius. "They can carry the load."

Leah hugged the old immortal as he led her back into the shelter. They entered under Chris' watchful gaze. He saw clearly that Leah's heart-wound had been mended. She and Mukda reminded him of Merlin and Morgaine as they had moved together through the forest – teacher and student of magic. Taking a cup of hot tea to both of them, he was pleased to see the look of peace in Leah's eyes. He steered her to an isolated place near the wall where they could not be overheard.

"Thank you, Chris," she said. "My hands feel like ice."

"How are the stars tonight?" he asked.

"Magnificent! The High Council embraces our embrace. From a place deep within my heart, Chris, I can admit how much I love you and how very pleased I am that you are in my life. For some reason it has been very difficult for me to accept the gifts being given."

"Feeling that you don't deserve a bloke like me, Darling?" he teased.

"I suppose that is it – at least not without a good fight," she laughed.

He rubbed her back gently as the group reassembled itself to hear from Jacques de Villey. Reaching deep into the backpack beside him, Jacques brought forth a treasure wrapped in an old white cloth with red markings, wrapped up a bit like a mesa. He unwrapped the cloth to reveal a dazzling ornate cross of solid gold. Many in the group knew it to be the Templar cross, with crosspieces of equal length.

"Jacques spread the cloth between him and the skull and set the gold cross within the deep red cross sewn upon the cloth. Glances were exchanged around the circle as it looked as if Jacques had produced two magnificent relics of the brotherhood.

Taking a few minutes to center himself, Jacques connected his filaments with the group and the relics. The intensity of his prayer was evident to the entire gathering. He cast his soft blue-violet eyes around the room at all those gathered and rolled up the sleeves of his camp shirt as his angular face broke into a boyish grin.

"I am very blessed to be here, My Brothers and Sisters," he began. Then bowing his head to Don Eduardo, he continued. "Thank you, Don Eduardo, for calling us to such a magical gathering." Jacques' English was excellent though heavily accented. His youthful charm was lost to no one, though his actual age was a mystery. Don Eduardo gave him an appreciative nod after Jacques' words had been translated for him.

"Before I begin my story, I must offer a disclaimer. I intend to speak my own Truth as well as the Truth of my ancestors. However, there may be no way to anchor it in what we refer to as history. History is no more than the opinions of those who were able to seize the power. In that sense it is a fairy tale. Nonetheless, it is important that this group hear what I have to say. Take what is yours and leave the rest for the hungry ghosts." Jacques' eyes twinkled mischievously as the group responded with subdued neighborly chatter. Jacques had a peculiarly shocking way about him, a trickster energy that Leah and Chris loved. He had certainly commanded the group's attention.

"Perhaps the best place to begin," he continued, "is with my own family. This Templar cloak and golden cross were given to me as part of my legacy. They belonged to a distant relative, Anselm de Ville, who rode with Richard the Lion-Hearted in the Crusades."

Chris felt Leah snap to attention next to him, her eyes widened in wonder. Jacques privately noted her response, but continued. "Anselm was a Templar Knight who was born into Gnosticism in the Languedoc region of Southern France. Our branch of the family moved north during the early years of the Inquisition to escape the burnings. Some went on to Italy where they became Catholic as the House of Savoy, while others migrated to Normandy, Holland and England, seeking their religious freedom. My branch of the family stayed in the northern village and changed the family name to de Villey.

"Anselm, who was, by vow, an unmarried Templar, left his memoirs and these artifacts with our branch of the family. They have been passed down through the firstborn son of each generation, until I inherited them. With them I inherited my place among the Templars, though we have not been a public organization since those harrowing times. Within our family and within the Templars, we carry Truths that have wrought extremely cruel persecution upon us as well as others. Many have died for these Truths – gladly have they died for these Truths in silence. Had they not, I would not be here to share them with you this evening. Some of these Truths will not surprise you, others will perplex you, and still others will shock you. Again, I warn you to take what you can hold and leave the rest behind.

"From the memoirs of Anselm de Ville, I have learned that our family was of the bloodline of the House of David - offspring of Jesus and Mary Magdalen. Our family comes through the female lineage, that is through the firstborn daughter of Jesus and Mary. Her name was Tamar.

"Many of the Templar Knights were of the bloodline of Jesus. All of the knights were commissioned with protecting this bloodline and the Gnostic Truths that it upheld.

"The core of the Gnostic teachings is the true words of Jesus, which, in every way, uphold the Feminine Aspect of God. We see God as both masculine and feminine – the feminine being equated to the wisdom aspect, the Sophia. The connection to God is direct, without priest, guru or other go-between. We have no need for churches.

"I think all of us in attendance tonight are walking that path to Divine Union. Mary Magdalen, Mary Salome, James, Thomas, Simon and other disciples brought these concepts to southern France when their safety was at risk in the Holy Land. It is a path of personal attainment, not hierarchical power.

"The Church of Rome had no tolerance for these concepts of freedom, or for the presence of the feminine as represented by the bride of Jesus, who was, in fact, his principal disciple. Invested in the submission of women, the church epitomized the patriarchal takeover of the western world as we track it in mythology.

"The Gnostics were quiet in their ways, but the church, much like the empires that have come and gone over time, felt it necessary to terrorize everyone into submission or kill them. It is interesting that this institution has lasted much longer than most empires. It speaks to the power of religion-based fear.

"The Templars have seen to it that the bloodline persevered throughout those perilous times. They were formed, initially, to retrieve the Ark of the Covenant, the Emerald Tablets of the *Akhus*, from Solomon's temple in Jerusalem. Along with the tablets, they brought with them to France the writings of Jesus, which were hidden beneath the temple by his followers. The Gnostics subsequently buried them in the Egyptian desert after laboriously copying these true scriptures for the followers of Mary in France.

"The Templars also confiscated a fortune in gold from beneath the temple of Solomon that was removed to France as well. Though the Knights themselves were vowed to poverty, their community was quite powerful and wealthy. In fact, the bloodline has remained wealthy in France because they were original landowners during Roman occupations in the Languedoc.

"You notice that the cross is not a crucifix. The equality of the branches speaks for itself. The Gnostics do not dwell on the crucifixion or the idea that Jesus died for our sins – because he didn't. What he did was to prove beyond a doubt his and our immortality -our birthright is resurrection. All of you are informed of that Truth already. The cross speaks of the balance between the masculine and feminine in all things. It speaks to the four directions and the power of earth, water, wind and fire. It also represents the mundane world on the horizontal axis and the mystical world aligning Heaven and Earth on the vertical axis. I could go on and on in that regard, but would rather shift my presentation just a bit.

"The cross on this Templar cloak represents the Red Ray of Will and Power, and on a higher level the Ruby Ray of Transcendent Magic. Who were these men? What was their relationship with the Order of the Ruby, the sisterhood and the magi? What happened to the magi from the time of Simon Magus until Merlin? When did they next surface on the planet? This is complex, but it is partly why we are gathered here at Tres Cruces.

"I would just like to reveal to you some of Anselm's memoirs as an offering of continuity. The magi survived the Dark Ages and the Inquisition because they were highly skilled alchemists. Alchemy has a lot of faces, as we know. It can mean invisibility – blending in, transmutation – changing form, and transcendence – shifting realities. Historically the magi have been system-busters, anarchists and zealots as well. Their highest magicians were and are Order of the Ruby.

"From Anselm's memoirs, I have gleaned the following. Simon passed the leadership of the magi to Galains, the grandson of Mary and Jesus through James, Joseph of Arimathea. Galains' father, Jesus Justus, was taken under the wing of James, who trained the eldest son of the Master to be the Father of the People.

"Like his father, young Jesus held the kingly lineage of David. Galains, his only son, joined a celibate Circle of Twelve, the Grail Table, which James initiated, as the Circle of Alains. In later times, it became the Round Table of Arthur – a group of dedicated warriors who served the bloodline, just as the twelve at the Last Supper had served the Master. We see here the seeds of the Knights Templar.

"As Peter has stated, because Galains chose the celibate life, the kingly lineage passed to Galains' uncle, Josephes, the second son of Mary and Jesus from whom the Fisher King lineage of both priest and king emerged. The magi lineage passed from Galains to his apprentice. Down through the ensuing years the lineage of magicians worked in secrecy among the Druids, until the Merlins emerged.

"Camelot was a template for a future Golden City. It required immense magic to put that template in place within the grids that Jesus, Simon and James had prepared.

"Camelot was not meant to succeed in this dimension. It *was* a seed. We should feel no remorse about Camelot. At that time, the stars touched the Earth and great souls reached higher dimensions, because the task was immense. The magi are particularly adept at working with illusion, so what we may think transpired is hardly a credit to their art. The Grail Castle appears in this reality to those with eyes to see it."

Jacques oration was skillful and captivating. Having no shortage of dramatic expression and charm, he paused to allow his last statement to sink in before continuing.

"After the demise of Arthur and Mordred, the work moved into higher dimensions and has continued to this day. The magi became invisible once again - transcending the dimensions to keep the bridge between the worlds open. That time at Camelot brought many branches of the bloodline together, and the magi were part of that bloodline. In France the female lineage of Jesus had spread to many regions, though it was concentrated in Provence, where Mary had lived. The House of Acqs came from that blood, as did my family, the Stuarts, and the Merovingians. To be perfectly honest, that blood is just about everywhere in the western world right now - none of it with any particular privilege.

"The magi, at a soul Mission level, began sending only a few of the order into Britain and western Europe from that time forward, but those who did incarnate were powerful wizards. As I understand it, the Templars were the guardians of the magi invisibility. Like the Rosicrucians and Freemasons in later years, their organization provided a smokescreen that allowed the magi to keep their arts alive during those dark times. These organizations also provided access to a personal alchemy by which men could overcome their base nature and open to the Divine.

"We need to ask ourselves just how much these organizations create a mental distraction for those who seek power in something less than its impeccable state of being. The Priory of Zion did the same for the bloodline. To varying degrees, these organizations were privy to secret knowledge and kept the Gnostic traditions of the Divine Feminine alive. To be a smokescreen is, perhaps, not too flattering to the ego, but a tremendously important detail in the Divine Plan."

The group's subtle laughter signaled their agreement with the importance of every detail of the Divine Plan. Jacques acknowledged this and continued. "This brings us to more recent history, when a brilliantly adept brother emerged to demonstrate his alchemy. The fires of the Inquisition were in full blaze when an illegitimate son was born to Queen Elizabeth of England in 1561. His father was the Earl of Leicester. He became Sir Frances Bacon – a true genius of the Elizabethan era who founded both the Rosicrucian Order and Freemasonry. He was a High Initiate in touch with an ancient, powerful alchemy.

"As Sir Francis Bacon, he, and a few associates, penned the plays and sonnets of William Shakespeare. Those plays and sonnets are filled with the overtones of Rosicrucian symbology and wisdom. When that life became endangered through political manipulation, he contrived his own death.

"Shakespeare's death is a mystery as well, for when that aspect of the Mission, or embodiment, if you will, was completed, he appeared in the courts of Europe as the Comte de Saint Germain. His life as an alchemist is exemplary, for he was moving energy in his own life as well as in the governments of France, Russia and the future United States and our own order.

"A secret agent and diplomat to Louis XV, the Comte frequented the courts of Paris, London, the Hague and St. Petersburg and, using numerous other identities, was seen all over Europe. He had strong connections to India and often disappeared to retreat there for long periods of time. He never showed signs of aging, and assisted many with his rejuvenating elixirs.

"Speaking twelve languages fluently, Saint Germain was an accomplished composer, musician, poet, and artist, to name a few of his interests. Whatever he did, in whatever dimension, he mastered. He was Order of the Ruby and remains the Grand Master of the Amethystine Order of the Magi. Having ascended seventy thousand years ago, he has embodied consciously since that time in service to the Mission.

"Our beloved Saint Germain was a powerful source of revolution in France, Russia and America – a magus in the tradition of Simon himself. In yet another lifetime, his soul incarnated as the Merlin, Emrys of Camelot, to name but one of many embodiments within the Order.

"Saint Germain was, and still is, deeply invested in the concept of Democracy, having appeared to dispel the fear around those who gathered to sign the U.S. Declaration of Independence. His magical oration declared that "God has given America to be free". He worked with Franklin and Washington to weave the fabric of Democracy into the foundation of the United States. As Francis Bacon he had written *The New Atlantis*, about America. From the Golden Cities of Mount Shasta and the Grand Tetons, he has held an intent that America could anchor freedom – a necessary component of ascension, for the world.

"When I think of Saint Germain, I feel a connection to the greater purpose of true Democracy that has, perhaps, been closeted away in recent years by those who would take the power personally, denying the Grail Codes. Now our beloved leader has ascended once again, and from those higher realms believes most definitely in Earth's ascension and mankind's transmutation of the material.

"Many believe that he designed and birthed the Rosicrucian and Masonic Orders to protect the magi. Who are we to argue that? It makes perfect sense that he would weave a tight web of invisibility for us before leaving the planet. Now Saint Germain guides the Amethystine Order from the ascended realms."

Jacques became silent then picked up the gold cross. Making the sign of the cross before him in the circle, he rose and touched the cross to the crown chakra of each member of the group. While he performed this ritual, the skull emanated a ruby light that filled the room. It felt warm and loving and very energetic.

Upon returning to his place in the circle, he touched his own crown with the cross, then he rewrapped it in the garment of his ancestor. Jacques placed the gold cross on top of the red cross and folded the garment around it with great tenderness. The ruby light diminished but the warmth and energy stayed within everyone's luminous field.

The journey of the magi, both then and now, felt complete.

Brotherhood

Jacques and Peter opened the circle to discussion after Jacques tucked the cross away in his backpack. Brian, who had wept unabashedly during the blessing with the cross, thanked Jacques for helping him remember something important about his soul.

"I have been struggling to know how I fit into this gathering, My Brother. I know I am not of the Ruby Order, but find myself called to be here, like so many of my Andean brothers," Brian offered, sweeping his hand out to connect with the Indians who had come to be with them. "When you laid out the Templar artifacts I knew who I had been, and now believe that I am called here to serve as a warrior guardian of the Ruby Order once again."

Don Eduardo slowly nodded towards Brian, affirming that he had been a member of the magi warriors. Leah had been watching Brian's energy shift from the vigilance of a wounded apprentice to the centered strength of the spiritual warrior. Her heart leapt with joy for Brian's profound awareness.

Reaching into his pocket, Brian withdrew the pouch containing the emeralds given to him by Don Eduardo. "I return these to you, My Brother, for they are not mine to keep or use," he said, passing them around the circle to the *ylloq'e*. Pleased that Brian had found his own way with the emeralds, Don Eduardo blew into the pouch and passed them to his wife, Doña Felicia, who was sitting behind him. She spirited them away while turning her twinkling eyes towards Brian in blessing. The emeralds had come full circle, for it was Doña Felicia who was their true guardian.

By way of explaining her astonishment at Jacques' discussion of the Templars, Leah shared with Jacques that an Anselm de Ville fitting the description of his ancestor appeared in her family tree as well. With a great deal of laughter, it was decided that they were likely distant relatives of both blood and soul.

Susmo, who had been deep in thought, suddenly spoke aloud. "I am remembering a story which my father told to me many times. In this story seven women came to a certain village in the mountains with a mystical alchemy. They were called witches or *brujas* by the local people and stayed very much to themselves. What manner of sorcery they were practicing was imagined into the stories of that village since their arrival in the mid-sixteenth century.

"My father felt they had come to escape the Inquisition. These women had come from Basque, Navarre and one from England. Later on, a Count appeared in that village who took up living in the hacienda of the seven sisters. He was mysterious beyond imagining. The women were said to be dreamers, *naguals*, and he an adept of great power.

"I am just remembering this story and wondering if it was not another projection of the Master Saint Germain. The women married into some of the families who had become the landowners at the time of the conquest, and with mixed marriages being very common, their esoteric genetics found their way into the work of the women shamans and *brujas* of the villages in that region.

"Those women were said to be ageless beauties of great wisdom. Do you suppose the Count had formulas for regenerative elixirs?" Susmo offered his conjecture to the group with a quizzical look on his face.

Don Eduardo enjoyed a great laugh when Susmo's comments were translated and offered that, when he was a boy, Saint Germain had appeared to the elders of their tribe numerous times and had taken them through an interdimensional portal right there at Tres Cruces. It was not much of a stretch to believe that he had been there in the sixteenth century. The full attention of the group was given to Don Eduardo, who offered a *kint'u* to the *Apus* before speaking.

"Let's speak of tomorrow, My Brothers and Sisters. We will want to see the sunrise, of course, so I suggest sleep as soon as we break the circle. Our courageous women will continue with work they started today. Hopefully they will complete that work and be ready to begin dreaming the following day."

The women looked around the circle at each other, creating an instant weaving of focused intent to accomplish that part of the Mission. Don Eduardo continued. "The men of the Ruby Order will meet together for the entire day, doing the work they will need to finish before the dream can become reality." The men connected as the women had, setting an intent to move energy swiftly, as the planetary alignment was fast approaching. "The warrior magus, Brian, and our warrior priests will search for that interdimensional portal while holding us in their protective bubble of light to provide us with the opportunity to move energy without restriction. Brian," he said, looking him squarely in the eye, "holds the portal in his luminous memory, for he accompanied the Grand Master as a warrior magus when he last took our elders through – a time when I was just a boy."

Brian, whose Mission was being accelerated by leaps and bounds before the group, looked flabbergasted. Don Eduardo laughed with gusto, slapping his knees and wiping tears from his eyes. "It is time to sleep!" he announced abruptly, sending the group into peals of laughter. The *ylloq'e* had moved tremendous energy in seconds, leaving everyone in a state of great anticipation about the coming day but also supporting each of them in the work they would do for themselves and the planet. The group broke up with lots of chatter and many hugs for Brian, Peter and Jacques.

After getting the sleeping arrangement established again, the group went about readying themselves for bed. Leah zipped up her parka and braved the wind for a final outhouse run and tooth brushing. On her way back to the shelter, she found Brian and Natalie gazing at the stars together, unperturbed by the stiff, cold wind.

"Looking for that portal, Brian?" she asked, as she came to join them.

Brian laughed, giving Natalie a squeeze. "I am just trying to quiet my heart, Leah."

"A little bit of overload, perhaps?" she teased.

"No. I would say that my circuits are thoroughly blown," he replied. "Talk about death to the old way of being. I am going to have to worry about that portal tomorrow."

"Just as well, Brian. I am hoping we women finish with our work early enough to journey into the jungle to a magical place tomorrow."

"Magically wet, I hope," Natalie offered. "I am one woman out of eleven in dire need of a bath or shower."

"Could be," she winked. "Spread the word. It's good motivation to move out of ego."

"I think it will work, Leah. I'll get on spreading the word first thing in the morning."

"Good night, Beloveds," she said, kissing each on the cheek.

Waiting patiently for her near the shelter, Chris locked his arm in Leah's and steered her around to the windless side of the building.

"How are you feeling, Love?" he asked.

"How do I feel? Well, Chris, it feels like the roller coaster finally stopped to let me get off. I am darned happy that Jacques showed up to put a few essential filaments in place for me. I am ready to do what we came to do – whatever the heck that is."

"That's My Mate," he teased. After deflecting the punch she sent his way, he added, "This has been one intense day for all of us. Is Brian okay?"

"Brian will be fine. He looks like he has finally found a reason to be here – at Tres Cruces and on the planet. Of course there is the matter of finding the portal, but I believe he will not have a problem."

"No, he won't. His Mission has been activated a bit ahead of ours. I suspect we will need the protection of the warriors for our work."

"I am grateful for all of them. I am most grateful for the humor of Don Eduardo and Master Mukda. They are teaching me to appreciate humor as a way to move energy quickly and painlessly. It is good for serious people like myself to observe this level of mastery."

"It is an art form, isn't it? Say, was it just this afternoon that I bathed your serious, but gorgeous, body?" he mused, unzipping her parka and taking her in his arms.

"Too much has happened since then, Chris. Remind me," she replied, reaching inside his open parka to feel his warmth.

Staying together long enough to rekindle the Divine energies they had shared in the jungle, Chris and Leah opened themselves to the work of the Dreaming Paths and rejoined the group to sleep.

Leah slept deeply without remembering a single dream. In that respect, the night seemed somehow out of place, but she felt a deep level of renewal and looked radiant upon waking. Over half the group, including Chris, was already outside awaiting the sunrise, causing her to scurry around locating her outerwear and boots. "Sunrise is not a requirement of the work, but who would want to miss it?" she thought, taking a hot cup of tea from the cook on her way out the door. She joined the circle of *waykis* as the first rays of the Sun were coming across the jungle canopy to the east.

Each *wayki* greeted the Sun in his/her own way but all were wide-eyed, drinking in the golden energy of *Tayta Inti*. The light shimmered over the treetops until the entire solar disc lit up the mountains and the day began to warm.

Don Eduardo and Susmo came to greet Leah with warm hugs and huge smiles. The *ylloq'e* had Susmo translate for him as he explained her duties for the day. It was clear to her that he wanted the entire group in the Fourth-Dimensional frequency before dinner, though that is not exactly how he presented her work.

This would be the final day of bridging realities, of being in the Third Dimension at all. The women dreamers would be required to hold higher and higher frequencies as the intensity of the work increased. Acting as vessels of the Divine, a dreamer's regression into states of desire, suffering, fear or any negativity would put everyone in jeopardy. A few shivers ran through Leah's body as Don Eduardo and Susmo took their leave, informing her that the men of the Order of the Ruby would not return until dusk. Master Mukda would be speaking after dinner.

"You look a bit shell-shocked, Sweetheart," Chris said, walking up and waving his hand in front of her eyes.

Leah jumped. "Oh, my God! You gave me another fright, Chris. Where was I this time?"

"Certainly not in your body, Leah. Was Don Eduardo a little challenging?" he asked.

"That was it!" she exclaimed. "How long have I been up? Maybe fifteen minutes? He just cranked the energy up a few notches, my body reacted and I was somewhere else. The new roller coaster is faster, and it's only going up."

Chris laughed. "I love you, Leah. You're lucky, you know. No one else could possibly understand you."

"You are right, Darling," she replied, seriously. "I think we should eat a good breakfast this morning. It's going to be a long and intense day. It sounds to me like we are entering a phase of the work that is moving beyond the material or human. Nothing wrong with getting a good meal in beforehand, eh?"

Chris put his arm around Leah, kissed her on the cheek and sent a dragon's dose of balancing energy into her field from his heart. Don Eduardo had really knocked her for a loop – he was sure with good intentions. "It's not like you to be so concerned about food, Mate," he said soothingly, "but I will join you for breakfast."

"How silly of me, Chris. I don't feel myself. Are you doing something to help me? My body and whole field feel tingly right now."

"Good. I think Don Eduardo activated this aspect of the Mission for you, Leah. We are, in every way, depending on the women dreamers to prepare an energetic space for us."

"You are probably right. I am feeling more stable now. What would I do without you, Chris?" she asked.

"Overeat, is my guess," he quipped. Smiling, he pushed her uncombed hair away from her face. "It's not likely that Don Eduardo would have activated you in that way if I had not been here to help or he would have stabilized you himself, Leah. The energy you took in was ten years' worth of work by ordinary human standards."

"No time to waste, I guess," she answered, sipping her tea. "Just a warning, Chris – I am sure to let go of the hotel in Lima today and everything it signifies. I deliver my life into the hands of the Divine Plan and whoever of our starry family happens to be directing this effort."

"I understand, Leah. I understand completely. We both will do what we must do. Just know that at some level beyond the illusion, we cannot be separated."

Leah moved to stand before him, looking squarely in his eyes. "Chris," she said, "there is a time coming soon when we will speak to each other only with our eyes and thoughts, and beyond that by combining our fields."

"You must be accessing new gifts of sight" he mused. "Surely they will help everyone with the challenges ahead of us. As for me, I have read your thoughts, eyes and your field in and out of this reality for longer than you could guess. Our love will in no way be betrayed."

"Thank you, Darling," she replied, lowering her eyes. "I guess we must be about our day."

Everyone had wandered back into the shelter for breakfast and the stowing of sleeping gear. It was not long before the men of the Ruby Order set off for the day, followed by the warriors, with Brian in the lead. The women sent a glowing love light with both groups of men - each group on their separate quest.

As the women gathered on the sunny side of the shelter, Doña Felicia and her two companions, Doña Lucia and Margarita, joined them. They sat behind Leah, as if protecting her back. She was whispering prayers of gratitude to them and to Chris for stabilizing the enormous energies delivered into her field by Don Eduardo.

It was time for certain codes and gifts to be activated. Leah was aware of her expanding consciousness as she took her seat in the circle. Energy was going to be moved in a decidedly different way today. She caught the wise eyes of Doña Felicia as she drew the group's assemblage point to attention. It would have surprised her to know that the wife of Don Eduardo had no more idea of what tomorrow would bring than she did. It was enough for each of them that their eyes had met in solidarity to the Mission.

"Beloveds, are you ready to fly?" she asked.

"It is what we came here to do, isn't it?" Georgia offered, touching her hands to her heart before extending her arms to the group.

"No argument there," Sonia replied. She looked around the circle of assenting women. "So, what is the game plan, Leah?"

"Are you willing to move a lot of energy in a short amount of time?" she asked.

Everyone agreed and she continued. "We must be ready to dream tomorrow. That means holding an impeccable vibration, without distraction, desire, or loss of focus, while the group accesses the filaments of Higher Consciousness necessary for the unfoldment of the Mission. We need to be completely free of density. We need to be crystal clear. In a nutshell, that means that we let go of everything we are carrying today - be it painful memories, hopes and dreams, thoughts of loved ones, and the list is really quite long. That list includes me. Let go of any attachment to me or each other. It will hamper all of us. Are you with me?"

Again everyone assented. "There is a place for sensitivity and a place for something like ballistic enlightenment – thunder and lightening, if you will. Are you willing?" she asked again, looking intently around the circle.

"Go for it, Leah. We promise we'll still love you when you're finished dragging us through the muck," Ellia offered with a twinkle in her eyes.

Leah could not contain her amusement. The whole circle had a good laugh, including Doña Felicia and her companions. Leah watched the filaments fly into a new, higher assemblage point. From that space of unconditional love, the women began a process of clearing that was as intense as it was profound. When they could not grasp the memory, thought or feeling holding them back, Leah was right there with it.

An hour into the work they started a fire and began burning the remnants of their lives. Six hours later, the smoldering embers told their stories to the Fire Spirits. The group was clear. They had just enough spunk left in them to journey down the jungle path to bathe and wash their hair in the waters of the pool where Leah and Chris had been the day before.

"Yesterday," she thought. "Could that have been just yesterday? I wonder how our men are faring?"

•

Don Eduardo led the men to a secluded spot near the mountain. The object this day was not a physical workout, but a gathering of spirit. The cooks had given them a box of lunch fixings and extra water that they stashed in the shade of a rock before taking their places in circle. It was a remarkable gathering, for most of the group had attained a fair degree of enlightenment. For those who had not, this meeting would open portals to the light for them.

Don Eduardo was the unofficial head of the circle, with Susmo sitting at his right to translate for him. Chris, sitting across from Don Eduardo, was asked to help with Spanish-English translation when Susmo needed his help. He was happy to be of service.

Once the logistics were worked out, Don Eduardo set the energy in motion with a short introduction. "My *Wayki* Brothers, it is good to be in circle together. We have much to share with each other today. As you can see, we number ten. This is not a complete and sacred number for the Order of the Ruby. That is because two of us are women about some work today more important than our recapitulation. We will welcome them into our circle tomorrow for the first meeting of the Order of the Ruby on *Pachamama* since the Kumaras came to prepare this planet for consciousness. On the inner planes, we have met often. Today we will weave the filaments of brotherhood, for we have much to learn from each other.

"*Wayki* Peter, on my left, will begin our circle," he said, turning towards Peter, who showed no signs of surprise. This was, after all, a circle of masters. Don Eduardo continued. "From each of you, we are interested to know how you overcame the trials and tests of *Pachamama* to gather your light. Tell your story - a sharable experience - each of you – and make it a good one," he joked. "We want to be entertained," he concluded, slapping his knees in laughter. The men loved his energy and lightly slapped each other on the back in laughter as well.

Peter took a few moments to connect with the scope of his life – searching through his memory for those important tests on the path. When finished assessing his spiritual journey, he opened his eyes to face his brothers.

"I feel honored to start this process, my Brothers," he began in his warm and amiable style. "When I look back upon my life I see many tests - but a common theme. I believe that is what we would want to identify and share in this circle. I also believe that my theme is a common one amongst the magicians, so it may ring true to many of you.

"I would call my test the abuse of power. Like most of us, I was not born knowing that I was of the Ruby Order, or even of the Amethystine Order. My grandfather, the Merlin at that time, watched me carefully, but allowed me to stumble around finding out what power really meant to me.

"I pursued the powerful path of academic hierarchy to find it empty of power. It was an illusion – a creation of its participants. It taught me something about creating reality, I must say. I watched power being abused in that setting and was tempted numerous times to abuse it myself. A mysterious strength within me resisted those temptations – not without a lot of sweat and tears - believe me.

"My formal training in the Merlin lineage began when I was twenty-five, and I soon learned that the abuse of power in our lineage is unforgivable. We are not permitted to dabble in black magic. We will lose our power along with our lives. I am grateful to the unseen brotherhood for their guardianship during those trials. I trust that there has been good reason to salvage me in that respect," he laughed.

"So my grandfather was my first teacher outside of life itself. He was a wizened old man with a white beard and mustache. He looked every bit the Merlin, whereas I have always tended towards the distracted professor image. He and I were quite different in this life.

"You can imagine him as a real character, for he was. His name was Rupert Wilshire. There are still many practicing Druids in the United Kingdom, and grandfather was their Archmage – though this was unknown to the rest of the world. They have missed him since his death, for I cannot play that role in my life.

"Grandfather never missed a chance to test my impeccability and right use of power through the ten years of my training before he passed over. He would love for me to share one story that I have never felt right about telling. Obviously the story was waiting for this moment to be shared with a group that would understand. I think that I can be in a place of non-ego to relate it, since years have passed in silence. It relates specifically to the moment of my enlightenment."

Don Eduardo nodded his approval, knowing that much was to be gained by all the men through Peter's story. Peter had been trained to watch his ego – a trait obvious to the whole group and one that pleased Don Eduardo, Master Mukda and Chris to no end. It was the only way Higher Self could predominate consciousness.

Peter fell silent, going within once more to gather the pieces of memory necessary to tell his story of awakening. The group sat motionless, holding space for Peter, who emerged from his meditation to continue. "During my training, I would share all of my experiences with Grandfather. There was no one else I was permitted to speak to about the training, not even my wife, Eileen, after we married. She still does not know who I really am.

"One day, shortly before his death, Grandfather asked me to lead a ritual for the Spring Equinox gathering of Druids at Avebury. I had no notion that my training was nearing an end, at least in the earthly realms, so I agreed to lead the ceremonies from a place of ego. Even though my ego had been under vigilant surveillance for years, there it was, right in my face. Grandfather was giving me the power, and my ego set about to destroy it without a thought to the lineage of Merlin that I carried.

"So I left my house all puffed up to do this ceremony, and the first thing that happened was a flat tire on the car – right in my own driveway. I fixed the flat, got on my way, and the next thing that happened was a minor car crash in town. I had been oblivious. I settled claims with the woman whose car I had hit and went on my way, though a bit wary of what would happen next." The group chuckled at the story and the expressions on Peter's face while he told it. "So then I was driving to Avebury, which is some distance from my home in Wales, and there was a cloudburst that nearly drowned me and the car in a low-country washout.

"By this time, I was shaken and began looking for the meaning in all of the occurrences. I decided that I was either being deterred from the ceremony because it was not meant to be, or someone's magic was being used to deter me for reasons I could not perceive – though Grandfather crossed my mind more than once. I sat at the washout and asked for help. I actually got humble in a big hurry.

"I asked the powers that be to give me a sign or an opportunity for right action that would lead me on my own path to the light.

"Amazingly, the car started up and I continued on my journey – looking for signs along the way, mind you," he added with a sparkle in his eyes. "As I neared Avebury, I began to feel quite confident that I would make it to the ceremony in time, my ego taking control again. Then I spotted a car on the side of the road with the doors flung open. I slowed down to see if someone was in the vehicle and saw a woman lying on the back seat. I didn't see anyone else, so I stopped to see if I could help.

"As hard as this is to believe, this young woman was in the midst of birthing a child. My ceremony was in half an hour. She was desperate for help and didn't give a damn if I knew anything about the birthing process nor if I had to be somewhere else. I had been on hand for the birthing of our two children and had actually facilitated the birth of Eileen's and my second daughter. What was more important? I felt ego pulling me to abandon her and some other part of me wanting to flog my ego for such a thought. I remembered having asked for a test, a way to discern right action.

"My heart reached out to this woman and I rolled up my sleeves, looking around for anything that would be of use. I had my pocketknife, a gallon of spring water in the boot of the car along with my Merlin garb, and a lunch I'd packed in a kitchen pot. I sped around gathering my resources while sending Grandfather a waveform of apology for letting him down, if in fact that was what I was doing.

"The woman, Desiree, had been on her way to the hospital in Avebury, but started out a little too late, having waited for childcare to come for her other little ones. I asked where her husband was. She told me she had sent him away months before, stinking of alcohol and brothels.

"I began to sweat. Was this woman a messenger to my own soul to beg forgiveness for the behavior of my youth? Not certain, I begged forgiveness anyway as I emptied out the bowl that held my lunch, rinsed it and filled it with spring water.

"Desiree was pushing the baby's head through the birth canal – a quick glance told me no complications with position. So I let her work away, encouraging her as I could, while I ripped a big piece off my purple cape and soaked it in the water. Oddly, the water took on a shimmer when I did this. I supposed that Grandfather would have something to say about ripping the cape, but I let the thought go.

"Soon I was guiding the baby's head while his shoulders and torso popped out of Desiree. When the baby was fully birthed, I laid him on her stomach so she could hold him. I prayed over the pocketknife while running the blade through a lit match. I must say I did a neat knot on the cord then severed it with the knife. Desiree birthed the placenta while I washed the boy and wrapped him in the remainder of my cape. His little body began to shimmer as well.

"Then the most amazing event in my life took place. A shaft of light came down from the heavens and engulfed the boy and me in its light. I felt a stirring in my chest and knew that a great White Heart was born there, for one was born in the boy as well. I saw his future and my own in that moment. The most profound level of awareness of brotherhood occurred in that moment – something I had never experienced with Grandfather or any other man.

"I saw clearly that Grandfather's path was not my path, that the brotherhood was preparing to complete a Mission greater than any one of us, and that ego was not to be confused with power - nor was my magic to serve desire. When the boy and I were fully activated by the light, it disappeared.

"Desiree had witnessed that light with eyes as big as saucers. She was speechless as I handed the baby to her. I busied myself salvaging the placenta, which she'd wanted to keep. I emptied my picnic pot and donated it to her with the placenta on behalf of her bravery. Oddly, Eileen never asked the whereabouts of her pot.

"Desiree put the little one to her breast and he began to suckle. It is a miracle for me to see that perfect acceptance of life outside the womb. He looked so innocent, wrapped in the cape of the Merlin. I credit the miracle of that day with the opening of my heart. From that day forward, the ruby light began to grow within me.

"I stayed with them until Desiree could be driven back to her home to be cared for by her neighbors. I have visited her family often over the years. Jamie, now twenty-five, has begun his training as my successor. I see it was necessary for the Merlin lineage to shift, and the magic along with it. We were not to serve the Druids, ourselves or anyone but Mother Earth, the stars and the Mission. I have wondered on occasion how much of that day was a magical creation of my Grandfather and/or the brotherhood.

"I never spoke to him about it, and he never sent me out on such an assignment again. It was certainly a piece of work! Oddly, my insurance agent never heard from the woman I had hit – and it was a fair amount of damage! I am not altogether certain what was real and what was illusion that day, though Desiree and her son have stayed in my reality.

"Thank you for listening to the first and last telling of this tale. I believe my greatest test was to keep that story within my own heart for twenty-five years. That silence gave me my power. I am grateful for brotherhood, *Waykis*." The group nodded their approval of Peter's story, but said not a word. It was by unspoken agreement that each man would tell his tale without comment or question. It simply was what it was, and in that *being* there was power.

Don Eduardo's glance at Demetri, who sat to Peter's left, indicated that it was his turn to speak. Demetri cleared his throat and ran his hand through a head of unruly hair while he summoned up his greatest lesson on the path. Before long, he was ready to speak.

"I admit to being born a warrior – a zealot at heart. Because of this aggressive streak, I happened to meet my teacher. He was not a martial artist as you may suspect, but a healer/magician in a neighboring town. My parents took me to see him hoping he could tame me," he laughed. "Eventually, he had some success with that task, though my parents did not live to see it.

"Vladimir Petroff was a displaced Russian of the Orthodox persuasion, who had come to Cypress from Istanbul to study with the Order of Saint John the Beloved. Many magi over the years have been affiliated with this Order, though John the Beloved was more aligned with the Brotherhood of Oracles - the Prophets.

"Vladimir took an immediate liking to me, or at least that is what I used to think as a boy. Now I know that he saw my White Heart lying dormant within me, wrapped in a tight cloak of aggression. I was one of those kids who would pick a fight just for the fun of it.

"Vladimir saw me once a month until I was an adolescent. He never did try to cure me of my aggressiveness but redirected the energies to more spiritually oriented battles. I learned to channel the energies into the vibrations just above ignorance. Then when I turned thirteen, he had me move to his healing center to become his apprentice. There I began to channel the energies into cleaning and gardening, which, he claimed, were the first stages of enlightenment.

"Not conscious of my White Heart, I had no idea why I would want to be enlightened anyway, but had had little choice about my new life. I think I had exhausted my parents. I am grateful that they didn't turn me over to the Greek military. Surely it would have been delighted to have a kid like me. I think my parents were really very spiritual, not traditionally, but with the occult. Vladimir told me that my father had been his student for most of his adult life. It made me a little curious about Vladimir's age, but I had enough sense not to press that question.

"I learned to love gardening – still do," he pondered. "The cleaning was for women, and I resented it enormously. As a result I spent three years gardening and eight years cleaning, just to get it right.

"It was at the end of those eight years, when I was on the threshold of a new life as the cook, that the first dream of my training came to me. As it turned out, Vladimir did most of his teaching during Dreamtime. It had taken me eight years to become conscious of the dreams. Naturally, he engaged me in battle. Night after night I would exhaust myself in my sleep fighting with him.

"He pushed me harder during the day with the cleaning, until I reached a breaking point. It was then that I became vulnerable in the Dreamtime. We never discussed these dreams, by the way. He found a way to beat me, by taking on the form of a dragon.

"Now a dragon is a formidable opponent, My Brothers – one worthy of a chivalrous knight. I used to wake up with mild burns on my arms and legs from the dragon's fire. I was not afraid of the dragon or Vladimir. Fear has never entered my field. I was not interested in losing to a Dreamtime archetype, but he was wearing me down. It is of interest to note that I never stopped to wonder why Vladimir was challenging me in this way. My ignorance amazes me now.

"One day, in this weakened state, I was mopping the tile floor on the veranda when I felt a searing heat on my left leg. I looked down to see my pant leg burned off. Quickly I looked around me, but saw nothing. I continued my work, and the next thing I knew the right pant leg was missing and the leg was mildly burned. I spun around and began to race up and down the veranda with my mop, looking for whoever was annoying me. As I rounded the corner, the dragon lashed out at me. We were in full combat, I with only a mop to defend myself. The dragon was ruthless, and I found myself losing ground."

Demetri became very excited telling the story, with beads of sweat breaking out on his forehead. "The dragon played with me for perhaps ten minutes before launching an all-out attack that laid me flat at his feet. As he stared down at me, blasting fire in my face that reeked of garlic, I realized I was not dreaming. Or was I dreaming? Which was the dream and which the reality? Was this reality real? I had the most profound thoughts thus far in my life in that moment. Who was this dragon, other than Vladimir?

"I surrendered – gave up my mop, so to speak – and the dragon blew fire into my White Heart, igniting it in violet flames. The next day, I moved into the kitchen and began learning how to prepare food with love. I may look like a zealot to you now and I assure you I will rise to any worthy cause, but I guarantee you, there is not an aggressive bone left in my body – and I am not such a bad cook. The dragon came to teach me in my dreams and continues now though Vladimir has passed from this illusion. The Divine Plan has brought my life full circle with the appearance of my Spanish apprentice who came to me with this same aggression. He is mopping the floor by day and fighting an angry bull by night."

Uproarious laughter accompanied the finishing of Demetri's tale. Demetri was wiping the tears from his own eyes. He had the most exuberant personality of the group, prompting everyone to hold him in their heart. He lovingly roughed up Julio who sat at his left side, giving him the attention of the circle to tell his tale.

Julio did not have to look very deep within or very far back on his path to see where his consciousness had lifted. It was all still fresh in his mind. He had an amazing heart-light for one so young. Raising his downcast eyes, Julio held a hand to his heart and began in Quechua, the language of his heart.

"My heart has been opened, fired and tempered by women – two very special women. The first of these women was my mother, Francesca. My mother had the sight. She was a woman shaman of much importance to our region. Her way was quiet, invisible, and she taught me to live in that way as well.

"She saw my White Heart when I was a baby, and raised me to follow the Path of the *Ylloq'e* which I follow now with Don Eduardo. Mother opened me to the magic during Dreamtime and when I was old enough to communicate with her in this reality, she began instructing me. She carried the codes of light for the Sapphire Sisterhood of the Sun, as does my sister, Angelica. I don't believe mother was a magician, but I cannot say for sure. Everything about her *was* magical.

"During her life, nothing spectacular happened to further my light, but in her death, my heart was forced to open fully. It opened in grief. It poured out its grief like a river flooding its banks when the snow melts.

"Her death was not necessary – from one miscarriage too many in a woman past her time of safe birthing. She was the victim of a culture that cannot separate wisdom from desire. It is our peculiar kind of greed for a woman to have so many children. Though it is old in our culture, it makes no sense to me – so neither did her death. It was not long ago, so my wound is fresh. Grief is a wonderful expression, for it frees the pain within your heart.

"It has been hardest for me to release the resentment I hold for my father and the attachment I had to my mother. I have no doubt, she is still with me. She appears as an eagle or condor whenever I am in need. I dream of her still, but her sweet smell and gentle ways are no longer part of my life. I had to grow up suddenly. I am not resentful of that. I am happy with my life.

"When I was maybe three years old, a woman came to visit Don Carlos, who has a hacienda near our village. I played there with my brother and our friends often, because my father gardened for Don Carlos. This woman looked to me like a Goddess and I could not take my eyes from her. I had never seen someone with blue eyes and blonde hair. I thought she might be someone like *Mamacocha.*

"I followed her everywhere and in my childlike way, I fell deeply in love with her. My mother understood my obsession, because this woman was sisterhood. "We are all one big family," she told me many times. Near the end of that first visit of many, the woman asked Don Carlos who I was. She knew nothing of the sisterhood or my mother at that time. She was attracted by the love I had in my eyes. She had a sight of her own.

"Since that time she has supported my education and our family. The death of my mother opened her heart with grief as well, which deepened the love between us. She is my *madrina,* my second mother. She is Leah.

"Leah took me to the mountains to meet Don Eduardo after mother died and I have begun my path of the *Ylloq'e* with him. As I came through my manhood rituals, I began to feel more of a burning love for Leah. I know it to be without reason or provocation. I suppose it was a natural response to manhood.

"Now she has come to me on the arm of her true love and, once again, I have had to let go of the woman I have loved through an important time in my life. I am grateful to both her and Chris for helping me understand that the only true love is within."

Julio glanced at Chris with a shy grin. "Though I am not yet fully enlightened, my White Heart has grown much bigger because they have been kind and loving in every way to me. I have detached from the unrealistic way I related to Leah and feel blessed that she is my *madrina* still.

"My heart grows even larger to see how radiant she is with our brother, Chris. I intend for such happiness in my own life. I have much to learn and am grateful to be part of this circle," he concluded.

Demetri gave Julio a brotherly squeeze of the shoulders and Chris sent a flood of love and light his way as the young man concluded. Shy of the attention, Julio shifted his enormous dark eyes to look at Maharajah Ramandi on his left, to continue with the next story. Ramandi entered into prayer, his beautiful face in repose. When his energies were focused, he slowly opened his eyes and spoke.

"Abundant blessings I wish for each of you, My Brothers. This circle has a considerable power with its intent. I acknowledge each of you as a master. No one of us is greater than another. I truly feel that vibration in this circle.

"I am a prince in a long line of princes. As most of you know, it was a distant Raja in my family who visited the babe Jeshua after his birth. He gifted the child with gold, for we are a family of considerable wealth. We are no longer political heads of state but have substantial landholdings where many people live and a vast majority of them work for us. It remains much like a principality since our influence is great within the government.

"When I was growing up, I wanted nothing more than to be like every boy I saw playing in the streets of our principality. I had a sense of guilt about my station in life from an early age, wanting to hide my wealth, run away from my future, and become a normal boy. Instead, a loving mother and six older sisters raised me to be a sensitive and devout man.

"When I was eighteen, my father began to worry about me and sent me off to America to college. We were tutored in English from the beginning of our education, so I was not handicapped by language and did very well in my studies of Political Science.

"However, in hindsight, I was much like the child in a candy shop with my first taste of freedom – and the candy shop had everything. I indulged – in sex of all kinds, in drugs of all kinds, in alcohol of all kinds, in cars of the best kind, clothing and so forth. My funds were unlimited and not monitored. I skied in the mountains, sailed in the oceans, visited New York regularly for shows, and spent summers traveling the globe. In short, I had all the life I could want in four years.

"Through it all, I maintained high grades and really did learn an enormous amount about the world and myself. I had such a good time I stayed for graduate school and earned a Master's degree in Economics. All of this I did while my sisters married or spent their idle time sewing for their future married lives.

"When I returned home, my mother and sisters were shocked, but my father was really quite pleased with me. I remember him telling me that he had allowed me that taste of the world because my life would have little room for that kind of freedom in the future. He did not even ask me what I had done. I was not sad, but rather grateful. He was a wonderful man. Elderly when I was born, my father would not live past my thirtieth year.

"On my return from America, Father had picked my brain to know all that I had learned about government and economics. I shared it all with him and what I had learned of countries around the world. He did not criticize or question. He just took it in.

"My magus training began at that time as well. I lived the double life of an apprenticing prince and a magician. Mother knew nothing of the magic, though it quickly became my passion. The best teachers were brought in to help me with mastery of my body, my mind and spirit. Nothing was spared to train me for my dual responsibilities.

"My enlightenment came through discipline and traditional initiatory passages bestowed on me by the swami who has guided my spiritual work over many years. However, I became aware of my White Heart and opened to the work of the Brotherhood of the Ruby with my father.

"For several years before he died, Father involved me in the workings of the government. He knew that he would pass soon and wanted the principality to be left in capable hands. In retrospect it was for this reason that he had picked my brain when I returned from America. He did not agree with all I had learned.

"I remember one incident above all others where that magician shifted my consciousness. In the mountainous region of our holdings there are a number of mineral deposits. A firm from England offered an equitable – in actuality a very profitable – contract to mine precious metals from our lands.

"I looked over the contracts carefully and researched what they proposed very thoroughly. I advised my father that it was an economically sound offer that would enhance the wealth of the family by providing jobs for our people and the contract for us. I followed every rule of my schooling to arrive at my decision. He allowed me complete control of the situation until it reached a point of decision.

"It was then that he took me into the hidden temples beneath our palace and introduced me to the codes of the brotherhood. He asked me to sit on the prince's throne before the Disc of the Sun. An eternal flame burned in the low altar before the disc and many butter lamps had been lit around the temple. It was a beautiful and mysterious place, with the light bouncing off the carved rock wall where gold and gemstones were set in sacred symbols from the stars. I was in the center of the brotherhood in India and had lived above it my whole life without knowing it. Mother and my sisters were oblivious to it as well.

"As I watched the Disc of the Sun it became increasingly fluid until I could see a group of aliens within it. I was introduced to the Siriun High Council, who worked with the Galactic Federation. Father told them of our opportunity with the mining operation and they asked for my thoughts about the offer.

"A tremendous vibration filled the temple as the elders spoke to us. I forced a weak voice to reply to them as I had to my father. They conferred about what I had said while I wondered what role they played in the governance of our lands and former principality. When they had finished among themselves, their leader turned to us and gave me a look of scorn. I felt myself shrinking to the size of a chick-pea before them. Then the elder spoke.

" 'Who is this arrogant idiot, Ram? Surely not your son?' he said, his voice booming. I was, by this time, the size of a grain of rice. 'He is not fit to rule. He has squandered your wealth, indulged his every desire, and filled his mind with nonsense because you gave him the freedom to do so. All this he did with not a thought for another human being. Now he pretends to know what is right for this principality that will eventually have the misfortune to call him Maharajah. What have you to say for yourself, Ramandi?' he concluded.

"What voice has a grain of sand, My Brothers? I could say nothing. My ego had been deflated to nothingness in less than three minutes.

"I began thinking of Father and his relationship with the people he governed. I remembered a time when we acquired more land and the people who went with it became part of our holdings. He did not force our beliefs on them or our ways. He listened to them and actually incorporated some of their ways into ours.

"These people loved my father for treating them as if they were important to him. He treated everyone that way. The revelation to me was that they *were* important to him. These thoughts began to penetrate my consciousness as I cowered before the Council.

"I was shaken from my reverie by the voice of the elder who had been reading my mind. 'Did they teach you to serve your people at the university, Ramandi?' he bellowed.

" 'From my present prospective,' I replied, meekly, 'it seems I was taught more about the management of people and money – control, I suppose.'

" 'Nice observation,' he replied, then continued. 'Listen to me carefully, young Ramandi. I will tell you this only once, though I expect you to be in regular contact with us when you assume your father's position. You bear the White Heart of the Ruby Order which is part of the Brotherood of the Magi.

" 'Once your heart is activated, you cannot be a fool again. You cannot be insensitive, arrogant or ignorant. To be so would jeopardize the Mission. This Mission is much greater than any personal quest you might know. This is the brotherhood, Ramandi, and not a college fraternity. Do you understand?'

"I nodded my head slowly from that state of abject humility, as he continued. 'The Brotherhood of Magi has certain ethical rules, which guide their lives on Earth. In addition, the Ruby Order has a very strict Code of Ethics, which, if broken, will cause your certain death. We advise you to find out what these are from your father. They support impeccability and service.

" 'You must pay particular attention to service, Ramandi, for you are a prince. The codes state that those who reign over or manage others must do so with sensitivity and acceptance. You have already ruminated on these traits in your father. These are Codes of the Holy Grail, Ramandi. To serve is to harmonize, love and bless. It is not to control. You are to do no harm.

"Now let us look over the proposed contract for mining on your lands, Young One. Your half-witted training caused you to see opportunity for personal gain – masked quite cleverly by your ego as jobs for the people.

" 'I would ask you about Mother Earth. Does she gain when her precious minerals are taken from beneath her skin? What of these people who live and would work in that area? Don't you know that changing the metal content of the land shifts the frequency, creates disharmony and depletes the natural *prana*? How will these people avoid ill health and mental imbalance?

" 'Ramandi, when in human bodies, we are no more than a reflection of the Mother. What we do to the Earth we do to ourselves. Please spend your spare time ruminating on this and return here in one month to learn more. Is that clear?'

"Of course it was painfully clear. Father continued to bring me back to that temple, teaching me little by little to summon the Council myself. Just before he died, I had my last session with him and the Council. It was a test of all they had taught me. What a joke it made of my Master's dissertation.

"At that point I had attained some wisdom and my White Heart had grown to a fitting size. Near the end of that session, the acting elder projected a light towards me as Father stood behind me, his hands upon my shoulders. That light filled my heart until a ruby glow began emanating from my White Heart. I was ready to serve, and I wept.

"So my story ends, Brothers. Humility opened a doorway for my Higher Self. My father died within the month and I have held our principality within my heart since that time. I am in regular contact with the High Council, who told me most definitely to be here at Tres Cruces with all of you. I am so grateful for all that is my life and I am humbled to be in your presence. Peace." With that Ramandi gave a traditional bow to the group and rested his left hand on Chris' knee.

Chris took a deep breath, focusing his attention within. Bringing forth the major awakenings of his life in remembrance, he searched for the one worthy of the occasion. He could tell stories of profound initiations at the hands of his teachers, the Ascended Masters and the elements, but he chose a story of the loss of innocence instead. When the remembrance was fully in his consciousness, he opened his eyes, removed his hat, and ran his hand over his silvering hair. With a slightly crooked grin, he began.

"Brothers of the Ruby, how good it is to be in your company in this reality. How grateful we all are to Don Eduardo and the High Council for summoning us together at this auspicious time," he added, bowing his head to Don Eduardo. "I am moved to tell a story from my childhood. It is short and simple, yet it was the first of the many times my life changed completely in the wink of an eye. It feels important for me to bring forth this foundational initiatory piece of my path.

"I was a precocious child - always wanting to be with boys older than myself – always trying to prove that I was a big guy. At the same time, I was unusually sensitive to my surroundings, the feelings of others as well as my own, and all of nature. Sometimes the precociousness and sensitivity danced together in a magical way, but all too often they presented me with challenges far greater than my years.

"When I was eleven years old, my mates were twelve and thirteen. We went out to the bush not far from our neighborhood. For some time, we had been building lean-to shelters out of natural materials, setting up camps and trying out survivalist techniques that we had read about.

"On that day, the oldest of us, Davie, produced a B-B gun. We were each to practice with this gun, shooting tin cans then turn it on some prey that would become our dinner. Since my father had taken me to the Outback shooting occasionally, I proved to be a highly accurate shot with the tin cans. As a result, I was given the task of shooting a bird in flight."

Chris stopped and laughed. "I shudder to think how much testosterone was summoned forth to succeed at this task – at that young age. There must have been plenty of it for my sensitivity was four sheets to the wind. I shot the first bird that flew by my spot in the brush, a plump bronze-winged pigeon. When the bird hit the ground, so did my heart. My mates were cheering and applauding, while I burst into tears. It was as if two opposing forces within me collided and exploded. I would never be the same.

"I lost those mates because I cried – not much of a loss in retrospect. More importantly, I lost my innocence. I had killed a living being. My instinct was to pick the bird up and try to revive it but I had hit it squarely in the heart. Alternatively, I thought of burying it – wanting it out of my sight, for it was too painful. Instead, I dropped the B-B gun, walked away and never looked back. I have not been one to eat flesh since that moment.

"Most importantly, that event brought to me the first of the lessons of magic I was to learn in this lifetime. When you kill a bird, you lose your freedom. It is a simple enough metaphor for one enlightened, but for an eleven-year-old boy, it became a living nightmare.

"Within two weeks, my father left my mother – never to return again. I have not seen him since. For years I felt he would return to free me from an already possessive mother who then projected her sense of loss and abandonment onto me. That projection cost me my freedom, until my own interest in alchemy created a portal of self-liberation. It has always felt to me like my first initiation onto this path – the first remembrance of who I am.

"Secondarily, it taught me that I was my own best mate – to love myself, if you will. I feel really lucky that I learned that lesson early on. The subsequent lessons of my life have been ceaseless, and I see no end in sight," he concluded raising his eyes to study the patterns of the clouds above them. "Thank you, Brothers, for allowing me to share this part of my life with you. Can I suggest that we share our lunch while the Sun is high?"

There was no resistance to Chris' suggestion, as all the brothers welcomed the break to stretch, relieve themselves, and break bread together.

When the group reconvened, it was Master Mukda's turn to relate his story. His meditation was so deep the group thought he had dozed off. When he began to stroke his long white beard, the men came to attention. A gentle smile came to his serene face as he opened his twinkling eyes to the circle. Laying his staff in front of him, on the Earth, he began.

"My Brothers, I wish to tell a tale about navigation. Since this event took place in my life, I have learned to transport myself with some ease, but in the context of this tale, I was a neophyte. This embodiment has been a little more than I expected in terms of length, but I surrendered my expectations to the Divine Plan and continue to serve in whatever capacity I am needed. I don't choose to hold a Three Dimensional frequency very often now, so I am grateful that this group is already anchored in the Fifth Dimension. Thank you. I am delighted to be here and am ready to offer whatever I am called to give.

"Now, to the telling of my tale! I have studied with great masters who have since passed from this plane. Some of them ascended in conscious death and some of them attained vibrations within their perfected bodies that allowed them to leave this plane alive, so to speak.

"One of these masters, Yunkia, first taught me how to project my etheric double. It would be fair to say that I was at least as precocious as Brother Chris," he added, reaching to his right to rub Chris on the shoulder. Smiling, Chris raised his right hand to touch Mukda's hand in communion of Spirit.

"Master Yunkia," he continued, "taught me the difference between my intent and my will. I had already distinguished between thought and intent, which I refer to as the portal to magic. He told me to take command of my energetic body using my will, for intent was not strong enough to project the double. Will, to me, is the portal of mastery, a stepping-off place for true ascension.

"The etheric double is the body of energy available to each of us, yet this body in most people is scattered to the four winds. Perhaps I was forty years of age when these lessons were presented to me – a temple monk high in the mountains of Tibet. When I was born, the monks had searched for me, as I was expected, and had taken me from my mother when I was quite young, so temple life was really all I had known. So, at this time we refer to as the middle years, I began trying to pull my energy body together using my will, unaware that Master Yunkia had an awareness of my every thought and action. I may have been the sole source of amusement in his life. He was a blessing for me, and I was happy to accommodate with all manner of blundering.

"I am sure you are aware that mastery of the energy body creates a superhuman capability within us, but the path of mastery is not without risk. Master Yunkia neglected to point out the risks to me as I gradually gained control of my energy body. As you undoubtedly know. the vehicle is not a thought projection, nor astral traveling - products of mental and emotional control - but rather the energy– the filaments, from the Sixth Dimension.

"The greatest risk is to fall into sorcery, the use of will and energy for self-gratification. This risk never occurred to me, having been brought up in the monastery. My risk came with the imploding of realities, the loss of the stability given to us by form.

"Firstly, I came into my heart with my intent, and from that place was able to access will. Will cannot be accessed from the mind or heart alone, but a concert of the two. However, in trying to describe the energy of will in right action, what comes to mind is the opposite or opposing face of pure love.

"We have mysticism and we have magic, two facets of mastery. We have love as light and light as love, and we have energy within the mastery of our Higher Selves. My practice involved three phenomena: the lifting of boulders; the movement of weather; then teleportation.

"Perhaps thirty years passed in the mastery of energy, but that is a Third Dimensional reference only. Each step along the way was a battle between expectation and will. Will cannot be summoned with any expectation. It is surprisingly difficult to organize something as random as the etheric double. Wanting to succeed is the worst formula for success in this regard.

"I practiced first moving larger and larger stones. These stones could be moved easily with physical exertion, but the training was to move them without exertion – purely with will. Imagine that you have done this – elevated a fairly large stone in front of you. What I can tell you is that twice the energetic mastery is required to lower it. As a result, many a stone dropped, and the magical part of this is that they dropped not below their hovering form, but wherever they felt like dropping – onto my toes, into my tea, sometimes jumping up and down for long periods of time."

The group laughed heartily as he continued. "Yunkia offered me no support in getting control of the situation, but was laughing louder and harder than you, My Brothers." Mukda leaned back with a sigh. "At last I managed to elevate and lower large boulders without mismanagement of the energy. Then I moved on to the weather. You can imagine!! I produced thunderstorms that would not cease, lightening striking all around me, snow in the summer, and long seasons of drought. Everyone in the mountains knew that a monk was mastering energy. Their tolerance was part of the landscape, though they all prayed that I would not be too long at this stage of my training. As with the boulders, reversing the force of the will was the most staggering task.

"By far the most challenging aspect of my energetic training was teleportation – teleportation without an instruction manual." Master Mukda began to laugh hard, tears springing from his eyes. Don Eduardo could not help joining him, since the two had both experienced these trainings in their own fashion. Mukda continued. "I used to lie on my mat and project my double to sit with my brothers in prayer and meditation. I rationalized this practice of will fully aware that I had picked an aspect of monastic life that bored me. I used vast amounts of energy to project my double to avoid a practice that would have replenished my energy. As a result, I began to diminish in power and was unable to bring my double back to me.

"Yunkia was tremendously amused, as I found myself in meditation for most of the day, missing meals which were scant to begin with. Eventually, he would come to retrieve my double, leading it through the monastery back to my mat. When I changed my attitude to one of gathering energy in meditation, the double became more powerful and easily found its way back to my still figure.

"These exercises allowed me to extend the range of my double beyond the monastery to the mountains, the villages and lakes nearby. I began popping up around

Tibet and was soon experiencing the entire Earth through my double. All of these teachings were an excellent precursor to interdimensional travel. I had to learn to navigate the double before I could navigate higher aspects of self and ultimately my entire multidimensional being.

"Without question, these experiences moved me beyond my culture, my geography and my genetics. Limitations fell away as the years went by until, one luminous day, I found myself in the ashram of Lord Sananda on the higher planes. From that moment on, I moved beyond the limitations of form, feeling myself more comfortable in the ashram than here, but quite willing to serve wherever I am called.

"I will end this story right there, saving the experiences with Lord Sananda for this evening. I thank you for your attention to this odd tale and hope that it might, in some way, assist each of you on your own paths, or at least provide good humor in the moment," he concluded. "I might add that a woman would approach the work I did in a vastly different way, and likely succeed at it in a fraction of the time."

The group broke into laughter and applause as the spell he had cast upon them broke. Without question, they were sitting in the presence of an Ascended Master who marked his time in the Third Dimension as a Bodhisattva – one who serves humanity from a place beyond the ego. How fitting that he had spoken of the blunders along his path of mastery with humor.

Master Mukda turned to Sheik Fakoum on his left, nodding for Fakoum to begin while he lifted his staff to lean it against his shoulder. Fakoum raised his eyes and hands to the heavens as if to say, "How am I to follow you, Brother?" This brought smiles to the faces of his brothers at the same time it spun a web of rosy light around the group.

The sheik lowered his head and hands to the prayer position for a few moments before facing the circle. Stroking his long beard, he spoke. "My Brothers, I have led the life of a mystic. My story can be naught but a poem – a poem of the surreal. Have you ever sat in contemplation of a flower? I have done so for hours. A flower, like everything else in this Universe, is an aspect of the Divine. At the time of my encounter with the flower, I knew this on some level of my being, but in my consciousness, I did not believe it was so.

"Mine was a great sufi master who also apprenticed me in the dervishes. At dawn this day, of which I speak, he took me to the garden and asked me to meditate before a yellow lily. I was to sit there until the lily spoke to me.

"A simple exercise in patience became a journey through the dimensions. Meditation practice had prepared me for those spaces in time when the mind becomes restless and wanders about aimlessly. For hours I practiced stillness in no-mind. I observed the changes in the atmosphere around me without taking my eyes from the flower. Droplets of dew crept down each petal into the cup of the flower, where they were consumed as the nectar of heaven's essence.

"The lily breathed in my respiration, restoring its life force with my respired waste. Our breathing became rhythmic – transcendent. She quivered in expectation of the breeze and drank in the golden filaments of the Sun. In time she became so transparent to me and I to her that we merged in our Divine Oneness. This experience of ecstasy took us into dimensions beyond, but within, the garden – dimensions of pure light and sound. It seemed that conscious lifetimes were lived in that space of time.

"My Brothers, I am here to assure you that ecstasy does not keep time. I was, for hours, within the enchantment of the lily. She allowed me to understand that ecstasy is our natural state of being – all else is the illusion. A sleeping cat is in ecstasy. A singing bird is in ecstasy. It is the preoccupied mind that separates us from our true nature.

"I carry that lily in my heart and in my luminous body to this day. We cannot be separated in death or life. I have had an infinite number of experiences similar to this one in my years of awakening. My field has expanded to encompass all that I have known in Oneness – and now I add this experience and all of you into my field with the lily and all else.

"My sense of wonder is saturated for the moment. To say more would be foolish. Thank you, Beloved Brothers, for sharing your experiences this day - for sharing a part of your essences. I recognize your many gifts and am humbled in your presence."

Sitting in contemplative silence at the conclusion of Sheik Fakoum's poetic delivery, the circle of brothers was, like the lily, soaking in the dew drops and golden filaments offered by the sheik. He had said little, yet he had shifted the group's assemblage point into a profound recognition of Divine reverence for life. It was some time before anyone could bring their entranced attention back to the purpose of their gathering. Sheik Fakoum lightly touched the right hand of Jacques de Villey, prompting him to bring forth his story.

Jacques rubbed his hands together, against the chill of a lowering Sun. His youthful eyes were bright with intelligent energy as he took a sip of cool tea and began.

"My Brothers, I have had an unusual life. Being born into a family of magicians who had never been separated from the gnosis, my identity was reinforced to me on a daily basis. I knew who I was from the day I was born. Due to that reinforcement, I have never gone astray from my Truth. This does not mean that I was not a terror of a child, for I was. My mother grayed at an early age," he laughed.

"Father was a stonemason and an active member of the true Masonic Order, but he was not an alchemist. Charles de Villey, an uncle of sorts, was the magus. It was Uncle Charles who saw the makings of a White Heart within me and who took me under his tutelage when I was young. I note how fortunate some of us have been to begin our training as boys.

"Uncle Charles had come through the same lineage of magicians as beloved Saint Germain. These were alchemists who worked with balancing planetary energies in preparation for ascension. They also held the formulas for the elixirs of the early brotherhood, including the elixirs of eternal youth. Uncle Charles had known Saint Germain during his European embodiments – his stories were more than fantastic, and over time I heard them all. At the higher levels of initiation, I was given the elixir formulas to pass on to my apprentice – who, incidentally, has not yet incarnated.

"Uncle Charles ascended around the turn of this century having been embodied for over four hundred years. I began my apprenticeship with him in the early nineteenth century," he said, with a broad grin. "I am still quite young for our lineage." Many an eyebrow raised within the circle.

"Some of the lessons inherent in my path have related to my lineage's rules of celibacy – truly the most difficult trial has been to accept a kind of separation that the gifts demand of you. To maintain the high alchemy, it is necessary that no one be allowed to share your field until the apprentice arrives. It is painful to watch your family of origin age and die, riddled with needless disease. It becomes part of your survival to regard the magicians as your family instead – for Charles and I were members of an authentic Magi Order.

"Now let me tell you where I was most severely challenged during my training. The magi of our order were overseeing the balancing of energies in the Americas. This has been part of our Mission since beloved Saint Germain set the wheels of destiny in motion prior to the French Revolution.

"Democracy was needed to balance the domination of monarchies and empires that had prevailed for millennia and to open the door of liberation leading to ascension. We were active in many parts of the world, initiating these energies. As a young apprentice I was appalled at the injustice present all over the Earth, but particularly in these democratic initiatives. We watched high vibrational initiatives turn into corruption, slaughter or sublimation of all who were different, financial dominion, greed - as we know, the list is long. I wanted intervention to right the wrongs, to bring equality and true justice without prejudice.

"Uncle Charles told me that I was an opinionated lout and very nearly boxed my ears," Jacques laughed. "I admit that it took many years for me to relinquish my opinions and accept that injustice is illusion – an illusion that accompanies moving energy. I learned that the magi set energy in motion for the highest ultimate good then withdraw their powers to allow mankind to find the appropriate movement to balance the energies. I learned that the magicians work with light and dark, yang and yin, for both are required to move energy. Thus it is the height of folly to judge their work at face value.

"Our Mission is to instigate change, not to manipulate how it unfolds. Obviously the lesson was relinquishing control, for that was not part of the magi's Mission, but I also had to let go of judgment, opinion and that sense of injustice that sprang from pity and my own high opinion rather than compassion. Beyond that surrender lie the intricacies of the alchemist, the understanding of illusion, and, in time, an ability to grasp the larger picture. Because I was able to initiate the surrender, the door to mastery opened, and my White Heart entered my reality.

"My lineage requires that one live an extraordinary life – a life outside the human condition. Discipline is part of every magician's life, but he who would achieve that extra-human position has no pity, no need to control, no desire, no judgment, and, as you can see, no deterioration. True power resides in that place – all other power is an achievement of the ego.

"It has taken some time for the balancing energies initiated by my lineage to find their way into the light. I understand the need for the darkness, for every seed begins its journey within the dark Earth and moves steadily towards the light, where it drops its seeds again to initiate a new cycle.

"We are here together, Brothers of the Ruby, for the first time in this dimension. The seed has at last pierced through the soil to reach for the Sun. Ascension, once the culmination of an individual's quest for true power, will become a collective enterprise. The people of the world once isolated and narrowly defined in their culture now share an awareness of each other that is, very nearly, global. We have moved into a stage of the Mission where the recipients of initiated energies are impacted immediately. I am grateful to be of service to Mother Earth, her multitudes and to each of you in whatever way I am able. Thank you, Beloved Brothers of the Ruby."

Susmo, next to speak, was staring at Jacques as his fingers idly twisted his moustache. His stunned expression suggested that he felt a mere mortal sitting next to a master of Jacques' attainment. Reading his mind, Jacques reached into his left pocket and pulled out a vial of liquid. Offering it to Susmo, he said. "My Brother, I offer you the elixir of regeneration, if you are willing to walk the path."

Susmo laughed, pushing the offering away dramatically. "I am in no way ready for your elixir, My Brother, but I thank you for the offer. I am still trying to comprehend my own desires – a sure sign that I am not ready to part with them yet." The group gave him a round of applause with joyful laughter and a few playful whistles. Jacques slipped the elixir back into his pocket and good-naturedly hugged Susmo, kissing him on the cheek. Altogether, it was an artful transition to set the stage for the telling of Susmo's tale.

"Brothers of my heart," he began. "Life has forced some very powerful transformations on me – perhaps the most powerful being just the other day. Lacking the perspective which time and distance brings, I will not speak of that event. Our Brother Fakoum has reminded me of an experience during my early years of training – an experience with the spirit of a plant. It was a significant turning point in my life.

"I was young, in my twenties, when my father asked me to accompany him to the jungle. He was dealing in antiquities but also looking for a piece of property. My father had many landholdings in the mountains but was, for some reason, looking to have a port on the Madre de Dios River.

"Wealth has had a way of putting you above reproach in our country. I believe my father, a descendant of land barons with vast holdings, may have used that to his advantage. I do not fault him that. It was the system. All of that changed with the reform and the loss of our lands, but wealth, sometimes a curse, has always been with my family in this land.

"Once we arrived in the jungle, he hired an *Ayahuasqero*, Don Pedro, to entertain me with ceremony while he went off with a number of women, as was his custom. I am being honest. My father was who he was, and I loved him. Unfortunately, I was, in many ways, made in his image.

"I had known about *Ayahuasca*, the Vine of Death, since I was a boy. Hearing the stories of those who had participated in the ceremonies made me reluctant to do so myself. Taking the substance of the plant shifted reality dramatically, after the prerequisite latex purge had caused you to vomit and shit to a point where life really didn't matter anymore. I suppose that was exactly where the plant spirit wanted you to be to talk some Truth into your consciousness," he mused. giving his mustache a twitch.

"At any rate, I went ahead with the ceremony, rightly believing it to be part of my training. We spent the afternoon preparing the plant extract, beginning with the harvest and ending with the bottling of the alkaline psychotropic extract. Father had not prepared me with fasting and cleansings, so it was a gut-wrenching experience from the first sip of the potent extract.

"I sat in meditation with Don Pedro while he sang the songs of the plant spirit, dashing off into the jungle regularly to empty my stomach and guts. After my fourth ingestion of the extract and trip to the forest, I began to hallucinate. Don Pedro skillfully led me into my first small death.

"Before entering into communion with the spirit of the plant, it is necessary to see yourself as you really are. This was painful and frightening. I think it is similar to what one can experience after death, when your own demons terrorize you. I did not think I would survive the night at all, but a warrior was born within me during the process.

"I encountered an ugliness that I carried through my bloodline from the conquest of these lands and from the old country. It was my father's lineage trying to free itself from the guilt and shame of domination. Here I am, a *mestizo,* carrying the blood of both sides of the conflict within me. It needed to be resolved, and I was the one who had chosen to find peace within.

"When the awareness of my forthcoming obligations was complete, the plant spirit came forth and the fear rose within me. In retrospect it was nothing to fear, except that it came as a serpent-dragon and scared me half to death," Susmo said, laughing.

"When my heart quieted again, the plant spirit took me flying over the jungle, giving me a freedom I had not known before. I was instructed about many aspects of plant life, coming away with a motivation to preserve the plants and to know their spirits. This was actually the *karpay* of the *pampa mesayoq,* an Initiation of the plant medicine. Don Pedro was such a priest and could provide this *karpay* for me.

"I went back to the jungle many times, and properly prepared, communed with the Spirit of *Ayahuasca* to further my learning in this *karpay.* Each time I released more of myself to meet the spirit, yet I had clung all of these years to an aspect of my desire body inherent in my father's bloodline.

"Finally I have released that need to measure or know myself through dominion over women. I can see that when the reform took our lands away and freed the Indians to their own sovereignty, my father transferred his need to dominate to women, who were barely a step above the Indians with respect to human rights.

"I am deeply grateful to Don Eduardo and *Waykis* Chris and Leah for assisting me in this final release. I see portals opening for me into realms of realization that I could not previously comprehend. I am grateful to the Spirit of *Ayahuasca* for initiating me on my path and to the spirits of the many plants who have come to me since.

"I feel blessed to have been able, in my lifetime, to come into a more loving and supportive relationship with the Indian tribes than has been the history in my family. My father was their friend and a high initiate in their priesthood, but he died with his sense of superiority. Since he passed, I have often felt him communicating his gratitude for my healing of the bloodline, for I have come to understand that it heals all those who have come before you and all those who will come after.

"I do not see these loathsome qualities in my own children. Now it is my conviction that my sons will live their lives in right relationship with all of life, including their women, as I come into right relationship with women myself.

"Dear Brothers, I feel your support and am enlightened by the sincere and amazing stories you have told today. I now ask Don Eduardo to conclude the telling of tales and move us onto the next level of our Mission here." With that, Susmo turned to Don Eduardo, who had a very pleased look on his face. Eduardo rubbed him on the back, tossing him around a bit to show his appreciation of Susmo's rapid evolvement. Then the *ylloq'e* became very serious as his tale began.

"My Brothers, collectively we are a powerful group of *waykis* who have trained through the ancient lineages of the magi. In the stories you have told today I have heard the Truth of your greatness. I have heard tales of self-realization in which each of you has fought your own battles of consciousness to arrive at the portals of high magic –The Great Service.

"In your tales, you have captured the essence of the Grail Codes, the Codes of the Ruby Order and Universal Law. None of us is perfect – perfection is not our calling - but we are authentic, impeccable, and wise.

"Tomorrow, Leah and Doña Felicia, who complete our Circle of Twelve, will join us. These Sisters of the Ruby and the Sapphire will bring a new level of sensitivity to this circle and balance the energies needed to manifest our Mission. I would like each brother and sister to bring the object of power most dear to them to tomorrow's meeting. These we will lay upon the table to initiate our work. Chris, make sure that Leah is informed of this request."

Chris nodded his head as Don Eduardo continued. "I suppose you are waiting to hear a story from me," he said, as if taken by surprise. The group prepared for the *ylloq'e's* humor by leaning a little bit forward, engaging him with alertness. Deftly, he reached into his baby alpaca-skin coca bag, saluting the mountain as he filled the inside of his cheek with a handful of coca leaves. He removed his felt hat then his colorful knit hat that fit snug to his head. A few gray hairs streaked his shiny black hair, which he parted above his forehead for all to see.

"I am not demonstrating a new style of hair," he said, his eyes alive with laughter. "I want you all to see this scar on the top of my head. Hair has never grown on this scar. You can see it is shaped like a jagged lightening bolt." The men leaned towards him to see the scar that was as prominent and jagged as he had described. Then, as quickly as he had removed his hats, he placed them back on his head – felt hat atop the knit one.

The *ylloq'e* continued. "What you have seen is the scar from a lightening bolt. I come by my insanity naturally," he added, slapping his knees and provoking laughter around the circle. "In my culture, it is the fastest way to become a *paqo* - perhaps because there is some risk involved. I was a boy at the time, which especially marks you for the training. Mine was not a family of *paqos,* so the lightening chose me. What kind of experience is this? En-lightening!" he joked.

Don Eduardo was unable to be serious about his own life, since he had detached from it long ago. "I don't remember pain because the shock was so great it moved me beyond any feeling immediately. I remember the light and the strong desire to move towards it, to be engulfed in it. I remember clearly the kind voice telling me that it was not my time to leave *Pachamama* and that the light would wait for me. This is a disappointment regardless of your age.

"I resigned myself to live again and found myself on my sleeping mat back in our home. I was being tended by the *pampa mesayoq* who had some experience with the situation. It is not that uncommon as the lightening is very *salk'a* in the mountains. It makes you *salk'a* when you have been marked with it – especially when it is the crown of your head.

"My parents told me that the light, which bounced me off the ground around the llama herd I was tending, had engulfed me. The light killed one young llama. The whole village was preparing an offering with the meat. My body had thrashed uncontrollably on the rocky ground, leaving me with bruises all over my backside. The *pampa mesayoq* was treating these with plant extracts when I awakened. My body was in pain then and many days passed before I could walk. My mother consoled me, telling me that a great light had entered my being and shone from my eyes. This was my first awakening to the path.

"Three years later, when I was initiated into manhood, the *kuya hampeq* read the coca leaves for each of us. When my reading came, my parents came to sit beside me. The coca reader threw the leaves, gasped, threw them again, then again and finally looked at the three of us with an expression of agony on his face. My mother went into fear and put her arm around me. My father pushed her arm away and sat more erect.

"I began to pray to the *Apu* for the strength needed in my future, because it did not look promising in that moment. The priest told us that I was marked for the life of a great *ylloq'e* but that I would need to chase the lightening, inviting it to strike me twice more. I had never heard of such a thing, though often those who were coming into their power did seek the lightening to strike them, to bring in the light and the community's acceptance of their powers. Three times seemed unreasonable by any measure.

"I felt the call of destiny but longed for the contentment of a normal life. Each of us has felt this paradox, I am sure. I was sent out into the mountains that summer, calling to the lightening. The pumas and condors befriended me as I climbed into the remote areas near the snow.

"My intent was pure and I was without fear. It did not take long for the lightening to find me. On this occasion, the only observers were the pumas I was traveling with, for even the condors were not flying on that wild day. At that level of light initiation, you were on your own to survive.

"Oddly, when the jolt went through me that time, again entering the crown, I did not thrash and go into shock. The initial strike of my boyhood had opened a portal for the light. I did not go to the light but traveled to the peak of the mountain instead. I was greeted by the *Apu* and *Ñusta* - the Masculine and Feminine spirits of that mountain.

"The spirits asked me to be the guardian of that mountain, a mountain called the Blazing Spirit in your language. The light within me increased markedly and I regularly communicated with the spirits. The gifts of seeing, hearing and sensing opened within me.

"Twenty years passed before I was struck a third time, quite unexpectedly when on a pilgrimage to *Apu* Ausangate. While high within that range, I made offerings at the seven lagoons. It was a pilgrimage. I was accompanied by the firstborn son of Doña Felicia and myself. We were both found by the lightening, he receiving his opening to the light and I, my final initiation. Again I had no shock or pain, but was taken out into the heavens to *Chaska*, the Dog Star – the Eye of God. There I met with the Siriun High Council to receive my Mission in the Ruby Order. They activated my White Heart and saved the life of my son, because I was not there to attend him. I was then known as a *ylloq'e* throughout the Andes and have been able to find many of the Brotherhood of Magi to help weave the foundation of our work. I have brought many of them with us on this journey as warrior brothers.

"That is my story, *Waykis*. The lightening has given me permission to be as crazy as I care to be, but it has also helped me to anchor the Source within my physical form. It was a lot to hold onto in the beginning, and now, as I begin preparations to leave the planet, it is all that I wish to be.

"Doña Felicia has also been kissed by the lightening. Together, we are as one soul. When we go, we will go together. Until that time, we are committed to the completion of the Mission. Forgive me for becoming a little melancholy, My *Waykis*. Once in a while, my Higher Self decides not to be a rascal and takes me completely by surprise."

With that, Don Eduardo completed the circle amidst cheers and plenty of backslapping. Gathering their belongings, the men trekked off to rejoin the group at the base camp. Hot tea and cookies were shared by all before stepping out into the chill wind again to witness the setting of the Sun.

Order of the Ruby

Steaming bowls of soup brought the group together around the kitchen fire. Social chatter was lighthearted since there was an understandable confidence surrounding the work of each small group that day. It had been an intense day for all of them and there was need for levity. Following the soup, there came squash pancakes, cucumber salad and fresh caught pan-fried trout. The cooks had had a full day as well.

Chris caught Leah's eye but waited to join her until she and Ramandi had finished an animated conversation. Lagging behind in the feasting, Leah had barely finished her soup as Chris approached her. One of the cooks slipped between them, exchanging her soup bowl for the main course. She looked at her plate, then at Chris.

"How am I going to eat all of this, Darling?" she asked, bewildered.

"Reminds me of the Last Supper," he replied, winking at her.

"Do you think it is?" she asked, wide-eyed.

"I would eat it if I were you, Mate," he replied with mock seriousness.

"Do you know something I don't know, Chris?" she asked.

"Of course not, but I have my hunches. I am sure Don Eduardo will give us some idea what we are doing next. What I do know is that you are to bring your most sacred item with you when we meet tomorrow."

Leah held her hand to her chest to feel the sapphires within her medicine pouch. Then she thought of the pendant of Qoyari and something else of immense importance. "What if I were to bring several sacred items?" she asked.

"No one will fault you for being a spiritual pig, Sweetheart," he teased. "Bring what you are moved to bring and I am certain it will be perfect."

"Thank you for your wit, Chris," she replied laughing at herself. "It is funny how I still react to such a request as if there were rules I have to follow – and at this level of play!"

"You don't strike me as one who would play by the rules at all, Leah."

"I don't - rebel all the way, in fact! On the other hand, I acknowledge the conditioning to them. You know, Chris, I just can't eat all this. Will you help me?" she pleaded.

"To be honest with you, I only ate the soup. I am not much of an eater either," he replied, taking her plate and passing it to the warriors. "Either one of us would be a cheap date."

Chris warmed her heart while simultaneously arousing her curiosity. "How do you live in Perth, Chris?" she probed. "Do you socialize much, eat out, play any sports? I'm curious."

He recognized her need to ground herself with practicalities. "You would be surprised to see how I live, Leah," he offered. "I own a cottage on a serene piece of land in the rolling hills of the bush – out past Kalamunda. A creek runs through the land allowing me to have gardens everywhere. I try to grow a lot of my own produce, though it has taken some time to bolster the soil. You could say that I am very reclusive. Since I gave up women, my only sports are cycling, kayaking and windsurfing - though I do keep up my aikido practice," he teased.

"Well, I asked for that one didn't I?" she laughed. "Is that how you have always lived?"

He laughed. "I wish. This has been since returning from the Outback. I found myself in continual upheaval in the city - though Perth is mild compared to most. This is self-preservation. I have learned to monitor my frequency and protect it. It's all part of the alchemy, Leah. Are you going to tell me how you live, or is this a one-way inquisition?"

"I have a little place in the hills, south of Carmel, but not quite to Big Sur. I was lucky to inherit a cottage in the redwoods overlooking the sea. The ocean puts me to sleep at night, and awakens me in the morning. Two amazing dogs keep me company when the grandchildren are not around. My youngest son, Charlie, and his family live in Santa Cruz, and take care of the dogs and house when I wander. I am an avid gardener, but lately I am never at home. It sounds like you have more time at home than I do."

"For the moment only. My guess is that as the Mission gets cracking, we are going to be living the whirlwind. One day, the wind will quit blowing and we will somehow find a bit of stillness."

"Sounds like a genuine vacation," she laughed. "This seems like a bizarre conversation for the circumstances we are in. I must be trying to ground myself."

"Of course you are, Mate, and I am happy to oblige. When you come to WA (Western Australia) next, I will greet you with a bouquet from the garden and cook a meal from the land. It will be an alchemical affair all the way around," he laughed. Then, taking his turn to change the subject, he softened his voice and asked. "Is your circle of women ready to dream?"

"It feels like everything is in place, though I haven't a clue what we're doing."

"I don't think anyone really knows at this point. I wouldn't want to guess, but I am willing to open the doors."

"Well, I, for one, am ready to charge through them. We are clearly moving into the energies of the alignment," she added.

"Only a few days until we are aligned with the Great Central Sun," he replied quietly. Chris and Leah had moved to a place against the wall, where they could speak freely. He was just about to ask her if he could fill her teacup when Jacques strolled over to talk with them.

"Good evening, Leah, Chris," he said, kissing both of them lightly on the cheek. They both greeted him with warm hugs, conscious of a most inviting softness about him. "I am curious about our common relative, Anselm de Ville, Leah. How did you come to know of him?"

"Quite by chance, Jacques," she replied. "My mother had once given me the genealogies for both sides of her father's family. The family was quite proud of her great-grandfather's lineage, which included an Archbishop of Canterbury. He had traced it all the way back to Charlemagne the Great who, as I have researched it, was of the bloodline of Jesus and Mary through the Merovingian descent.

"Of course that bloodline had its fair share of Crusaders and Templars as well. I did not look at my great-grandmother's genealogy for many years – obviously not until I was ready to understand it. It was primarily the genealogy after arriving in America, but the beginning spoke of the history and mentioned Anselm and the Crusades of Richard the Lion-Hearted. It included a family shield that was fascinating. In the top left corner was a tower and in the top right corner, the rampant Davidic Lion - Mary Magdalen and Jesus, left and right – feminine and masculine. That is all I have had to go on," she concluded.

"Our lineages come through the feminine side of the messianic bloodline, Leah. Have you had much of an opportunity to research the family in France?" Jacques asked.

"Very little, Jacques, though I have been to southern France. Provence will always take up a big space in my heart. I imagine you have a massive amount of information – all in French."

"I do. I would be more than willing to share it with you, even translate it for you," he offered, with a smile.

"How interesting that would be," she replied, glowing. Jacques' kindness and generosity struck a cord within her.

"Actually, I would like to invite both of you to stay with me awhile, when you have the time."

"Oh, Chris," she sighed, "wouldn't that be wonderful?"

"It would, Leah," Chris answered, smiling. "When would you have the time to work France into your life? I would like to spend some time with Jacques as well."

"I am committed for a year and a half before I can schedule some time. Would that work for you two?"

"Fine with me, " Chris offered.

"I am in no hurry, Leah," Jacques replied. "Write it into your schedule for the spring - more like two years from now, then send me an e-mail. Here is my card, Beloved Cousin," he said handing her a simple calling card with his name, address, phone and e-mail written in a flowing script. "Plan to stay awhile so that we can explore France and northern Italy together."

"We will, Jacques. I have so longed to walk in the footsteps of Mary and the lineages of blood and soul that are there for me. Thank you, Beloved Brother."

"It is my pleasure to host both of you. In the meantime, Leah, take this humble offering from one who loves you as the Goddess." With that, Jacques drew the vial he had offered to Susmo from his pocket and put it in Leah's hand. It was a small dropper bottle. "You are ready for this, Leah. Take only one drop each night before sleeping."

"What is it, Jacques?" she asked.

"The first of a series of elixirs holding the secret of immortal life, My Dear," he replied, looking somewhere deep within her being. "Forgive me for teasing Susmo with it this afternoon," he added, glancing at Chris. "It was made specifically for you."

She was speechless, looking at him wide-eyed in astonishment. "Chris," he continued, "when you come, I will teach you to make your own."

Chris laughed, lightly touching Jacques' shoulder. "Very well, My Brother. I have much to learn from you."

"And I from you, My Brother," Jacques added. "It will be outrageous fun as well," he laughed, returning the brotherly touch. "I see Master Mukda preparing to gather us in circle, Beloveds, so I leave you until tomorrow. Good evening."

"Good evening, Jacques," they both called after him.

Leah looked at the vial, then at Chris for some explanation. "Put that in a safe place, Love," he told her casually. "Jacques is going on two hundred years old."

"Get out of here, Chris!" she exclaimed. "Are you serious?"

"He would have no reason to lie about his age, Darling. He looks fantastic, don't you think?" he mused.

"To say the least, Chris. What a wonderful invitation to stay with him. I can hardly wait," she said excitedly.

"One drop a night, Leah. All you have to lose is your mortality," he whispered, kissing her softly near her ear. "It will be a great opportunity if the Divine Plan unfolds in that way."

"True enough. So much could happen to change it all. If it is to be, it will be," she added good-naturedly, pulling out her medicine pouch to tuck the vial within it.

•

Master Mukda established himself before the altar as the group filled in the circle around him. After placing the golden skull in the center of the circle, Don Eduardo had a few words with Master Mukda, calling Susmo over to translate. Then he took his place in the circle next to Doña Felicia.

Master Mukda motioned for Leah to come and speak with him as he used his staff to shift his position to one of greater comfort. Setting her tea down on the floor, Leah rose and walked over to the master. She knelt on one knee before him to receive his message.

"Give me your hands, Beloved," he said, a twinkle in his eyes. Leah held her hands out, slightly cupped, not knowing whether he intended to inspect them or put something in them. Mukda reached into his pocket and produced an elaborately decorated silk pouch. Ancient symbols woven in shades of silver, blue and violet took on a luminous quality as he put the pouch into her waiting hands.

Arms sinking, Leah felt the weight of the pouch and its contents. "What have we here, Beloved Teacher, and how can I serve you?" she asked in wonder.

"It would serve me, Leah, if you would place these stones in a Star of David around the golden skull," he answered, solemnly.

"As you wish, Master Mukda," she said, smiling. Then she spilled the stones into her hands and gasped.

Mukda laughed. "They are nice specimens, are they not?" he noted, his eyes filled with light.

"Blue diamonds?" she queried, her hands electric with their energy.

"Indeed. Do you like them?"

"They are quite beyond words!" she exclaimed. "Can I ask you where they originated?"

The diamonds were enormous and perfectly faceted. "They did not originate in this dimension, Leah. That is all that I can reveal to you at this time."

"What do they represent?" she asked. "We have the rubies of the Ruby Order and the sapphires of the Sisterhood. What of the blue diamonds?"

"The light of the planet Venus is blue, is it not?" he asked.

"Truly, it is," she replied. Then with a sudden realization, she added, "Do they represent the Kumaras?"

"And the Christ Consciousness Initiative," he replied.

"Thank you, Master Mukda, for the privilege of setting this grid for you," she said, lowering her eyes.

"With every privilege, there comes responsibility, Leah."

"How well I know, Beloved Teacher. How can I serve this initiative?" Leah answered.

"Beloved Leah, within the context of your evolving consciousness, you have truly lived authentically. Promise me that you will continue to do so as the fullness of the Mission comes upon you."

"I promise, Master Mukda. I will not shirk from the responsibility that comes with that awareness, nor be other than who I am."

"Even if who you are seems outrageous to you?" he asked, laughing.

"Even so," she replied, with a great smile. "I will find some way to live it authentically."

"You were well chosen, Child. Now set the grid. When this journey has ended, the diamonds will be yours, a gift from Lord Sananda and Lady Nada."

A tear rolled down Leah's cheek as she rose to set the grid. Somewhere deep inside her, a memory of the Masters created a longing to be with them. As soon as she turned around, she caught Chris' eyes. As it was poised upon her cheek, ready to drop, he saw the tear turn into a tiny white dove that flew in circles around the group. It was the Holy Spirit, the Feminine Aspect of God. He knew that her field had been activated in a subtle way to the Mission, for it pulsed blue light just as the diamonds did while she set the grid.

When Leah came to sit at Chris' side again, she sat staring at her hands for a short time. Electric with charged energy, they were emanating blue-white light.

"How beautiful," he remarked, whispering in her ear.

"Look at the Matrix, Chris? It is completely cosmic tonight," she responded, trying to shift his attention from her hands.

The space around the skull was filled with sparkling filaments of light. Geometry emerged from geometry as the filaments were continually rewoven.

"So are you, Leah," he replied, touching her lightly on the back of her neck. He read the energies from her body immediately – blue light, Venus, the Kumaras. "Thank you, Mukda, on behalf of the Mission," he thought, sending that thought form across the room to the master.

Acknowledging Chris, Master Mukda tapped his staff several times on the floor to get the group's attention. He sat like a Buddha atop several rolled sleeping mats, his eyes twinkling above his round, flushed cheeks. His richly brocaded Tibetan robes fell in folds to the floor.

Clearing his throat, he harnessed the attention of the group. "Beloveds, before we begin tonight's adventure, Don Eduardo would like to discuss tomorrow's schedule."

Don Eduardo nodded to Susmo for translation and Sonia prepared to help with the English. "*Waykis*," he began, "we look ready to begin the next step in our Mission. In the morning after breakfast, we will journey towards the mountain. *Wayki* Brian has reported to me that our warriors located the interdimensional portal today. When we reach that portal, a group of warriors will stay in this dimension to guard the entrance and a small band will enter the portal with the brothers and sisters. Bring any sacred items with you, a bottle of water, but nothing else. The cooks and Susmo's young warriors will stay here to guard your belongings.

"*Waykis*, we are moving outside of time, but we will be cared for in every way. Please, arise before dawn. We must begin our work with the sunrise. Thank you, *Waykis*," he concluded, bowing his head.

The group stirred with excitement, then settled down again as Master Mukda tapped his staff a few times on the cement floor. When he was ready to speak, he pointed the activating end of his staff towards the skull. The cement building fell away as a whirling weblike cocoon of light-energy surrounded the group. The cooks, rancheros, and young warriors, who were not of the brotherhood or sisterhood, fell away.

Mukda laughed at the startled faces of the group, then, holding his left hand to his heart, he began to speak. "Beloveds, forgive my theatrics. I find this building somewhat dismal, don't you?" he teased. The group laughed agreeably. "Do not worry about our companions, for they are having a wonderful show of light and sound, and are not aware that we have gone. As I am speaking, the great Golden City of Shambhala will begin manifesting around us. Shambhala has been a Golden City of the Piscean Age, working in concert with its two points of articulation, the Golden City of Mount Shasta and the Sun Disc here in the Andes, to hold an ascended energy within the auric body of our Mother the Earth.

"Shambhala has been the retreat and advanced learning center for those in the latter stages of ascension. As Earth ascends, Shambhala will become her reality and new Golden Cities at higher frequencies will emerge. One of the central cities of the Age of Aquarius will be Camelot at Glastonbury in the United Kingdom, the heart-center of the planet. Another magnificent anchoring of light will occur somewhere in America and then, there is this beloved land in the Andes.

"Camelot was activated by beloved Master Jeshua, his brother, James the Just, who was Joseph of Arimathea, and Simon the Magus, before Master Jeshua began his public life. In fact he had not yet journeyed to India for the first time. These young masters anchored a vortex of light there, creating a bridge between the worlds.

"The bloodlines and soul lineages of Master Jeshua and Queen Mary Magdalen in the persons of Merlin, Morgaine, Mordred and Arthur were born into that vortex to facilitate the next stage of activation for this futuristic city. The blood crystals of Arthur and Mordred, spilled upon the land as they ended each other's lives, contained a memory of the Grail Codes and the Golden Cities. In that regard, the loss was on the Third-Dimensional level only. Having completed their ascensions long before that time, they are all actively engaged in manifesting this Golden City for the coming age.

"Having very little to say but much to show you, I will talk briefly then lead you in an ancient chanting ceremony that will appropriately end our evening forays into the history of the magi.

"I was born high in the mountains of Tibet and was given to an order of magi there at a young age. This order dated from the time of the first colonization from Ancient Mu. Our history was written in the language of the stars. Don Eduardo and I are brothers in the truest sense of the word.

"In time I mastered the ancient languages and was admitted to the Hall of Records to work at our continual process of translation. It is how we kept the language of the stars alive. Within that Hall of Records I learned the history of the Earth and her genetic seedings from the stars. Beyond that, there were records of starseeding successes and failures on other planets in our solar system as well as those in distant galaxies. It was a repository of records from the stars that just happened to include the Earth initiatives.

"These experiences opened my cosmic body at a young age, and the monks began training me as an oracle of the stars. Don Eduardo has described those in the Andes who speak with the *Apus*. I believe the training is similar."

As the group listened intently to Master Mukda, the vortex of light slowed until it was replaced with a formless, shimmering presence. "We are entering Shambhala, Beloveds. Please, do not allow yourself to be distracted. We do not want fluctuating energies to distort the field around us at this time.

"In speaking to the star beings, especially the Siriuns, I learned about the role of Earth as a genetic laboratory. Most of you are aware of this already - the starseedings, aborted experiments, and all. However, when the average human hears of this, the collective ego suffers much pain and denial because it fears that we are not in control. I ask you, how are we to shatter the limitations of this dimension if we deny our origins? I would like you to be aware of yourselves in all dimensions – to honor your cosmic body with that acceptance."

The shimmering lights of Shambhala began to take form around them. Pillars of light surrounded them while vibrations of love and joy permeated their bodies. Being a group who had experienced Fifth Dimension in their everyday lives, they recognized the frequency as one of heart activation and compassion. However, few of them had experienced this frequency at a complete cellular level.

To several in the circle, it seemed more than they could hold, like an explosion of energy within the body, centered at the heart. Mukda asked them to calmly integrate the energy as an activation of charge to the electric field. He asked them to call on their magnetic fields to stabilize the charge. In this way, it would become a dimension they would always be able to access.

He monitored a crescendo of energetic implosion, then the balancing, and, finally, the integration of Fifth-Dimensional frequency. As this occurred, more of the Golden City revealed itself around them – the details of a temple in which they sat with many beings of that dimension sitting around them. Their circle had expanded markedly.

"Beloveds, there are an increasing number like yourselves who are holding higher frequencies and the awareness of themselves at that level. In this awareness is an unfolding part of the Mission and the gift of being together in the Golden Cities. As more and more individuals come into this awareness, the consciousness of Fifth Dimension will expand until, one day, all those on Earth will be experiencing this as their reality."

He swept his arm beyond the circle, indicating Shambhala and all its inhabitants. The group saw beyond their temple to a vast city of light. "The Fifth Dimension is Love. It is Christ Consciousness and Heart – *munay*, to our brothers in the Andes," he added, smiling. "It has been the initiative of the Piscean Age. As this frequency stabilizes on Earth, there is no need for it to be held in Shambhala. Do you see? Shambhala will be everywhere, and what we will hold in our Golden Cities is the Sixth Dimension.

"The Aquarian Age is one of energy accessed through the heart. Mastery of energy requires mastery of will. This will be the spiritual work of the new age. Now that you have been activated to this dimension, I would ask that you begin making it your primary reality to help those light beings around you here in Shambhala to anchor this on the Earth.

"Now I would like to cease talking so that you will turn your attention to the inner voice. Let us join our brothers and sisters here in meditation," he concluded, bowing his head and folding his hands in his lap. The group found the still point within, filling the temple with heavenly sound. They were transported into spaces of inner vision, deep tranquility and expansion.

In every space accessed by Leah, she found Chris. He, likewise, experienced her in all of his awareness. Each of their hearts expanded to contain the other as the Grail Cup accepts the elixir of Truth and Light.

In oneness, they reached out to hold hands, allowing the expansion to enter the physical field. Feeling a more profound expansion, they were able to bring every member of the group into their unified heart space. Many in the group had a similar awareness, as all hands joined in one. In a timeless reality, they remained in that meditation of oneness until Master Mukda gently tapped his staff on the temple floor, drawing the group's attention back to his presence.

"Beloveds, we must journey on. There is someone waiting for us beyond Shambhala. Chant with me a Mantra of Transcendence. Open yourselves to an even greater aspect of being," he urged, as he led them into the mysticism of sound. As members of the group ceased focusing their minds on the mantra, it began flowing from them unabated, becoming a song of spirit. A luminous egg of light filaments, the vehicle of transcendence, formed around them in the temple of Shambhala.

Then, at one point in the chanting, the egg reached a destabilizing frequency. Everyone in the group felt it warp as their energetic bodies received a gentle torque. The sound of the mantra wavered, and then stretched as the luminous egg turned inside out.

Opening their inner eyes on the higher plane, the group found themselves in a space of golden light, facing outward in their circle. They could not see each other, but knew that the circle was still intact. As Master Mukda gradually brought the chanting to an end they became aware of an angelic sound filling the space of golden light.

Telepathically, he asked the group to turn and face a low altar that emerged from the golden light in front of Leah and Chris. Upon the altar, there burned a rainbow flame. Master Mukda orchestrated the circle from his position in the rear, asking individuals to move once again until they were sitting in a Star of David. Chris and Leah sat together at the point in front of the altar and Mukda and Don Eduardo held the opposite pole in the rear.

When all were in position at points and junctions of the star, the limitless space behind the altar began to emanate a shimmering blue light. Moving towards them, the light stopped on the opposite side of the altar, where a core of golden light began swirling at its center. The golden light took form and four robed beings emerged into the blue light. Two stood forward towards the altar, and two stood some distance behind them.

The golden light developed a brilliant white center as the form within defined itself. It became so intense, that it masked the countenances of the four beings. The light flared then receded to reveal a tall man in radiant golden robes. Burnished red hair fell in waves to his shoulders, framing a kind, bearded face. Emitting a soft light, his blue eyes were doe-like and seemed large for his face. Before his heart, he held a golden chalice studded with blue diamonds, rubies and sapphires.

Many of the Ruby Order recognized Lord Sananda in his Jeshua embodiment, his guardians, and the Maxine Flame of the rainbow warriors. Those who did, rose to their feet then fell to one knee as knights and ladies before their King. As the remainder of the group followed suit, all of their rugged outdoor garments were replaced with the same shimmering robes of Lord Sananda's guardians.

The Master and his guardians walked around the altar to stand before Leah and Chris, whose heads were bowed respectfully. The guardians standing ahead of Lord Sananda touched the robes of the two beloveds, drawing their attention to the Master before them.

Lord Sananda placed the chalice into the upraised hands of Chris, who drank of the elixir within. His body pulsed with blue light as he returned the chalice to Lord Sananda.

Leah looked into the Master's eyes – the eyes of love and compassion – while taking the chalice and drinking the magically replenished elixir. A smile came to her face after drinking the sweet liquor. She returned the chalice to Lord Sananda, silently whispering her gratitude for the lifelong guidance he had given to her. He returned her smile, and handing the chalice to one of the guardians, laid his hands upon their heads in blessing.

The blue light moving through Leah suddenly flared as she received his gift into her field, then he withdrew his hands, took the chalice from the guardian and moved around the circle to Ramandi and Ellia, who sat behind and to the right of Chris at a junction of the star. Each member of the group received both elixir and blessing, until Lord Sananda and his guardians returned to the altar.

Lord Sananda seated himself upon a richly brocaded golden cushion that the two rear guardians withdrew from beneath the altar. When the group had also settled on cushions brought to them by assistants of the ashram, Lord Sananda began a telepathic discourse to the group.

"Beloved Children of Light, welcome to one of many ashrams in the ascended state. I am deeply moved by the sincerity and intent of your group. You are about to embark on a Mission of some importance – to each of you as individuals and collectively.

"For those of you who are not familiar with this ashram or my teachings, I open the door for your return to me in meditation and dreamtime from this point in your earthly life onward. As many of you already know, I am available to each of you whenever you need me in all dimensions. You will come to understand this as a partnership.

"I would like to speak to you about commitment – commitment to your individual Missions and to the greater Mission of planetary ascension. The Christ Consciousness Initiative is accelerating on planet Earth and each of you has made a commitment at the soul level to participate in this Mission.

"Please do not associate the initiative exclusively with me or with my life as Jeshua. There are many at this level of consciousness and beyond who have been instrumental in the Earth initiatives.

"My beloved brother, Sanat Kumara, has been holding Earth in an aura of hope for millions of Earth years. My role has been as a way-shower through many incarnations in human form.

"Our work with Earth began when the Galactic Federation asked for intervention. Earth was staggering with imbalances among early life forms. This seems ridiculous to you, I am sure, but any form of consciousness can create havoc. This imbalance became so great that the Federation leaders exiled Earth from the Galactic Federation. She was incapable of impartial and balanced membership. Her overseers – planet lords from distant galaxies - were exiled from the galaxy until they could heal the imbalances in their own desire bodies, a process that is still not complete. Had we not agreed to intervene, Earth's position in the galaxy might have been terminated.

"We are the planet-tamers from Venus - our base in your solar system. However, our interest in consciousness is intergalactic. In agreement with the Federation and the Siriuns, the most favorable way to accomplish our Mission was to begin with a rebalancing of the energies on Earth, including the electromagnetic field polarization.

"We established bases within the Earth at each of her present poles. At that time those regions were lush, almost tropical lands. We worked energetically to establish a polarity closer to what presently exists; though this has shifted many times.

"When the last equalization occurred, the poles reestablished themselves again, shifting ice, water and land. Very few land-based life forms survived this shift, and much of the ocean life died as well. This was the time when the dinosaurs – a great imbalance of reptilian life forms – were eliminated. They were not the only existing enigmas of alien experimentation, but a good example to bring forth to you.

"Our efforts have been aided primarily by the Siriuns, Arcturians, and Pleiadeans, who have, along with others, shared their expertise in repopulating Earth. We sent a great many of our race to help hold a consciousness conducive to seedings from the stars. We have received assistance from the Arcturians who have been continually transmitting a love consciousness from space to Earth.

"Our initiative has always been futuristic. In Truth and Light, we have planted the seeds of consciousness amongst the star-seeded races of Earth. Through the language of the stars, we have encapsulated Earth's history and that of mankind in sacred documents, edifices, and within the cellular memory of some human lineages who have been working with us throughout the ages. All of these documentations exist off-planet as well, within the libraries of Venus, Sirius and the Galactic Federation.

"Souls nearing the completion of incarnation cycles of growth on Earth have secondary agreements to uplift human consciousness. There are many vehicles of this commitment, including light codes of consciousness, exemplary lifestyles in dedication to holding consciousness, and lives of imparting wisdom on all levels.

"Yours is a group of many such souls. Know who you are. You have incarnated in all races, have played every role imaginable, and now have come in service to something greater than your individual soul. This is the Mission. I am no greater than you are. I am simply more conscious of the God-presence we share.

"One day each of you will be a light-bearer of consciousness to humanity. One day each of you will hold Earth in your aura as my brother, Sanat, has been doing for millions of years. This, my children, is commitment. It is time for each of you to step out of your cycles of incarnation into your cosmic self. This opportunity is at hand. It is time for some of you who have already come into that awareness to move one step beyond in your service to embrace yourself in your God-presence. All of this you will do without ego.

"Do not mourn for the past, thinking life on Earth to have been simpler and more pure. It is illusion. Dwell in the present, and from that position of God-awareness, create a future that honors God in all things. Create the bridges to the Golden Cities.

"Please release any fears that may remain within you concerning the future of Earth and mankind. Live your life's purpose without this fear in the present moment. If you fear destruction of the Earth, you will call it to you. Your own consumption will consume you – this in accordance with the Universal Law of cause and effect. Do not be part of the overconsumption on the Earth. See the Earth as a vessel of love, much like the chalice from which you drank."

"Lord Sananda held the chalice before his heart again. "This is the Grail Cup of Loving Service to the Mission. From this Grail Cup, you have shared the elixir of the Bodhisattva, the elixir of True Service to Earth. This service requires commitment to something greater than your self. Each of you drank from this cup willingly, with full consent of your Higher Self. Worship no one but learn from everyone. Design your own path of return in accordance with the will of your soul.

"In preparation for your present collective Mission, allow me to say the following. Each of you has been selected because you are able to hold a certain light frequency. Many lifetimes have helped you prepare for the task that lies ahead. Shed the fear that you may not be good enough and complete this part of your assignment in glory.

"As the planets align Earth with the Great Central Sun, portals will open to those who are ready to enter the higher realms. What you will experience as awakening and activation will prepare you to live Christ Consciousness every day. As a result, your individual Missions will rapidly unfold. I will not reveal the details of the group Mission to you, as it must unfold - as it will, from the mystery, as a mystery. However, I will assure you that, we, the Kumaras, will guide and assist you within the guidelines of the free-will agreement of the human experience. The Mission is unquestionably in your hands, Beloveds.

"I ask you all to chant with me as you return to your reality," Sananda concluded. Held spellbound by the discourse; the group never blinked an eye –inner or outer - as an enormous golden Disc of the Sun emerged behind the altar. Shimmering with golden light, the disc sent forth a tone, reminding Leah of the sounds that Chris was able to speak from his heart. Each of their hearts began to bring forth that vibration of joy, raising a chorus of heavenly sound. The disc sent forth more sound and the ashram was soon filled with a chant of the Bodhisattva. Drawn irresistibly within, each member of the group closed their eyes to the ashram, the Sun Disc and Lord Sananda while chanting from their hearts.

Lost in that sound until the persistent tapping of Master Mukda's staff drew them from their inward journey, the group members slowly opened their eyes to the firelight dancing on the cement walls at Tres Cruces. Master Mukda was still sitting on the pile of sleeping mats, like a wizard perched on a fallen forest giant. White light pulsated from the tip of his staff as he watched the ruby light retract from the circle into the golden skull.

Not a word was spoken to break the magic as Master Mukda went outside to stand beneath the stars, and the group quickly prepared to sleep. His enchantment would hold them in the space of magic for the entire night. The history of the brotherhood was complete.

As did most of the group, Leah and Chris wandered out under the stars before sleeping. When they made their way back to their quarters, Leah strolled past Master Mukda, brushing him on the cheek with a kiss. No words were spoken, but their hearts merged in joy. It was with a still mind that Leah snuggled deep into her sleeping bag facing Chris. Stroking her cheek, he quietly asked if she had taken her drop of Jacques' elixir.

Leah held her medicine pouch close to her heart. "No, Darling," she whispered. "I think it best to begin in Lima, when time has become linear once again. What do you think?"

"I would be inclined to trust your intuition, Leah. Right now you look pretty near immortal to my experienced eyes," he replied, lifting her chin slightly.

She smiled then pursed her lips playfully, inviting a good night kiss. Chris bent over her as she rolled onto her back. Withdrawing her left hand from the sleeping bag, she ran her finger along the ridge of his nose then drew circles on his forehead before slipping her hand behind his head to draw him near. His eyes lit up as their lips met in deep communion. Thoughts of the future danced briefly in his consciousness, but he dismissed them to the moment of bliss. As silence finally took over the night, they drifted off into a dream-filled sleep, Leah in Chris' protective arms.

Long before dawn, the eerie chanting of the Indian women roused the group from slumber. Like a flock of discordant birds, the reed flutes of the men soon accompanied them. For Leah, their voices were an enchantment that beckoned her back to lives past. Drifting in and out of Dreamtime, she was finally awakened by the persistent affection of Chris, who heard the music as a kind of bugle call.

"Good morning, Mate," he whispered in her ear while playfully tugging on her ear lobe with his teeth.

"It couldn't possibly be morning, Darling. Let's go back to sleep," she pleaded.

"It's Don Eduardo's version of morning, Leah," he replied, kissing her neck. "You know, I adore your neck. I will surely miss it when this Mission is over."

"Now that is an interesting thing to bring up at this particular moment in time - or no-time, as the case may be," she remarked, separating herself from him, slightly irritated.

"I am sorry, Love. It really is time to get up. You were far away from Tres Cruces and it is time to be present."

"You're right, of course, but it is cold, dark, and so darn early," she cried. "Here it is, the Mission, and I want to sleep in."

"What were your dreams, Leah?" he asked, abruptly changing the subject. Chris unzipped his sleeping bag and was layering on clothes while she told him of faraway beaches, sea breezes and tasty fruit drinks.

"It sounds like a well-deserved vacation," he laughed.

"There were exotic temples in the mountains, where huge energy lines crossed as well," she went on, dreamily, while reluctantly inching the zipper down on her sleeping bag.

"When you come to see me in WA, I will take you to the place of your dream, Leah," he said, pulling warm pants over his long underwear and hiking socks.

"You know it? I have seen many beautiful places on Mother Earth, but not quite like this dream."

"It was Bali, Darling. I have a witch-doctor friend there who would love to open the temple gates to you. One temple is built upon the crossing dragon lines of the Earth."

"Exactly as I saw it. Where were you in that dream, Chris? You were not obvious to me," she asked. "Oh, Chris," she added, "would you reach into my bag and pass me that clean pair of fleece pants and the black socks?"

He passed her pants and socks to her and put on his outer jacket. "Do you remember the monkey hanging from the tree outside the temple?" he asked with his crooked smile.

"Very original, Darling," she replied, matter-of-factly, pulling on her fleece outer-pants. "Tell your friend to expect us. It is an important place for my own growth."

"How about a little fun, Leah?" he teased. "Life has many ways to help us grow."

"You are going to change my life, aren't you, Mate?" she asked, turning to hold him in her gaze.

"I would do anything for you, Leah, but you know that I cannot and do not want to change you. Let's say I will offer you possibilities you had not dreamed of, love you could never have imagined and all the exotic fruit juice you want to drink. I would invite you to enjoy life, laugh and get your Mission accomplished while doing it."

"I wonder, at times, why I make life so difficult for myself?" Leah asked. Then she added. "Don't answer that. I have a few beliefs to change about being good to myself. Thank you for providing the challenge. The magic has been happening to me all along. I just need to get myself out of the way."

With that, they both stood up, tied their boots, and stowed their bags and mats in their duffel bags. Leah made a quick trip outside then joined the gathering group in circle. She returned to find Chris in conversation with Don Eduardo and Brian. Still chanting as the cooks poured hot tea for the bleary-eyed group, the Indian women soon raised the pitch of their voices, signaling the end of their song. Chris moved into the circle to speak as Brian and Don Eduardo slipped outside the building.

"A cheery good morning to you, Mates," he began, raising his teacup to the group. "Apparently we need to arrive at today's destination before sunrise. So we are asked to have a bit of breakfast, prepare our day packs with water, our sacred items or mesas, then hike over to the face of the mountain with our tribal guardians. Lobo and our young warriors will stay behind to guard this space and hold the energy for our return. I cannot tell you when that will be but suspect it will be after the planetary alignment."

"*Wayki* Chris, what about provisions?" Susmo asked.

"A natural concern, Mate," he replied, tipping his cup towards Susmo. "Today, we are moving outside time, Mates. All of the rules change. If you find yourself stuffing your pack with power bars, concerned about survival, know that self-preservation has a powerful hold on you. Break it. It is time for us to trust in the Masters, the Mission and the Divine Plan."

"Hear, hear," Peter shouted, raising his teacup. The whole group responded, shouting "hear, hear" while raising their cups towards Chris. Feelings of fellowship, magic and hilarity released within the group, weaving an assemblage point of infinite possibilities. Chris winked at Leah, who was observing the scene with awe. He had somehow enchanted a circle of sleepy men and women who were now moving about filled with an excited energy. Unable to remain detached from the weaving, both she and Chris plunged into the milieu of laughing *waykis*.

Within an hour, they began trekking towards the mountain, leaving the cooks and young warriors contentedly behind to guard their camp. In the lead were the Indian men - the warrior magi who had been out with Brian the previous day to find the interdimensional portal. Brian and Don Eduardo had left before breakfast. Following the warriors were the women of Leah's circle and the Indian women, Doña Felicia, Doña Lucia and Margarita. Leah and Chris walked together between the women and the men of the Ruby Order.

Brian had led Don Eduardo through the darkness to the east side of the mountain, where his group of warriors had detected the interdimensional portal. Don Eduardo felt the thick ridge running around the outer edge of the carved stone doorway. He moved his hands from the ridge inward to the middle doorway, while deepening his breath and focusing his intent. Brian watched Don Eduardo touch the stone interior of the final inner door to center himself before it. Putting his hands together as if in prayer, the *ylloq'e* breathed an ancient and magical invocation asking *Apu* Kañacway to safeguard his passage through the dominion of the Ñaupa, the primordial and often malevolent beings who lived within the cracks and crevices of the stone. Then, spreading his hands as if parting an ocean, he moved through the stone into the mountain.

Brian's mouth dropped open as the woven bundle slung over Don Eduardo's back disappeared into the stone. Paradoxically, he was pleased that he and the warriors had found the correct portal, and dismayed to be left behind, alone and in the dark. He heard Don Eduardo's loud, cackling laughter from within the stone and was told, in perfect English, that preparations needed to be made for the group and that Brian was to sit tight until the *ylloq'e* returned. With a slight smile and pounding heart, Brian adjusted to the idea that his thoughts were being read and moved to stand with his back to the portal to guard it. Leaning against the cold stone, he chanted his own prayer of protection while looking out over the jungle canopy towards the east.

As the sky began to hint of dawn, he saw two ghostly beings approach him. Silently repeating his chant of protection and invisibility, he watched as they slipped between the cracks into the great mountain just to the right of the portal. He rubbed his eyes and wiped the cold sweat from his brow with his gloved hand. It was a lesson to him that protection for this group would necessarily be interdimensional. It didn't matter whether the beings were real or the product of Don Eduardo's magic. He took them seriously.

A sudden gust of wind came from within the mountain, blowing Brian's hat down a small embankment. As Brian went to retrieve it, the *ylloq'e* stepped out of the stone and stood above Brian, slapping his knees with laughter. Running his hands through his blonde hair, Brian shook his head at Don Eduardo and laughed as well.

The elder's woven bundle was missing from his back, and an hour of time had lapsed. He reached down to help Brian up the embankment then cocked his head to the south, where the first of the group of brothers and sisters could be seen in the predawn light. Spreading out towards the north, east and south of the portal as they approached, the warriors created a guarded space for the women dreamers and the Ruby Order to stand along the rock wall of the mountain to the south of the portal.

Don Eduardo asked Chris to join him at the portal to discuss plans with him for translation to the group. It was obvious to Leah that the days the two men had spent together before her group's arrival in the *ylloq'e's* mountain village had been focused on the coming events. There was a certain orchestration in the air that bespoke high magic, and yet the two brothers moved in complete service to the Mission, and not to themselves. It made Leah, and others in the group, think of the Codes of the Grail. Their focus was not on the great wizardry of which they were both capable, but rather the safety of the group as well as the quality of the communal experience.

Chris came back to stand in the path next to Leah. As he walked towards her, a spontaneous ray of ruby light leapt from her heart towards his heart. He took it into his heart, pulsed it through his entire field and sent it back to her like a meteor shower of exploding rubies and starlight. She caught her breath, closed her eyes, and smiled as if touched by heaven. His words filtered through the starlight to reach her consciousness while she kept her eyes closed.

"Well, Mates," he began, "we have reached the portal of Tres Cruces. What we must do is simple. As the direct rays of the rising Sun fully engulf the portal, the doorway into the mountain will open. Don Eduardo will prepare the doorway, ensuring our complete protection, and I will bring up the rear, doing the same. Half of the warriors will stay here to guard the portal; the other half will enter with us into the mountain.

"It would be best to stay focused, to remain silent and to move right along, because the direct rays do not linger on the doorway. Don Eduardo has been through the portal this morning to prepare the space within for us. We are walking into the *Ukhupacha*, the dark interior world of shadows - Fourth Dimension. It will measure our clarity and bring forth any remaining unconscious blocks to our work. There will be time to clear those blocks.

"Now Mates, let's face the Sun and await the signal to enter the mountain."

Chris took his place between Leah and Julio, who, in his calmness, looked mature beyond his years. He could feel Leah's heart beating double-time as he took her into his arms, resting his chin atop her head. As the jungle canopy began to shimmer, a pulse of attentiveness ran through the group. They were able to take the full sunrise into their luminous fields before the portal was in direct line with the rising Sun.

"As the doorway opened, Don Eduardo blew a shrill note on his flute and the line of women began following him into the mountain. As Chris and Leah reached the portal, he stepped aside to let the Brothers of the Ruby enter. Six warriors, including Brian, followed behind Master Mukda. Then, in the fading light, Chris partially dematerialized himself to slip through what remained of the portal.

Don Eduardo led the group into a large amethyst chamber lit by a single shaft of light from above. The floor, walls and ceiling appeared to be gemstone crystal, without seam or imperfection. Unexpectedly warm, the comfortable room could have held twice their numbers.

"The six warriors entered to stand before the portal, affording Chris the opportunity to fully materialize before rejoining the group. His commitment to the Mission dissolved any reticence to exercise the fullness of his power. He would do what was necessary to bring this aspect of the Mission to successful completion.

Giving the group the liberty of inspecting the chamber, Don Eduardo waited until curiosities were satisfied before calling them before him. With Chris translating, he asked Leah's group of women to sit in circle around the shaft of light with Doña Lucia and Margarita. The shaft of light fell in the middle of their circle. Doña Felicia and Leah joined the men of the Ruby Order, who were gathered behind Don Eduardo.

The *ylloq'e* explained that the circle of women would be exposed to fairly intense energies of the Fourth Dimension, which would afford them an opportunity to clear any remaining impediments to dreaming. They were to assist each other in this clearing work as sisters of light. The warriors were to be their guardians, and they would also experience the cleansing energies. He explained that the Order of the Ruby would be meeting in an adjoining chamber to prepare for their joint work with the women and that passage through this chamber required clarity beyond Fourth Dimension as well.

The women settled into their circle as Don Eduardo led the Order of the Ruby to a hidden doorway in the interior wall of the chamber. As he touched an impression in the crystal, a lock was released on the door, opening it into the next chamber. The passageway was close to ten feet long, and carved of solid amethyst. As each member of the order passed through, he or she would be challenged with an intense energy of clearing. Leah was asked to begin, and Don Eduardo and Chris stood at the opposite end to help each of them process their feelings immediately.

Leah stepped into the passageway without fear, but her heart was not tranquil. Midway through the passageway, she felt a surge of heat entering her field at her feet and exiting through her crown. Feeling herself engulfed in flames, she arrived at the end of the passage drenched in sweat and teary-eyed. When she had finished describing her experience, Chris spoke of it with Don Eduardo in Quechua.

"Any emotion?" Chris asked her.

"Yes, a great fear as well as anger and resentment," she replied, honestly, then added. "Maybe a little self-pity as well."

"Step back into the passage, Leah. Tell me what you feel now," he asked.

Cautiously, Leah moved backwards into the energy once again, but felt nothing.

"Excellent. There was an unresolved issue from the Inquisition, Leah," Chris said.

"What was it, Chris? Do I need to know what was released?"

"It is not necessary, Leah. You have carried collective energies in your body and your field because your soul agreed to help heal a collective memory. You've healed the personal stuff, so move forward into the future, Beloved."

"Thank you, Chris," she replied, bowing her head as she passed through the two brothers into the room.

Leah found herself in a circular amethyst chamber facing an enormous round table of amethyst. Twelve golden chairs with deep blue-violet cushioned seats circled the table. Directly above each seat a shaft of light entered the room, creating a circle of light beams.

As she walked up to the table, Leah traced part of the gold inlay with her fingers. The inlay marked a twice-drawn Star of David within a double-banded circle of gold. In the center, Don Eduardo had placed the golden skull. Within the two bands of inlay were twelve evenly spaced gold inlaid names written before each of the places at the table. Walking around the table, Leah read the names of the Ruby Order written in ruby and diamond-studded gold script. Stopping at the name 'Leah', she lowered her pack to the crystal floor, and brushing the dust from her hiking pants, took her seat at one point of the great star.

A shimmering violet light filled the room, which lent an air of mystery to the entrance of each member of the order. One at a time, they followed the names around the table to their seats. When all were seated, Leah found herself flanked by Doña Felicia and Maharajah Ramandi and directly across from Chris. She, Chris, Master Mukda and Don Eduardo formed a cross in the four directions. When everyone was settled, Don Eduardo touched the hand of Susmo on his left, indicating his and Doña Felicia's need for personal translation.

"Brothers and Sisters of the Ruby," he began. "It has been my task to gather all of you here. My directives have come from the stars. I am happy that all of you have managed to find this remote place. Thank you all for listening to the summons and responding as true members of the Ruby Order. My work is complete for I have brought you to this point." Don Eduardo raised his voice slightly as he concluded. "I would now ask the incarnate head of the Ruby Order to identify himself by bringing forth the first sacred object of our brotherhood."

The air was electric with anticipation, as each sacred object was retrieved from its hiding place to sit in the lap of its owner. Leah could not help but gasp as Chris slipped the chain of the golden Sun disc around his neck. Positively dazzling against his black shirt, the disc was illuminated by the shaft of light above him. The table burst into applause that caused a subtle flushing of his face. Don Eduardo had presented him with Inkari's breastplate during their days of private meetings. A shy smile swept across her face as Chris summoned Leah to bring forth Qoyari's pendant. It too was resplendent against her deep blue-violet fleece top. Once again, the table showed their great delight with wild applause and cheering. When the members of the Ruby Order quieted themselves, Don Eduardo spoke again.

"It was spoken in our prophecies that this time would herald the appearance of the new *wiracochas*, the Shining Ones. We have welcomed many of you and those you have awakened to our lands to activate all of you to your callings. It was also spoken that Inkari and Qoyari would return to light the lamp of the *Hanaqpacha*. What an extraordinary surprise that they are both *ylloq'e cuna* of the Ruby Order. May the first meeting of the incarnate members of the Ruby Order begin."

With that, Don Eduardo activated the golden skull, which was staring directly at Chris. A burst of ruby light engulfed him as a golden scepter magically appeared in his right hand. Amazed, Leah wondered if it was the scepter used by Inkari to claim Cusco as the land of the Children of Light, but she had little time to dwell on her thoughts as Chris began the meeting.

"Brothers and Sisters of the Ruby, we owe much to the wonders of science and technology, which has made it possible for us to meet on the Earth plane for the first time in our history. We have always been spread to the four winds, working only occasionally with one another. This is the Divine Plan, of course, but that hardly dims my wonder at this occasion. I know that each of you feels likewise."

A brief round of applause followed Chris' opening remarks, after which he continued. "We have much to accomplish during our time together and, I imagine, many places to visit for activation of our Mission, but we must begin our weaving here in this sacred temple of the magi. Let us pass this golden scepter around the circle, with each of us contributing to this weaving of *ylloq'e* magic. We men have already met to weave filaments of brotherhood amongst us. Now we welcome our sisters to weave the filaments of the Ruby Order.

"Our collective Mission will unfold as our work together progresses. At this time, I would ask each of you to bring forth the sacred object you have brought to the table. Tell us something about it and about your Mission and soul's purpose as you have known it in this embodiment. It would also be a good time to relate any other experiences or messages relevant to the Ruby Order." As Chris concluded, he handed the golden scepter to Peter Wilshire on his left.

Peter chuckled to himself at having received the first pass of the talking stick two days in a row. "Dear Brothers and Sisters," he began "the Divine Plan must be wise to the fact that Welshmen are seldom at a loss for words."

The group responded with laughter as Peter brought forth a bundle wrapped in deep purple velvet. He set the scepter crosswise on the table between himself and the bundle before unwrapping a glowing crystal orb. Within the orb, the group could clearly see the churning movement of liquid crystal energy. Peter brushed the glass lightly with the cloth, buffing away any fingerprints. The crystal ball sat upon an elaborately carved, low wooden stand on top of the purple velvet. Though it was no more than five inches in diameter, the radius of its light emanation exceeded eight feet.

Picking up the scepter, Peter touched it to the orb, causing a whirlwind of movement within it. As the churning crystals stilled, a smile came to his face. "What we have here, Brothers and Sisters, is Merlin's crystal ball. It has been in our lineage since well before Merlin but Merlin brought it to its full power. Touching the scepter to it has brought forth a message for our circle. It reads:

'Wayfarers of the Ruby, be steadfast and transparent in your quest for the Grail.'"

Peter paused a moment before continuing. "It does, indeed, feel as if we are on a Divine quest. The spirit of Merlin obviously accompanies us and invisibility is our ally."

Peter leaned back in his chair, running a hand through his waves of silver hair. "I know that my soul's purpose is *to guide*. This purpose applies in the magical as well as the mundane world. You might also think of this as navigating, showing the way towards the destination. It is what I am happy doing and how I am most appreciated. That is affirmation enough for me that it is my purpose. All of my lessons were presented to me during the crude stages of aligning with this purpose. It is hard to say more about it, so I will not. Just let me know where you want to go," he added with a laugh.

He continued after the group responded to his humor. "I do have an interesting observation to share. It is likely of some significance. I have been compiling the messages transmitted by the crystal ball since it has been in my keeping. Some of them have been personal, but many have referenced the Brotherhood of Magi and the Order of the Ruby. Most have been a bit of a puzzle, but I have a fondness for puzzles and undertook to solve them.

"What I glean from these messages is an imminent danger to our Mission. It may be here and now, or in the future. Overall, it would be wise to be wary. I would ask Don Eduardo to assure us that our guardians are capable of detecting and neutralizing evil energies or agents of the sinister force." Peter looked from Chris to Don Eduardo who, along with Doña Felicia, was receiving a translation from Susmo.

"I am not surprised," Chris responded, solemnly. "There has been little opposition thus far to a Mission which has brought the entire Order together in one place. I doubt that our mobilization on the planet has gone undetected." Master Mukda, Jacques and Ramandi were in immediate agreement with Chris, mumbling concerned assents while Susmo translated to Don Eduardo. When Susmo finished, Chris nodded to Don Eduardo, giving him the floor.

"*Waykis*, our guardians are well trained warriors who have never been to war. What can I tell you? We have no idea what form this evil might take or at what stage of our Mission it might confront us. We will warn *Wayki* Brian and my people guarding the portal to be especially watchful at sunrise each day. My men are all experienced to detect and neutralize dark energies, and I can telepathically communicate with them at any time. Thank you, *Wayki*, Peter. Your observations will be taken quite seriously."

"Jolly good then," Peter, replied. "May all of our troubles be small ones." With that, he touched the scepter to his heart and passed it to Sheik Fakoum.

Fakoum received the scepter with the kind of reverence integral to his nature. After holding it in silence some minutes, he set it upon the table alongside his name and brought his sacred object up from his lap. From wrappings of rich tapestry, he carefully lifted an ornate, ruby-studded, silver box, perhaps six inches long and four inches wide with a depth of several inches. Holding the box in his hands, he offered it to Heaven, then to the Earth, and finally, to the group. After placing it back on the table, Fakoum stared at it for some time before speaking. Then, closing his eyes to connect with its energy, he spoke of the box.

"Brothers and Sisters, this box has been held sacred in our lineage since the time of the Master. Balthazar, a magus of the Ruby Order, used this box to bring an offering of frankincense to the child, Jeshua, to honor him as a Kumara, a gift of light to humanity from the stars. Before the transition of Jeshua's guardian, Joseph, the aging king returned the box to the magi of our lineage. Within the box there are remnants of that holy offering." The sheik opened the box, releasing a dusky blue light into the circle. It was a sweet, gentle energy that seemed to embrace the twelve members of the Ruby Order. "Jeshua traveled upon the Sapphire Ray of Love and

Wisdom. Placing this sacred box on our table, I ask for the blessings of the Master for the work we are to do together."

The brothers and sisters of the Ruby Order gave thanks to Fakoum for so great a gift. He bowed many times then spoke of his Mission. "I have known for some time that my purpose is *to transcend.* Certainly we are all to transcend, but this purpose has become my life. It was necessary for me to transcend my powerless beginnings as a beggar-child. It was necessary to transcend my native Muslim religion to become a sufi in the universal sense of the calling. You are free to imagine countless opportunities to transcend along the way, including a few on this very journey."

Fakoum's humor was not lost to the group. He continued on, stroking his beard. "After receiving the directives to embark on this journey, including the details of the rendezvous with Demetri and Ramandi, I spent much of my time in prayer asking for confirmation. Previously, I had barely ventured out of my city of birth. The confirmations were everywhere. I dared not ignore them, but before making the arrangements, I had a dream.

"In this dream, I was asked to retrieve a pearl from an oyster that dwelt in the dark realms. The pearl had been stolen from my father's house in ages past by one of black magic. I was to retrieve the pearl and return it to my father's house.

"I went down into the darkness and forgot my Mission. I allowed myself to be seduced by the darkness. I was happily pursuing all materiality when, one day, I received a vision of true awakening. A woman appeared to me. She was a Goddess. From her endless compassion for all those lost in the darkness, she manifested herself to remind me of my father and the pearl.

"I wept in remembrance of my Mission and retrieved the pearl at once. I was guided back to my father's house by a white dove of peace and was welcomed unconditionally, like the prodigal son returned. This dream was a reminder of the greater Mission and my need to be here with my brothers and sisters.

"The next day, I purchased the first airplane tickets of my life to take me halfway around the world to this magical land. From the airline office, I went to my friend, Salkee, who is a jeweler, and asked for the most perfect pearl in his collection. When I arrived here, I presented that pearl to the Goddess of my dream." All heads turned to Leah, as Fakoum asked her if she knew this story of the pearl.

Tears of recognition were streaming down her face as Leah touched the pearl within her medicine pouch. "I do know this story, Beloved Fakoum. It is similarly written in the Gnostic Gospel of Thomas, the true words of the Master. It is a great favorite of mine. Though I cannot claim consciousness of that manifestation, I am happy to be of service to you and to this Mission. I struggle with the acceptance of my truest being, Dear Brother," she concluded, bowing her head to Fakoum.

"A tribute to those who have trained you, My Sister. I believe this story has significance for you and for all of us. Most of us have been guided to the remembrance of our true selves by the presence of inner Truth. We have lifted ourselves out of the darkness and aligned ourselves with our Missions.

"Like all Masters of the Ruby, we have practiced humility, or have had it forced upon us to help us differentiate ourselves from ego. We have learned to be invisible to those who covet power and yet, we have the true power.

"I believe my dream is calling us to be all that we came to be in order to accomplish our individual and group Missions. For example, you, My Beloved Goddess, will need to acknowledge who you are and be in that power to be of service. If you deny who you are, we will fail. It is the same for each of us."

Leah glanced at Chris, who was looking quite pleased with Fakoum's remarks. She thanked Fakoum, politely, hoping he would pass the scepter to Don Eduardo before embarrassing her further.

She took a deep breath as he did just that, fully aware that Chris was recollecting the dream in which they were all making love to her. Savoring the moment, she sat up a bit straighter to allow a surge of kundalini full access to her spine. While the rest of the table focused their attention on Don Eduardo, Chris noticed Leah's involuntary quiver as the energy exited through her crown. He silently thanked Fakoum for saying what he and Leah both needed to hear.

Don Eduardo received the scepter with a tear in his bright, old eyes. He had never dreamed of holding the symbol of Inca sovereignty in his hands, nor had he ever been on the receiving end of high magic. He made it clear to Chris that he was profoundly moved by his manifestation of Inkari.

When he could speak, he held the scepter high, thanking *Tayta Inti* and *Pachamama* for a long and happy life in service to the greater Mission. Then he placed the scepter atop his name on the table and drew a mesa cloth from his lap. Everyone in the group wondered what could be more sacred to Don Eduardo than the golden skull? Reading their thoughts, the ancient *ylloq'e* broke into a wide, toothless smile.

"Beloved *Waykis*, Brothers and Sisters of the Ruby," he began, motioning to Chris for Quechua-to-English translation. "This golden skull of our ancient brotherhood is of unspeakable value. Beyond sacred, it has come down to us from the first Dragon Lords - the first Shining Ones - on *Pachamama*. I do not wish to replace it with a more sacred object. However, borrowing from Sheik Fakoum the words of the great Master, I wish to honor each brother and sister at this table for retrieving the pearl and returning it to the house of our Father. Remembering your cosmic self is profoundly beautiful and seldom rewarded. Please accept my humble offering."

With that, Don Eduardo opened the old mesa cloth to reveal twelve dazzling ruby rings. A small gold name tag dangled from each ring. Passing the mesa to his left, Don Eduardo invited each brother and sister of the Ruby to find their ring and place it on their right ring finger.

"It should be a perfect fit," he said with a chuckle. "My gift has been *to manifest* and I have, over these many years, perfected the manifestation of gems. It has been a small challenge to ask for rubies mounted in gold to fit each of you perfectly. We will soon know if this feat has been successful."

Don Eduardo sat in silence while his brothers and sisters found their ruby rings. Leah, who wore the sapphire ring of the sisterhood on her left hand, found the ruby stone to be larger and heavier than the sapphire. Not being a good judge of carats, she could simply appreciate that the ruby was flawless, perfectly faceted, and a good three-quarters-inch in diameter. Don Eduardo was a true *ylloq'e*.

When all of the rings were distributed, Don Eduardo put the last one on his own ring finger. Then, folding the old mesa cloth, he asked if anyone had a poor fit. Each ring had fit perfectly. Don Eduardo slapped his knees and laughed until he cried. It was such contagious laughter that the entire circle was soon in tears. When they had all managed to regain their composure, he continued.

"Forgive my peculiar sense of humor," he said, pretending sobriety. "It has also been part of my Mission to manifest this meeting, which will activate the order's current Mission on *Pachamama*. I must, in all seriousness, tell you that this completes my personal Mission in this lifetime. I am ready and willing to leave the planet when my purpose has been served. Like all of you, I await the greater Mission to see if I can be of service or whether I have earned my freedom.

"What I can tell you, as the organizer of this meeting, is that our orders have come directly from the star, Sirius. I expect we will be in direct contact with the Siriun High Council before this particular Mission is complete. I have no exclusive information to share with you. It seems we are all at the same place of ignorance and I am most delighted to be in the company of such an ignorant group of *waykis!*"

Don Eduardo burst into laughter again, sending those at the table into tears once more. He waved his hands furiously in front of his face, indicating he had no more to say, and passed the scepter to Susmo, who had been laughing well before Chris had finished translating into English. Don Eduardo wiped his tears away and dug into his baby alpaca-skin pouch for a handful of coca leaves.

Leah's heart was bursting with love for the *ylloq'e* who had been her friend and teacher for so many years. Among other things, he had taught her that laughter and discipline, seemingly odd bedfellows, could be good working partners on the spiritual path. She hoped that the Mission would be in need of manifestation for some time to come.

Gaining his composure before the others, Susmo spent some moments holding the scepter in contemplation. Being on a Mission was a concept that had only recently entered his consciousness. He assessed the important aspects of his spiritual work to put his purpose into words.

When the group was ready to continue, he pulled his mesa from his lap setting it before him on the table. Placing the scepter to the side, he unwrapped the cloth to reveal a pile of stones. Of many shapes and sizes, the stones did not, in outward appearance, appear to be unusual. Yet Susmo handled them as priceless gems. His ruby ring sparkled in the shaft of light as he moved the stones out of the cluster into a circle of twelve, duplicating the seating at the table of the Ruby Order.

"My *Waykis*," he began, "I have with me a rare collection of stones. The shamans of many tribes throughout the Andes have gifted these stones to me. I have been fortunate in my work as an antiquities collector to travel a great deal in these mountains.

"Each of these stones contains a special power, for each has been struck by lightening. I have been taught to use these stones as healers because they balance energy. Here they will sit in circle, holding a place of balance for each of us and providing a connection to the lightning – giver of shamanic power.

"I know, from those who gave me these stones, that my calling in this life is *to balance.* It has been a lifelong lesson to keep my own life in balance. I have not always been successful in doing so. I have used the stones to balance the energetic fields of others. This has been a great learning experience in many ways, since I have had to discover my own boundaries and those of others.

"To be honest, until this journey I had been living my life unconscious of who I am and my purpose here on *Pachamama*. Oh yes, I had a spiritual life, made my offerings and sat in ceremony often, but I was not directed.

"What I am trying to say, My Brothers and Sisters, is that this journey has made me completely aware of myself. I can no longer hide, because my awakening came within this last week. I have little wisdom to offer you about our Mission. I am amazed to be on one, and am grateful to have been of some service to this Mission and to Don Eduardo. Thank you, Brothers and Sisters."

Susmo was solemn, as he passed the scepter to Doña Felicia. The journey had truly changed him – so much so that Leah wondered if his assemblage point had stabilized itself. She cast a concerned glance towards Chris at about the same time Don Eduardo smacked Susmo squarely on his back. Leah giggled at such instant manifestation while Chris looked on amazed. Susmo's energetic field flared out dramatically then reorganized itself in a more integrated way. Don Eduardo was laughing again at Susmo's stunned expression, while the remainder of the circle whispered to each other, creating a subdued mumble of voices. Magic was afoot in each moment of the meeting.

Master Mukda, sitting across from Don Eduardo, gave his staff a thump on the crystal floor to bring order to the circle. Chris sat back grinning, without any need to control the meeting.

Leah knew Don Eduardo's wife to be a soft-spoken woman with a gift for observation. She had been a spiritual mother to her, just as Don Eduardo had been her spiritual father. Doña Felicia sat with Inkari's scepter for some time, drinking in the energies and visions it provided. She felt the power of the ancient brotherhood move through her and saw the faces of the many *ylloq'e cuna*, both men and women, who had passed that power through the generations.

An astute dreamer, Doña Felicia drifted for some time, gathering her vision. Opening her brilliant brown eyes, she offered a shy, toothless smile to the circle. She was older than Don Eduardo, and the deep furrows of her weathered face were a roadmap of the spiritual path. Invisibility had been her strong suit, so speaking before the group made her uneasy. She began in a small, soft voice, to speak what was in her heart.

"*Waykis* of the Ruby, it is good that we are together and good to hold the golden staff of Inkari, a ray of our Father, the Sun. Inkari was the Son of the Sun. We have known for some time that *Pachamama* would choose to live in the *Hanaqpacha* (Higher Consciousness). Every day more of her people decide they would like to do that, too. You are here, in part, to show the way."

Doña Felicia placed a worn mesa cloth on the table. From a distant era, the cloth held the designs of the Incas – the Sun, the condor, and the teachings of the higher path. Dyed with sacred plants, its threads still held the scent of the Incas. She unfolded the cloth to reveal its patterns.

"As you see, I have nothing within the mesa, because the mesa itself is my most sacred item. Within this design is our cosmology. It is like a map to help find our way home – a constant reminder of who we are and why we are here. It is, within the weaving that we know not to fall into the darkness and lose sight of the pearl.

"This mesa has held countless *despachos* (offerings) to the *Apus*, the *Ñustas* and *Pachamama*. Some might say it is very valuable as an antiquity, but I tell you it is worthless without the wisdom that accompanies it.

"I am a weaver. My purpose is to weave. To understand my purpose, you must first understand how we weave. This cloth will be our guide. When we make the loom, it is understood that the frame represents our relationship with *Tayta Inti*, the

top of the loom, and *Pachamama*, the bottom of the loom. The guiding threads that
are the two sides are shafts of light from *Mamaq'illa* (Mother Moon). When we
begin a weaving, we create an interior support with tightly woven threads. Help me,
Leah, with the correct word for your culture," she asked.

"It is the warp, *Mamacita*," Leah replied, lovingly.

"Thank you, Child. This warp is the strength of the cloth, though it is unseen. It
represents the male energy part of us. Then we are ready to create a weaving with
the colored threads. Leah?"

"The weft, *Mama*," she offered.

"You might guess that this represents our feminine aspect, which brings forth
creation, like birthing a child. The weaving is a vision held in the mind and heart of
the weaver, and the act of creation is no different than having a child. It requires the
cooperation of the male and female energies to birth a child, a weaving or a spiritual
life. Life is given as the spreading stick – Leah, again please?"

"The batten, *Mama*," she replied.

"As the batten weaves its way between the warp threads, in/out, in/out,
inspiration/respiration, it gives the weaving breath – the life force. It is the male
energy again, manifesting the vision of the weaver.

"When the weaving is finished, it contains the vision of the weaver, and in our
tribe, the cosmological truths by which we live – the remembrance of who we are.
Everyone in our community learns to weave, though some become extraordinary
weavers. These are the great visionaries who weave into their cloths a vibration that
beckons the tribe into the future.

"We think of life as a weaving – a weaving of the filaments of light. Each person
is a unique weaving of these filaments, and yet we are all part of a greater weaving
that is the Divine Plan. The cosmos contains all of the possible threads needed for
the weaving. So in this old cloth are hidden the principles of balanced creation, the
symbols that guide us on our way home to the stars, and the vision that is our future.
The only part of this cloth that has changed over time is the vision of the future.

"This cloth contains a vibration of service. That vibration led us to the high
mountains, where we have kept the truth free of contamination for five hundred
years. The cloths that our extraordinary weavers are creating now contain the
vibration of freedom. As a people, our Mission on this planet is complete. Do not
mourn us if we leave you, gifting our bodies back to *Pachamama*. Do not judge
those of us who stay for what we might choose to experience next on *Pachamama*.

"Now it is your turn to hold the Truth and take it to even higher vibrations. Now
you must become the weavers of your own mesas – mesas of the *Hanaqpacha*."
Doña Felicia folded her hands as if in prayer and bowed to the group. She looked up
with a sweet grin on her face and passed the scepter to Leah, saying, "Be who you
came to be, My Child. You must step into your power."

Leah leaned over to give Doña Felicia a kiss on her right cheek as she accepted
the scepter into her left hand. Felicia held on to Leah's right hand for a short time as
Leah began to speak. "Beloved Ones, I feel an awakening within me as each of you
speaks. Like Brother Susmo, I have become conscious of the Ruby Order on this
journey. My time and attention have been directed towards the Sapphire Sisterhood
– a part of my consciousness since meeting Julio's mother, Francesca, some time
ago. I am a little challenged holding energy for both, and I am grateful to Doña
Felicia, Qoyari and Morgaine for good role-modeling in that regard."

Doña Felicia squeezed Leah's hand, then released it as Leah continued. "I cannot tell you much about this pendant. It is a paradox and contains a paradox. It doesn't feel like there is much to say about it and yet it contains the greatest Truth we could possibly understand. It is what it is and I accept it. However, I have with me another sacred item." Leah set the scepter down on her left side and brought a mesa from her lap. It was an old *vicuña* weaving from the high mountains of Peru. Eyes closed, she cradled it in her arms like a child.

Then, pulling back the mesa cloth, she revealed the head of a carved stone idol. Surrounded by green leaves, flower blossoms and petals, the idol looked out at the group with enormous round eyes. It was not a South American tribal image. In fact, it looked more extraterrestrial than it did human. It made Susmo think of the subterranean temple at Tiwanaku in Bolivia, where strange heads looked out from all four walls at the statue of *Wiracocha*.

Leah propped the idol up on the mesa cloth so that the group could see it – "or so that it could watch the group," Chris thought to himself with amusement. Now they could see a golden chain around its neck with a Disc of the Sun dangling from it.

"This Being," Leah continued, "came from the mountains not too far from Tres Cruces. Its discovery was both magical and tragic. Occasionally in the Andes, there are spontaneous fires. The villagers know them as Fires of Magical Return, because within the fires are found the golden relics of the Incas - for those brave enough to retrieve them.

"A man who was working in his field of potatoes witnessed this particular fire. According to his account, the fire was spontaneous, not caused by lightening or by man. He later admitted that he reacted in greed, thinking of being released from a life in the fields by coming into a weight of gold. He entered the flames to retrieve the gold of the Incas as his wife came running to stop him. It was too late.

"When the fire subsided, she found him on the ground, badly burned and holding only this stone idol. She wept profusely, as his risk had been for naught. Calling for help to family and others from their village, who were also in the fields, she was able to bring him home to his sleeping mat. His wife loosened his grasp on the idol and placed it on the window ledge of their mud brick house. The village *bruja* nursed the man's wounds, but he got steadily worse. His wife sent her son running a long way to the village of *Pakulmaka* to tell the story to Doña Francesca, Julio's mother, and to ask her to come see his father.

"Doña Francesca was the most respected shaman woman in this region. She mounted a horse and traveled with her daughter, Angelica, to see the man because she felt something very strange had happened and she wished to know the truth of it. By the time she arrived, the wife was also quite ill and losing life force. Francesca sat with the man only a few moments before making connection with a powerful spirit force in the house. The spirit force was one with the idol.

"She told them that possession of the idol would soon cause harm to the entire village because they did not understand the powerful spirit accompanying it. The family begged Francesca to dispose of the idol in an appropriate way, since no relic was worth the lives of their family or village. Francesca consulted the spirit of the Being while Angelica held space for her. She came to understand the needs of the Being, its origins and purpose. She agreed to take it with her. Unfortunately, the man died from the burns, but his wife recovered from her illness.

"When she returned to her village, Doña Francesca gave the idol to my friend, Don Carlos, a *mestizo* shaman who lived nearby. She told him that the Being came from the stars with the seeding of the great Mission of the sisterhood and brotherhood. The Being actually represents a stargate, a portal to the galaxy and our remembrance of who we are. It is an extra-planetary consciousness. The spirit told her that the idol had last been in the possession of Qoyari when she lived in that area. She had buried the idol as a gift for the future, asking that it make itself known at the appropriate moment.

"Qoyari had received the idol through the long lineage of the Andean branch of the sisterhood, which started with *Mamacocha*. *Mamacocha* had received it in ancient times from Mir-An-Da and Aman-Ra who began this Mission in old Egypt. It was their son, Mak-Ma, who had brought it through Atlantis to Titicaca Lake so long ago.

"Francesca told Don Carlos that the farmer had approached the relic in greed, not in integrity. The spirit demands that the keeper of this Being be impeccable, or die. It also demands that the keeper be actively engaged in the planetary ascension Mission.

"Francesca gave the stone idol, the Being, to Don Carlos, who kept very good care of it for many years. It is a living Being in need of nourishment, harmonious vibration and growth. Under those circumstances, it acts as a stargate.

"When Don Carlos prepared to retire from active duty, so to speak – to shift his pretext to his memoirs and more relaxation - he commissioned me with the care taking of the idol. Now I understand that the spirit of the Being was seeking the Ruby Order and wanted to be here with us.

"As my own life has shifted its focus, I have carried the idol with me around the world. It has opened me gently to remember who I am. Soon, as I come fully into that memory, I believe it will find a more stable environment back at *Pakulmaka* with beloved Julio. I am grateful for the opportunity to continue to serve the Mission in this way, and know that Julio will as well."

Julio returned a big smile to Leah. He had not yet been born when Francesca had brought the idol to Don Carlos. Leah relaxed, leaning against the purple velvet back of her chair. "Thank you, Brothers and Sister, for your patience with the long story I have told. Now, I will be brief with my purpose. I am here *to awaken*. My greatest joy comes from seeing the light of consciousness dawn in the eyes of my students – especially when they resolve an inner struggle to bring it forth. Because this is my purpose, I have received countless awakenings myself – through life, sacred places on the Earth and at the hands of my beloved teachers here and those from other realms. It is an energy that feeds me. It is about gathering more and more light.

"I would like to share that I have been receiving a steady stream of messages about paradox and power. It feels as if our acceptance of paradox is a necessary component of the transition to the *Hanaqpacha*. To create Heaven on Earth, it is necessary to be of Heaven and Earth, not one or the other.

"Perhaps that is the message brought to us by Beloved Fakoum – to accept the power of who we are within the humility of the Order. It speaks of magic.

"Magic brings me to my final observation. I am fond of Merlin, and I thank Master Mukda for the chance to look back on his relationship with Morgaine the other night."

Leah bowed to Mukda, who acknowledged her with a thump of his staff and a wink. She touched the pendant of Qoyari, remembering that Morgaine and Qoyari modeled to her the dual roles of high priestess and high magician.

"To make it brief," she began, "I have five different statues of Merlin, which I use in crystal grids, on my altar and around the house. I carry some of them with me when I teach. All of these Merlin statues had the magician's staff with its crystal ball tip in Merlin's right hand.

"Through one circumstance or another, all bona fide accidents, all of the statues have been broken at the right wrist, meaning that the power end of the staff and the right hand have broken free. By the time the fourth statue lost its hand, I fully expected the fifth one to break, so I put it in a place where it could not possibly be damaged. One morning after a very powerful dream showing me the limitations of magical power – forgive my vagueness, since the dream was immensely complex – I went to check on Merlin and, sure enough, the right hand had broken."

Leah laughed. "Can you imagine someone so dense that five statues had to sacrifice their right hands to get the point across, or someone so reluctant to come into her full power, as myself? I am grateful that all of you support me in taking up the Staff of Power with my left hand – the feminine hand – to live the Truth of my Mission and the greater Mission." Then, tipping the scepter towards Chris, she added, "I am uniquely indebted to Chris for volunteering to keep me out of the flames of the Inquisitors this time around."

Jacques winced slightly at Leah's reference to the Inquisition, since they shared a familial and incarnational history of burning at the stake. As she passed the scepter to the Maharajah, he kissed the sapphire ring on her left hand. She blushed slightly then shifted her sitting position to watch him speak.

"This golden relic of the Incas held the hopes and dreams of a great nation," Ramandi began, inspecting the scepter. "I do appreciate hopes and dreams. I am also conscious of those rare moments when light is birthed on the Earth. Such was the advent of Inkari and Qoyari to those who would become the Children of the Sun.

"My ancestor, Maharajah Ram, Melchior, followed a star to honor the birth of light of another great Master, Jeshua. I have followed an invisible star to witness the birth of this Mission – in many ways, a birth of light. It is appropriate that I have brought with me a relic of my ancestor from that ancient time."

Ramandi brought forth a ruby silk case brocaded with dragons and white flowers. The green vine of the flowers snaked through the design in a way that gave it fluidity as well as beauty. Rectangular and a little over two feet in length, it was not an identifiable case at all. Aware that the group curiosity was at its peak, Ramandi, a gifted showman, opened the case so that only Leah could see the contents. Looking within the case, her hand went to her heart as her eyes widened. Ramandi laughed. Then, leaning over to kiss her cheek, he asked if she would like to remove the relic from its case.

Leah leapt at the opportunity to assist Ramandi with his dramatic presentation for, more than anything, she wanted to touch the relic. Reaching inside the case, she used two hands to lift the ruby-and-diamond-studded handle of a broken sword from the case – the very sword that Ramandi had presented to her in Dreamtime. She held it high for all to see, turning it completely around once, allowing the jewels to light up the room.

Amidst the muffled approval of the brothers and sisters came a spontaneous shriek from Demetri, who sat to the left of Ramandi. Demetri's outburst caused Leah to jump with the sword in her hand. She quickly set it into the awaiting hands of the Maharajah. Everyone looked to Demetri, who wore the remorseful face of a schoolboy who had spoken out of place. He raised a hand to his chest while bowing his head in a gesture seeking forgiveness then waved a hand at Ramandi to continue.

Holding the sword to his heart, Ramandi spoke with passion. "My family has safeguarded this treasure for two thousand years. This is the sword that was broken over the knee of Melchior as he knelt before the child, Jeshua. The tip – the Point of Power, he gave to the child's mother, Mary, as a sign of subservience to the Master, Jeshua. The base he gave to the child's guardian, Joseph, who was the true king of his tribe.

"When Jeshua came to India for the first time to complete his training as a master, he brought the base back to my family, activating his own Mission. He left it with our family, since he had chosen to walk a path without possessions. The tip stayed with his mother. It has felt to me like a sword waiting to complete its Mission."

Ramandi laid the sword above his name with the handle facing Leah and the broken end pointing towards Demetri, who bent forward to examine it more closely. Beads of sweat were pearled upon the Cypriot's brow.

Ramandi continued his story, unfazed by his brother's behavior. "My purpose is *to unite.* I find, in my life, that unity must be accomplished by adhering to the Grail Codes of Service to the constituents.

"Since my father's death, when I came into that service, there have been countless opportunities to follow in his footsteps, bringing people together as participants in governance rather than subjects. Those to whom I delegate authority have come to understand these codes, and we have been asked to share our ways with other landowners who have large holdings and much responsibility. I do not feel that ours is the perfect system for many reasons, but if all people are honored equally, it can support Higher Consciousness.

"Coming from a long line of Vedic astrologers, my offering to the group must surely be the auspicious nature of this gathering. Like my ancestor, we have followed a star, perhaps brighter than the one that heralded the birth of the King of Kings. We cannot measure it with our sight because the Sun and Earth are both part of the alignment, but energetically we are witnessing a profound astrological event.

"One might expect that the return of the Shining Ones to the Earth be heralded by such an event, but consider that we are also aligning with the Great Central Sun – the Heart of the Cosmos – the Heart of God. The eyes of the Universe are upon Earth and those who serve her through all the dimensions. May we be especially receptive to divine guidance at this time. Thank you, Beloved Brothers and Sisters of the Ruby Order."

Ramandi held the scepter out for Demetri, who tried not to grab it from him. Barely able to sit still during Ramandi's short discourse, Demetri had thrust a leather-encased sacred item upon the table before taking the scepter. Perplexed by his mysterious behavior, the group needlessly braced themselves against the words of their most volcanic member.

"My most humble apologies for my outburst, Brothers and Sisters," he began. "When a Greek becomes excited, it is difficult to refrain from expressing exuberance. I have a most precious sacred object with me here. It was quite clear to me that I was to bring it, though it made little sense to me at the time. I have been the custodian of this object since my beloved dragon of a teacher passed over. It has been passed down through the Order of Saint John the Beloved, the guardian of Mother Mary, since he walked the Earth."

Unsnapping the end, Demetri opened the leather case, which was similar to the protective sheath of a hunting knife. He withdrew the object by grasping the soft, black velvet cloth wrapped around its end. With a bit of flourish, he thrust the tip of a shimmering, double-edged sword out over the table. "Beloveds," he announced, "I give you the Point of Power."

The energy emanating from the broken blade caused everyone to grasp their hearts. Ramandi was in tears immediately. "This Sword of Destiny and Devotion has not been united since the birth of Christ," Demetri continued. "The Point of Power was given to John the Beloved by Mother Mary when his guardianship of the Divine Mother was completed – before her ascension. It had been, many times, in the hands of Master Jeshua.

"As to the timing of the actual physical union of tip and blade with whatever power it unleashes," he said, glancing at Ramandi, "I leave to the impartial discernment of our brother, Chris." Ramandi nodded his head in agreement, then they, and the rest of the group, looked to Chris.

He was reflective for a moment, piecing together the magical puzzle that this meeting had become. "Soon, My Brothers and Sisters," he said, softly. "I suspect it will open a portal of some magnitude. We will allow the Divine Plan to guide us. Do each of you agree?" Those around the table voiced their agreement, contributing to an ever-increasing atmosphere of excitement and magic in the room.

Demetri laid the broken point-end of the sword above his name on the table – its jagged edge in perfect alignment with the broken end of Ramandi's sword. Many in the circle could see an electric, filamentous connection already being made between the two pieces of the sword as Demetri continued.

"My purpose is *to defend.* Who would have guessed?" he asked, laughing. The group joined in his laughter for a moment, and then he went on. "My mother tells me I came from her womb fighting – and so it has been in my life. It was through my magus teacher that I learned to defend with energy rather than physical force. Energy is a more powerful weapon because it is unseen and unexpected. He was not of the Ruby Order, but as a magus he knew of us. So he taught me to use energy impeccably in accordance with the rules of our order. He continues to guide me from the other side – a jolting experience at first, but one to which I have become accustomed.

"What I can offer the group are messages he has shared with me regarding this journey, our meetings, and our Mission. They are usually cryptic, owing to his trickster nature, but time and the unfoldment of this journey have helped me decipher them. There were numerous references to high magic and a most powerful experience for all of us.

"However, to corroborate the information given to Peter from Merlin's ball, we must prepare for major resistance from what he called 'the opposition'. It seems we must prove ourselves to be worthy of our Mission."

Demetri's eyes met those of Chris, then Don Eduardo, noting that they had taken the second warning seriously. Don Eduardo shut his eyes for a moment to connect with his warriors outside the stone portal into the mountain. They were chewing coca in a place of shade nearby the portal. He communicated to them a command to have at least one man at the portal at all times, making them aware of potential danger. One warrior jumped up immediately to take that position.

Then he moved his consciousness within the mountain to Brian and the other warriors. They sat as a group with their backs to the portal, energetically shielding the women, who were deep in meditation. Their position was perfect, but he asked Brian's Higher Self to urge him towards defending the invisible doorway to their meeting room, leaving five *waykis* at the portal. Brian stood up, then, meandering over to the doorway, stood before it.

Demetri, aware of Don Eduardo's activity, remained silent until the *ylloq'e* returned to the circle.

"That said," Demetri continued, "let me go on to topics a bit lighter. I was told that, on this journey, I would meet two dragons, a prince, several immortals and others who could attain immortality. Then there are the rest of us," he laughed, "Magicians one and all.

"How would one prepare for such a journey? I was told to bring the Point of Power, several changes of clothes, and my camera. Perhaps Don Eduardo can manifest some interdimensional film for a few group shots," he joked. Leah loved Demetri for all his craziness, and so could not contain the giggles that bubbled up from within her. They were innocent, playful and very contagious. Soon the whole table was laughing as Demetri went on with his nonsensical monologue – all of it accompanied by animated facial expressions that lent theatrics to his words. He stopped long enough for them to wipe their tears away, then concluded saying: "He did say one more important thing."

The group expected to hear one last joke, but Demetri's demeanor took on a sudden reverence. "He said that none of us would return from this journey as human beings. That is something I trust all of us have considered. Thank you, Brothers and Sisters of the Ruby, for allowing me to be who I am. I stand ready *to defend* you and this Mission as I am able."

After everyone took a very deep breath, Demetri passed the scepter to Master Mukda who, holding his staff in his right hand, reached over to take the scepter with his left hand. He had brought nothing forth to sit upon his lap when asked to ready the sacred objects. Mukda began to twist both scepter and staff, while staring at the table before him. Everyone around the table followed his eyes to fix their own eyes on the table before the master.

At first, a little wisp of vapor appeared. Then it grew into a cloud around a foot in diameter. Watching it coalesce, the group began to see a form take shape from the mist. Soon the mist vanished and they found themselves looking at a burning round lamp. The tiny flame grew, shooting up into a rainbow of light. The group applauded the good magic of their brother, who tamed the flame down to several inches.

"Beloveds, it is a wonderful experience to sit at this table with each of you. Sometimes life in the ascended state gets a bit dull. Oh, to be sure, we have a good time with our magic and have often taken manifestation into the arena of sport, but, for the most part, we hold a high joy frequency rather than the humor indigenous to the Earth. I might add that we regularly encounter 'the opposition' which makes this journey good training for all of you."

Looking at the little lamp, he spoke further. "Here we have a small child of the Maxine Flame, the flame expressing the Seven Vibrational Rays of light at once. No color is greater than any other color - or more important.

"The First Ray of Will and Power, is represented by the color red. The blue color of the Second Ray symbolizes Love and Wisdom and is the ray guiding our solar system.

"The Third Ray, Active Intelligence, is yellow. Those are the three primary rays from which the other four rays express themselves.

"These are the Fourth Ray of Harmony through Conflict, represented here by orange, the Fifth Ray of Science and Concrete Knowledge, which is green, the Sixth Ray of Devotion and Idealism which is purple, and the Seventh of indigo, the Ray of Ceremonial Order and Magic.

"As frequency is elevated, the individual begins to work with the Ruby Ray rather than red, the Sapphire Ray rather than blue, and so forth. Like the derivation of the I Ching in the Chinese cosmological system, all possibilities exist within combinations of these seven rays.

"Like the flame, my purpose is *to illuminate,* to bring light into the darkness or greater light into the light. It is why so many of you are working with me in Dreamtime. This is the mastery level of training for your ascension. Of course this purpose of mine began with self-illumination – the slow but steady process of holding more light. I had the help of many masters through the dimensions with my own training, each one taking me to the next step of illumination.

"There are other ways to become illumined. Don Eduardo is an incredible master of light through the power of lightening. But my way, and the way of many of you studying with me, is through the continual shifting of reality through self-correction towards higher frequencies of light embodiment.

"It would not serve you to describe my process with this enlightenment, for each of us will follow a slightly different path. Know that we have the endless strength and the support of the masters on our quest. Let us remember to call on them in time of need.

"I, too, have foreseen an opposition to our Mission, at this point and as the Mission continues to lead us into the future. There are those who covet the Earth in a way of greed. They act out of fear, unable to release themselves from material bondage or the need to control.

"As we know, there is no shortage of misused power on Earth, but perhaps it is good to remember that the abuse of power exists off-planet as well. Do not think that other dimensions are not challenging. Remember – outside the Heart of God, all exists to some degree in the duality of separation.

"Learn to use both, Beloveds, to move energy on behalf of the Divine Plan. Know that if we are challenged on this journey, it is because we are worthy of challenge and that we are capable of moving energy at that level. Remember the light and be free of fear.

"This little lamp will burn here to illumine our way. Those of you who have entered the Dreamtime with me, recollect your invincibility in that state and create it around you if need be. It will support the entire group in our efforts to complete this Mission. Thank you, Beloveds."

During the few moments it took for Master Mukda to pass the scepter to Jacques, Leah processed a rising fear. One warning of an impending conflict did not concern her, but three warnings had now been laid on the table. She was a fearless woman by nature, but as had already been clearly illustrated, she had little expertise where evil energies were concerned.

She closed her eyes and remembered herself in Lord Sananda's ashram dueling with Chris. Her energy was endless and she had never felt pain from a fall or blow. In fact, she was an all-out warrior.

When the fear had dissipated she opened her eyes to find Chris watching her. A hint of his crooked grin suggested that he was following her feelings as they cleared. In ways too numerous to conjure in her mind at that moment, she was grateful for the love and support of such a beautiful man.

Jacques examined the scepter carefully, turning it around many times. "Brothers and Sisters of the Ruby," he said, at last, "I perceive that this scepter is one half of a whole. What can you tell me about it?"

Everyone looked to Don Eduardo for an answer. "The scepter was manifested into Chris' hand by the golden skull," he reflected. "I never thought to ask if it was the true staff of Inkari, but I did assume that. Please give me a moment to consult the skull," the *ylloq'e* asked. The group closed their eyes in meditation to hold the space for him while he asked the skull about the scepter's origin and possible twin. After only a few moments, he returned his consciousness to the circle, chuckling to himself. "What can *you* tell us about the scepter, Jacques?" he asked. "You are correct, of course," he added.

Jacques' engaging smile warmed the room as he explained himself. "This scepter has an ascending energy – a clockwise vortex for those so inclined. It is telling me that a similar scepter exists that has a descending energy – a counterclockwise vortex. The former creates an energy that reaches towards Heaven, while the latter anchors Heaven on Earth.

"This scepter was truly Inkari's – brought from our Father's house to found a nation of light. When that nation lost sight of the pearl, the scepter was taken from them and returned to our Father's house. Its twin, the descending scepter, has never left our Father's house. Together they hold the principle behind the Star of David – Heaven and Earth meeting. When the two are united, the true ascension can begin."

His eyes glazed, Jacques had entered a trance state somewhere in the middle of his introduction. As it ended, he relaxed his gaze and set the scepter on the table.

Reaching beneath the tabletop, he brought forth the Templar cloak and cross that had so activated Brian. The cloak was folded with the cross facing upwards. He placed it above his name and laid the golden cross of equal lengths on top of the red cross.

"Sorry to have messed up the order of my presentation, but the scepter's message could not be ignored. I put forth the cloak and cross of my Templar ancestor once again," he said. Then, looking at Leah he added, "Forgive me, Leah, *our* Templar ancestor." Leah smiled at his needless acknowledgment, and Jacques continued.

"These objects are sacred to me not so much because they are my ancestor's, but rather for their representation of a dedicated group of men who were, and still are, on a Mission. Unlike the average man, whose Mission is the protection and raising of family, theirs was the protection and preservation of the bloodline and teachings of the Master Jesus. It feels appropriate that they be represented at this round table."

Jacques laughed. "My purpose is *to preserve*. At face value, it seems fitting for a lineage dedicated to youthful longevity and immortality of the body. However, it also applies to the Templar legacy, the formulas of the magi, the hidden teachings and so forth.

"In learning to follow this personal Mission, it was necessary for me to learn discernment. Without discernment, I might inadvertently preserve untruth. Learning early on to recognize the Truth in life, I spent many years filtering through the collective and cosmic rubbish dumps to salvage threads of Truth. When we are fully opened cosmic beings, we need discernment at all levels of consciousness.

"Now I see my purpose in a whole new way – to pre-serve – different, isn't it?" he queried. To many a raised eyebrow, he continued. "To pre-serve becomes a frontline assignment for the spiritual warrior. There are those of us anchored in Truth who are able to dance on the edge of the sword – to be of service to the evolution of consciousness. Slightly different from the concept of the Bodhisattva, who comes back to serve in compassion, we carry the warrior energy of serving Truth. Like the Bodhisattva, we ascend and return until our Mission is complete as incarnate beings, then we serve from the ascended state like our beloved Saint Germain.

"I feel complete in my discourse. However, I would suggest to Chris that this scepter be carried with us wherever we are taken on this Mission. I am very attentive to messages received in this way." Chris nodded his head in agreement as Jacques placed the scepter into the hands of young Julio.

Julio received the legacy of his people engulfed in a golden light. With a spontaneous expansion of heart, the group saw Julio's clarity as a true beacon of light for future generations of seekers. He would be a sought-after spiritual teacher some day – a teacher who would work with passionate integrity. His participation in this Mission would sow within him the seed of his expanded, powerful presence, but in the moment, seated at a table of magicians, he spoke as a young man, filled with the insecurity of one opening to far greater possibilities than he had imagined.

In passable English, Julio asked Chris to interpret for him, allowing him to speak from his heart. More than happy to do so, Chris connected his heart to Julio's as he began to speak in Quechua. "Respected Elders, Brothers and Sisters of the Ruby, it feels an honor to be in the presence of great *ylloq'e cuna*. I feel within myself that potential and am happy to have you as my teachers. I have much to learn and only a little to say."

The group held warm smiles for Julio as he drew his sacred object from his lap. He set a beautiful mesa cloth from his region before himself on the table. It was a fine cloth of naturally dyed alpaca in shades of red, green, gold and black. When the mesa was fully laid out upon the table, a stone sat at its center. The stone was rectangular, about four inches long and two inches square on the end. Polished smooth from lifetimes of handling its original carved form, it had an undeniable presence. Julio sat staring at it for a long time prior to speaking.

"These are my sacred objects," he began, at last. "My mother wove this mesa cloth for me while I was in her womb. It reminds me that she brought me into this world with joy. She did that for each of her children. Within the weaving is an intent that I live and love to the fullest capacity of my soul. With that intent, she aligned me with my purpose before I was born. She gave me this stone as well," he said, with some emotion.

"She gave this stone to me as she was dying. It was her sacred and magical stone. On this side facing me," he said, turning the mesa a full circle for all to see, "there is a portal, not unlike the portal here at Kañacway Mountain.

204 The Brotherhood of the Magi

"My mother knew that she was dying. She told me that her Mission was complete and she was free to go. It was in that beautiful place of acceptance that she taught me to journey through the portal of this sacred stone to the other dimensions. She said there had been dreamers in every generation of her family since the stone had first been carved. I would pass it to the dreamer in my own family to continue the lineage of magic.

"My purpose is *to bridge.* I am fortunate to know my purpose so young in life and direct my energies towards it. Because I loved school, I was advanced in my studies and sent to Paucartambo to be educated. I am grateful to my *madrina,* Leah, for supporting my education there by providing a space for me in a widow's home. In addition to mathematics, culture, science and geography, this education has given me Spanish, and now I am studying English. These are cultural bridges for our elders who understand only Quechua.

"Now I am preparing to attend university in Cusco to study medicine. I hope *to bridge* the old ways and the new ways of medicine for my people. I know that life has many lessons for me and that they will come to me because I act as a bridge. I do not know where my education will take me, but I am grateful to have the old ways and my *ylloq'e* teacher, Don Eduardo, to keep my heart open. Thank you, *Waykis,* and thank you, *Wayki* Chris, for helping me to speak from my heart."

Julio passed the scepter to Chris, who reached over to rub the back of Julio's neck. Julio had done very well for one so young. Chris set the scepter over his name on the table then pulled a worn leather amulet from under his opened black shirt. Overturning the amulet in his left hand, he grasped the contents and returned the amulet to its hiding place against his chest. Leah leaned forward and to her left to see beyond the golden skull as Chris placed something curved and ivory colored on the table. Tapered on one end and no more than two inches in length, the object was completely mysterious to the group.

Eyeing them all with humor, he looked directly at Demetri when he spoke in a contrived whisper, loud enough for all to hear. "Dear Brothers and Sisters of the Ruby, I have here the tooth of a dragon." Demetri jumped in his seat, shrieked and slammed his fist on the table, all in a second's time. Chris met him with a wizard's humor, raising his hands and breathing fire as if in attack. Demetri shrieked again and began laughing so hard he could not stop. The rest of the group snapped out of shock to join in the fun. It was quite a long time before order was restored to the meeting.

Chris rotated the tooth while holding it before him for all to see. "Allow me to continue, Mates," he said casually, when at last he could speak. "This really is the tooth of a dragon. I am not at liberty to tell you where I came by it, but I plucked it from the beast's mouth myself." The group was stunned. Leah stared at him in disbelief. "So, anyway, there it is, my most sacred item." He slid it to a place just above the ruby that dotted the 'i' in his name.

"Very well, then," he continued, aware that he had stretched even Master Mukda's belief systems a fair piece. "My purpose in this life is *to activate.* With activation, codes of consciousness can be opened for ourselves and the Mission, and we take a giant step, or as we say – a big kangaroo hop - on our journey back to our Father's house. People are not the only activators, for activation is contained in the land at certain sites, in the experience of life, and in vision or interdimensional experience.

"It has been a tradition of the magi that many of the men serve as activators for the women of the Sapphire Sisterhood who have carried the codes of Higher Consciousness." He glanced at Leah who was, at once, in agreement with what he had said and amazed at what Chris knew himself to be.

He winked at her, and continued. "I concede that I am far from activated myself. Activation seems to happen to the brothers solely through the challenges of leading a conscious life. I feel certain that one cannot turn away from it when a certain frequency is attained.

"From my experience, perhaps from yours as well, it seems that purpose is steadily pursued over the life of the initiate, though initially at an unconscious level. Becoming conscious of purpose feels like separating the weak threads of desire, which are entangled with the strong threads of purpose, to create a weaving of quality and integrity. As we do this, we are motivated less by desire and more by purpose.

"Within each of us is a unique approach to life that allows us to be individuals contributing our uniqueness to a collective Mission - a greater weaving. The Mission honors each of us in our uniqueness, our purpose, and our willingness to follow a path of mystery and magic. It is not for everyone.

"It feels as if the real power of our circle is emerging. We are brilliant, strong, magical, and a little bit crazy," he said, with a smile. "Together we have woven this cloth of solidarity in purpose. Let us, in that solidarity, be guided by the magic we know so well. If we meet conflict, let us meet it as true warriors, each bringing forth our own strength for the strength of the whole. If the doors open to higher dimensions, let us hold a frequency of attainment for all who would come with us. Thank you, Brothers and Sisters.

"We will adjourn briefly to consult with the warriors, collect our dreamers and see what Spirit has provided us to eat. Well done, Order of the Ruby," he concluded, setting the scepter over his name.

"Well done, Lord of the Ruby," they spontaneously shouted back at him.

The dragon's tooth discharged a puff of smoke – to their astonishment and amusement.

Valley of the Blue Moon

After considerable backslapping and hugging, the group picked up their belongings and began moving through the passageway to the entrance room of the Brotherhood's Temple within the mountain. Lingering behind, Leah and Chris came easily into each other's arms. After a deep, warm kiss, she looked into his eyes and began to laugh.

"Christian Kramer, you are absolutely outrageous," she whispered.

Smiling, he pulled her close again. "Guilty as charged," he whispered in her ear. "There are so few places where I can get away with it – and how to resist Demetri?! It feels purposeful, though. We are such an energetically intense group that the pressure needs to be released at regular intervals. Do you agree?"

"No doubt. My top was about to burst a few times," she replied, holding her hand on her crown chakra. "As an aside, just let me say that I have truly loved you as a human being and know that the Divine Plan will afford us some expression of that in the future."

"Let's set that intent right now, Leah," he replied seriously, while drawing her close again. Together they created an assemblage point for their love that could transit through all dimensions to the heart of God. Then, following Leah through the passageway, Chris said a fervent prayer that he would be divinely guided to steer the Mission to completion. "Thy will be done," he breathed as he emerged into the entrance room.

Ten women rushed towards Leah, as she emerged from the passageway, while the two Indian women joined arms with Doña Felicia. They had all experienced the profound release of unconscious blocks – memories so deeply buried that their conscious minds would never have unearthed them. Many of the releases were from past-life remembrances - patterns brought into this life from previous experience. To Leah and Doña Felicia the women looked brilliant – filled with luminous energy – ready to dream the dream.

The men were conferring with the warriors who were ready for anything but hungry for details of potential conflict. None could be provided at that time, but Don Eduardo promised to be telepathically open to communications. He dissolved through the outer portal to confer with the warriors on the exterior of the mountain.

The Sun was low in the sky as he warned them to be particularly watchful at dusk, when the *Ñaupa* were slipping through the rocks. Naturally the greatest time of danger from human aggressors was the dawn, when the *Ñaupa* made their return and the portal was open to those who could see into that dimension - like the sorcerers. If the slightest perturbation of the energy field was noticed, aside from the *Ñaupa* who would not likely be the source of aggression, they were to communicate with the inside guards, and with him, at once.

Don Eduardo returned through the portal to find the group in a great circle surrounding a large amethyst disc that was being lowered from the ceiling. As it slowly came to rest at table height before them, they saw that it was piled high with fruits, nuts, raw vegetables and sprouted seeds and grains. Pure water and juices of every kind were contained in pitchers of crystalline amethyst with matching glasses and plates.

Walking up to the table, Chris lifted a ripe mango to his nose. "Ah-h-h," he breathed, drinking in the aroma of the nectar, "our gratitude to the Brotherhood for looking after our needs. Come feast as Gods and Goddesses, Mates – beyond organic, I'm sure."

Suddenly famished, the group converged on the table, while Chris steered Brian away from the group to speak with him privately.

Chris gave Brian a warm hug across the shoulders as he pulled him aside. "Everything okay, Mate?" he asked.

"So far, Chris. I admit to being more comfortable fighting form rather than energy, though. Any words of advice?"

"There is really no difference, once you detect the energy. Our warrior codes are of nonaggression, making the first rule of thumb to wait until you are legitimately challenged. It's a tough one. Secondly, we yield when at all possible, allowing the energy or form to destroy itself with its own aggression.

"If all else fails, we fight to the full extent of our power maintaining a bubble of protection around us. This bubble can burst through its own weakness, in fear or, sometimes, through the workings of the Divine Plan."

"Understood," Brian replied. "I am relying mostly on past life memory as a warrior, Chris. I have limited sight for energy, and am not sure I can project a strong bubble."

"Give it a try, Mate," he responded. "Right now."

The group was oblivious of the two men as Brian projected his bubble of armor around him. Chris circled around it, examining its etheric, weblike structure. "You've got a few holes, Mate," he said, reaching his hand into Brian's bubble space. "Let's do some repair work."

"Okay, what do I do?" he asked.

"I am going to merge bubbles with you, Mate. Then we can use my field to repair your holes. You'll need to give me permission to enter your bubble."

"Permission granted. Where did the holes come from?" he asked, as Chris threw up a cloak of invisibility around them and entered his field.

"Anywhere," Chris answered, stepping behind Brian in a back-to-back position. "I've seen them come from negative thought forms all the way out to cosmic interference. It doesn't matter, as long as we repair them.

"Now, Mate, my bubble is holding your bubble. You can relax your intent about keeping it out there and use your intent to reweave the mesh. Draw on the Source energy which comes naturally and plentifully through your crown chakra."

Having Chris hold his space gave Brian the vision he needed to repair his bubble of light. This vision concretized his bubble in Brian's awareness so that he would never lose sight of it.

Chris, he realized, was doing more than holding space for him. In fact, Chris was activating Brian's own gift of vision on behalf of the Divine Plan.

When the work was complete, Chris stepped out of Brian's field and retracted his bubble. Brian followed suit, pulling in his bubble, then gave Chris a heartfelt hug. Chris charged Brian's heart and drank in the love Brian offered him. Words of confirmation were not needed. Brian knew that he could see any energy projected at him. Lifting the cloak of invisibility, Chris led Brian, who was adjusting to his newly opened gifts, to a spiritual warrior's feast.

Enough time was given for them to eat and drink fully, as well as to enjoy each other's company. Then the table, with all of their refuse, was raised again into the ceiling of the entrance room. As this was taking place, a hallway appeared at the side of the circular room opposite the entrance. Sonia, bold as ever, explored the hallway, pushing open doors, then turned back to the group with a wide smile. "Wouldn't you know?" she announced, laughing. "Here are the *baños* – men's and women's!"

Everyone had an opportunity to refresh before gathering back in the entrance hall. Having asked for guidance before speaking to the group, Chris began, "Brothers and Sisters, we will reenter the meeting room in a few moments to begin the next phase of the Mission. In gratitude, we leave our warriors here to guard this passageway, as it is our place of return to this world. We will take our dreamers with us, for their work is at hand. Leave all of your personal belongings, food and water behind. Bring with you only that which is sacred – including your humor," he added, with a smile.

After stacking their belongings along one wall, the group began to file through the passageway. When the Order of the Ruby returned to their chairs, they found that a second row of chairs had been placed behind and between their circle. The women dreamers were asked to take the chair on the right side of the brother or sister they were drawn to assist. Moving quickly, quietly, and without dispute, they seated themselves within seconds. Unattached to where they sat, the women's focus came quickly to the table and the sacred objects at each place. They became aware that the objects were holding an incredible power, but the floor was never opened to question.

Asked to put their own sacred objects on the table, all of the women brought forth their mesas and set them unopened on the table above and between the objects already present. They were immediately woven into the Power Grid of the Ruby Order. As Chris took up the golden scepter, a ruby glow emanated from the eyes of the skull connecting to his heart. Then the skull rotated full circle to connect its ruby light with each White Heart of the order.

When the skull had completed its circle, Chris asked each member of the order to bring forth their sacred gemstones to activate the inlaid Star of David within the table. He asked Julio, who held the single-terminated quartz crystals, to begin the sacred geometric grid. Each brother or sister was to call forth an intent for the Mission before laying down their stones.

Julio rose, pulling his pouch containing the crystals from his shirt. He held them to his heart for a moment, then to his Third Eye, and called out "Protection". It was a good start for the gridwork.

After Julio had circled the table and drawn the two triangles of the star, the group felt the first level of activation. Chris rose to place the ruby grid inside the quartz grid, calling forth "Solidarity". Leah followed Chris with the sapphires of the sisterhood, intending "Ma-at – Love without Reason". The amethyst crystals of the magi were laid down by Susmo, who summoned "Courage", followed by Doña Felicia's emeralds with her intent of "Vision." Two more layers of the star grid were laid out with Jacques' golden topaz and Mukda's blue diamonds, calling forth "Alchemy" and "Clarity", respectively.

The six remaining brothers placed their gems in smaller Stars of David at the junctions of the star – the interior points of the hexagon. In doing so, they reinforced the geometry of the star, at the same time anchoring a column of light between Heaven and Earth to stabilize the grid. They were: Don Eduardo with gold, asking for "Surrender", Ramandi with silver, asking for "Peace", Peter with amber, asking for "Divine Guidance", Demetri with aquamarine, asking for "Impeccability", and Fakoum with his pearls, calling forth "Humility".

As the sheik activated the final anchor of the grid, a column of light appeared from floor to ceiling passing through the golden skull in the center of the table. The apexes of the star tetrahedron were spinning in opposite directions as they had in their previous meetings, but were now anchored in the column of light. Without notice, the central column attached itself to the Maxine Flame burning from Mukda's lamp, and the column became a holographic rainbow of light. Master Mukda was quite pleased.

Scepter in hand, Chris plunged within himself for guidance once again, providing an opportunity for the group to stabilize their individual fields in the force field of the tetrahedron. All of their preparatory work made sense to them at that point, for theirs was not a simple task.

When Chris emerged from his meditation, he tucked the scepter within his shirt and announced, "We are asked to activate a dimensional shift. Please, Beloveds, detach yourself from this reality."

The energy in the room elevated itself spontaneously. He looked to Demetri and Ramandi sitting to the right of Leah, and, using the power of the magus, commanded, "My Brothers, join the Sword of the Master."

Ramandi grasped the ruby-and-diamond-studded sword handle, raising it up from the table as Demetri moved the tip into alignment with it. When tip and sword came together for the first time in two millennia, light shot out in every direction. Though physically quite strong, the two brothers found it difficult to hold on to the two pieces as the activation began. The circle found itself stabilized within a whirling vortex of violet light energy. All perception of the room vanished as the star tetrahedron took on the capacity of an interdimensional ship.

After moving through a rainbow of color, the light projecting from the sword diminished, leaving a soft golden glow surrounding it. At the same time, the vortex slowed itself, then came to a stop. The frequency was noticeably higher, though the space seemed not to have changed. Demetri and Ramandi sat staring at the sword, then lifting it together by the handle, demonstrated to all in the room that the two pieces had fused together without a hint of the fracture.

With a broad smile, Chris shook his head, and spoke. "There are no mistakes in the Divine Plan. It was destiny that the Master's sword be joined on this occasion. Truly there can be no separation as we journey towards our Father's house. Shall we see where our magic has taken us?"

With that, they began to look around at the familiar room, to find an unfamiliar archway where golden double doors appeared. Situated behind Leah, the doorway seemed to beckon them. Chris sought the counsel of his guides, asking what the group should bring with them. Opening his eyes, he found everyone awaiting instructions.

"Well Mates, it seems we are to bring the scepter and the sword with us and nothing else. Shall we go?" The group nodded their approval – Demetri deferring to Ramandi as guardian of the sword for the time being. As if in response to his deference, a ruby and diamond-studded silver sheath magically appeared around Ramandi's waist as he rose to leave the table. With a boyish laugh, he sheathed the sword and moved towards the doors.

As the group approached the archway, the doors magically opened before them. Ramandi and Demetri led the group through the golden doorway out onto a stone terrace bathed in sunlight. Tropical flowers surrounded the terrace and cascaded down the mountainside beneath it. Looking down from the mountainside perch, they saw a lush valley surrounded on all sides by snowcapped mountain peaks. Little villages spotted the landscape - most of them on the shores of a peaceful blue lake. Near the base of the mountain beneath them was a large village of tidy white cottages clustered around a central plaza, where several temple-like buildings were situated.

Leah and Chris came through the doorway last to join the others on the terrace. Looking behind, they saw the golden doors silently close, sealing the mountainside entrance to the valley.

Leah breathed deeply of the warm mountain air. "Well, Darling," she said, scanning the horizon, "we are definitely not at Tres Cruces."

"Look below, Leah," he replied. "It is a little paradise – like Shangri-La. No question we're still on Earth, but where?"

"It feels like Fourth Dimension to me, Chris. My light body is fully active. Should we look for a path down to the big village there?" she asked as they came close to the terrace edge, where Don Eduardo and Doña Felicia were standing.

"That seems appropriate," he replied, "but let's get the lay of the land from above first." They walked along the edge of the entire terrace, mapping in their minds the roadways, villages and natural landmarks of the valley.

"Look, Chris, over on that mountainside," Leah said, grabbing his arm and pointing off to the right of the terrace, beyond the lake. "Isn't that another golden doorway?"

"Eagle eyes, Leah," he said, squeezing her around the waist. "You seem to have an affinity for golden portals."

"This place is very familiar to me, Darling – from Dreamtime or past lives. I love it already!"

"Well, remember not to get too attached to it," he laughed, stroking her neck. She leaned back against him for a moment, drinking in his love. How good it felt to have him here with her. Leaning down to kiss her forehead, he whispered, "So where is the path, gorgeous? We have a crew to lead onward."

"Forgive me for trying to stretch this moment, Mate," she said, turning around to look in his eyes. "If I'm not mistaken, there is a narrow path along the mountain to the right of the entrance. Shall we look?"

"After you," he replied, lowering his hand to the center of her back with a gentle nudge. She responded to his playfulness by wheeling around to grab his hand.

"Come on, everyone," she called, leading Chris to the edge of the terrace along the mountain.

The group, who had been milling around in amazement at the sight before them, now turned to follow Chris and Leah. The path was masked slightly by some overgrowth of the jungle foliage but she found it.

"Handy little magician, aren't you," he chuckled, motioning for the group to join them.

"There is a strong remembrance guiding me here. I guess you could call it magic," she responded.

Making their way down the steep and tricky path, Chris asked Leah to lead the way while he, Julio, and Susmo positioned themselves at the difficult spots to be of help to those who needed it. She made her way along the overgrown path until the group came to a clearing on the outskirts of the village, where they stopped to rest and regroup. Pure water bubbled forth from the mountain there into a small stone pool where the group members, having felt the temperature rise as they walked down into the valley, took refreshment, splashed themselves with cool water and rested.

When all were thoroughly rested, the group walked through the narrow streets of the village past whitewashed cottages, heading towards the central plaza. Feeling it wise to move towards the major temples, Leah and Chris guided the group of twenty-four around a gentle curve in the street to spill out into the plaza. In the center of the plaza, a graceful fountain sprayed streams of water upward in a rotating spiral. Standing before the fountain was a small delegation of men and women dressed in white garments with violet sashes.

The group walked up the gently elevated steps of the plaza to stand before the delegation. Leading the delegation, a beautiful dark-haired woman with deep green eyes came forward to bow respectfully before Leah.

"Welcome, Sister," she said, grasping Leah's hands, "we've been expecting all of you." She felt the warm pulse of high life force in the woman's hands as well as the heart glow of sisterhood.

"Thank you, My Sister. I present to you a most remarkable group of brothers and sisters. We are at your service."

"Quite the opposite, Dear Leah. We are at your service. We will lead all of you to a resting place where you can refresh and change into garments that will better suit you here."

"Where are we, if we might ask?" Leah queried.

"Why, the Valley of the Blue Moon, of course. Do you not recall having spent lifetimes here in the study of the sacred teachings and preservation of the records?"

Leah looked at Chris in amazement. Then turning back to the delegation leader, she said, "Well, it does feel very familiar. I just couldn't put a name to this beautiful valley." Then feeling Chris' silent laughter, she added sheepishly, "Perhaps I will open more memory while here. What is your name?" she asked.

"We are an order here," the woman replied, in a soft-spoken voice. "Commonly, we refer to each other as brothers and sisters, so simply call me Sister Sarah. After you have rested, we will debrief your group as to our customs and purpose then give you a tour of our important sites. This evening there will be a celebration where we will all get to know each other. Tomorrow evening the planets come into alignment with the Great Central Sun."

"Thank you, Sister Sarah. We will follow you," Leah replied, bowing slightly. Having lost all track of time, she was grateful for the reminder of the alignment. She turned to the group and let them know what had been said, and then they all followed the woman while the rest of the delegation dispersed from the area of the fountain.

Walking in silence, the group entered a street that ran alongside one of the two temple buildings on the plaza. Adjoining one of the temples was a lower, two-story building that completed the block. Midway along the length of this building was an entrance with great wooden doors.

Knocking sharply on the door, Sister Sarah summoned a gatekeeper who opened the doors from the inside. She led the group into an enchanting courtyard where brilliant bougainvillea in all the shades of pink to purple cascaded down from rooftops and second-story balconies, framing the courtyard in flowers. Palm trees lined the walkways and orchids clung to the walls and flowering trees in a central garden.

A shimmering light filled the courtyard as the group came to stand within it. Sister Sarah began assigning rooms to the group by calling their names, as if they all had reservations. The Indians were assigned space at the far end of the courtyard, as it was their preference to sleep in their usual way of travel – all melded together as one body around a small fire. Men roomed with men and women with women until she came to Leah and Chris, who were the odd man and woman out.

"You, Beloveds, will be together in the room above the kitchen," she told them, pointing to a balcony overhead. It was very nearly an order.

Chris moved behind Leah to hold her in his arms. "I really like this place, Mate," he whispered in her ear.

"Well, this will be interesting," she whispered back.

Sister Sarah announced that they would meet again in the courtyard when the Sun sank behind the mountains to the west. At that time, they would begin their evening together. She advised them to rest or meditate until they were called, for it would be a long evening. Having carried nothing with them, save sword and scepter, the group found their rooms with ease, grateful for a chance to restore themselves.

Chris and Leah walked up the stairs at the side of a large kitchen onto the balcony overlooking the courtyard. Facing the courtyard, the door was almost hidden behind flowering vines and foliage. The swaying leaves of a palm shaded two chairs that sat where the balcony joined a high neighboring wall. Between the chairs, a low table held a tea service for two. Leah inspected the teapot, calling back to Chris who was trying to understand the latch on the door.

"Care for some coca tea, Darling?" she asked.

"Maybe later, Leah," he replied, intensely focused on the latch. "We have to solve the puzzle of the door latch before we have a room."

Leah started towards the door as he solved the puzzle. "Ah, there we go," he said, triumphantly. "How very clever of our hosts," he laughed peering around to see if the other brothers and sisters were challenged as he had been. With a good view of the courtyard, they saw a fair number of their associates fixated upon their door latches.

Leah laughed. "A hostel befitting wizards, wouldn't you say?"

"So it seems, Leah," he agreed.

"Let's explore the room, Chris. This could be a surprisingly good time."

After removing their dusty boots and socks, Chris took her by the arm, steering her into the room. The whitewashed walls were filled with niches holding golden statues. Leah walked to the nearest niche to look closely at the gold work. "Chris, these are Inca idols!" she exclaimed. "This is amazing."

Slowly they walked from one niche to the other, receiving a blessing from each of the relics they encountered. It was as if they were living beings rather than golden statues. More of a personal temple, the room was clearly meant for meditative pursuits and spiritual gatherings, not social activities. Colorful woven cushions filled up window seats splashed with sunlight, while the light wood floor reflected rainbows of light from crystals hanging in the windows.

"It is magical in here, Chris. I feel the presence of the Masters in this room."

"Where did Sister Sarah say we were?" he asked, setting the golden scepter on one of the tables. He massaged her shoulders while she drank rainbow light into her eyes.

"The Valley of the Blue Moon, Darling," she replied.

"Well where is that exactly?" he asked. "You seem to be the one who has been here before."

"I think we are still in Peru. I have journeyed to this place through the portal of Aramu Muru at Titicaca Lake, but you know, she is right. I have also lived lifetimes here in the temples and community. I have always loved it here. There is such peace."

"You're right, Leah. There is peace. Shall we explore further?" he asked, nodding towards a pair of double doors on the interior wall.

"Oh sure. I suppose there is more."

"I hope there is more. I fully appreciate this room, but doubt I can get any rest in the frequency here."

"Maybe we don't need to rest – ever again," she offered, dreamily.

"That could very well be true, Leah," he replied, his crooked grin spreading across his face. "But what if I choose to rest – for the simple pleasure of holding you close."

"Do you think that's allowed?" she asked, feigning innocence.

Reaching the door, he turned around and held her by the shoulders in front of him. "I think it's the law," he said, seriously.

"The law! What are you talking about?" she asked, laughing.

"It's the Law of Attraction - you know, Universal Law. There are higher forces at work here. Therefore we are given a room together," he teased with a charming smile.

"Then I would caution you to expect a test," she suggested.

"Help me with this latch, Wonder Woman," he laughed, turning his attention to the puzzle on the door. "We will meet whatever awaits us as magicians and warriors."

Leah looked over the lock. It was similar to a three-dimensional moving parts puzzle she had had as a youngster. However this one was profoundly more complicated than that puzzle because it had a Fourth Dimension, time. The sequence of the puzzle movement had a cadence.

"A bit symphonic, wouldn't you say?" she asked, peering intently at the latch.

"Interesting observation, Mate. Would you care to give it a go?"

"I could try," she said, taking the latch in her hand while she closed her eyes.

"What are you doing, Mate?" he asked, impatient for her to start the movement.

"I am listening – both to the symphony and to this man who keeps distracting me," she replied, elbowing him slightly.

"Okay, go for it," he challenged falling silent.

She listened further then suddenly began moving the puzzle pieces while singing the music held within them. It was remarkable for Chris to observe her flying fingers at the same time he was hearing the strange sound of the puzzle key. In a burst of light, the puzzle gave way, freeing the latch to open.

"After you, Wiz," she said, triumphant.

"I say we open the doors together, Leah," he replied, in frank amazement of her magic.

"Very well, on the count of three then," she said, taking the left latch as he took the right.

As soon as the doors cracked open, an energy drew them gently but steadily into the room. Light entered the room from a large window above a window seat, which was piled high with soft violet cushions. In the center of the room was a canopy bed with linens and pillows in muted shades of violet, blue-violet and rose with ivory. Fresh lavender roses filled the center of a sheer canopy, the ivory fabric of which fastened to the posts then fell gracefully to the floor. Large tiles of lavender and ivory ceramic checkered the floor, while ivory porcelain vases of violet and pink roses appeared everywhere - on the floor, pedestals and the tables near the bed.

The bed itself was of delicately carved wood that had been rubbed with a white wash. Candles for nighttime were plentiful – all scented with the oil of rose. Leah wept. Chris, close to tears himself, drew her into his arms.

"Someone really loves us, Darling," he whispered in her ear.

"It touches my heart to be honored in this way," she replied, when able to speak. "It seems sacred – beyond words."

"You are right, Leah. I am glad it was your magic that opened the door. This is a temple of the Divine Feminine," he said, stroking her hair. "The Mission aside, I wonder - was it holding the dream of you in my heart all my life that has brought me to this place with you?" he asked again, wiping the tears from her cheeks. Chris bent to kiss her, drawing her fully to him. He felt their fields merge then realized he was rapidly losing himself to her feminine power. He withdrew suddenly, holding her at arm's length. "Let's go have that tea, Love," he suggested briskly. "There are a few things I need to sort out."

Leah was a little surprised, though she had been drawn to Chris more intensely than she could remember. "Of course, Darling," she replied, agreeably but with a quizzical expression. "What is the matter, Chris?"

"I'll explain it over tea – on the balcony. Come along, Love, I need to move outside the energies in this room," he said, grasping her arm to steer her outside.

She gazed longingly at the room while being led from it and through the meditation room to the balcony. When they were seated, with teacups in hand, Chris took a deep breath and tried to explain his behavior.

"Let me see - where to begin," he faltered. "This is a magical place."

"No argument there darling," she agreed, smiling.

"Right," he replied, collecting his thoughts and deepest feelings. "Leah, I understand the nature of our love. My longing to merge with you does not come from my desire body alone, but the deep longing of my soul. It is cosmic in its nature – our love. Agreed?"

"It seems to be so, Chris," she replied. "Continue."

"In that room, with the simple act of coming together to share a kiss, I felt my whole being surrender to you – no, it was being consumed by you. It is a deeply held collective fear of men that we will lose ourselves to the feminine. Even with that understanding, I cannot believe that it is wise to willingly do so – especially in light of the Mission."

"I should think not!" she replied with surprise. "Surely you don't think I consciously tried to devour you?"

"Not at all, Leah," he replied, touching her knee." I think we had come under the influence of a charm or spell within the room."

"Do you think it is a test, or a trap?" she asked, setting her teacup down gingerly in its saucer. Leah leaned forward in her chair to look in his eyes.

"At the very least. It reminds me of the Siege Perilous."

"Which is?" she queried.

"In the tales of the Grail Knights, it is the thirteenth seat at the Round Table – the seat where only the man worthy of the Grail can sit. To sit there you must fight the well-armed knight – sounds to me like the ego and the desires that drive it. To be worthy of the Grail, you must live life authentically – otherwise, your life is the Wasteland."

"Translate that to our experience if you will, Love," she asked, taking up her teacup once again.

"Leah, if I am to be with you in that room or in this human life, it must be as the Grail Knight who serves the feminine without losing his soul to it. I must move from my heart and at the same time from my essence, the part of me uninformed by life. For me, for any man, this is a difficult test."

"What can I do to help, Darling? I don't fancy sleeping in these chairs," she asked, sincerely.

"Nothing, Leah. You are absolutely, exquisitely perfect as you are. It is I who must do some work here. We will try it again in a few minutes. Perhaps having the cognitive piece of the puzzle will help me. Hold space for me, just a moment, while I search myself."

She finished her tea while Chris moved deep within his consciousness. Literally this was his first challenge of the trip. He saw, within his field, the longing for Union. Aware that this ancient longing originated from the soul's experience of separation from God, he knew it truly could be healed through Union with another who, in her essence, was God. Surrender was necessary - consumption by the other was not.

This longing was not something superficial but existed in all humans at a deep cellular and molecular level.

If he were meeting Leah in a room of the Divine Masculine, she would be the one put to the test – but hadn't her life as a woman tested her ability to hold her power in a masculine world? He was the one in need of testing.

Chris realized that he was being called upon to summon forth a more subtle power than he had ever accessed before. Surely it was there because the test was at hand. He asked for it - intended that it enter his field – and a surge of energy charged his heart. Of course! He recognized this as a fundamental Initiation of the Beloved. If the two maintained sovereignty so that the whole might create itself from a place of equality it would be the highest form of union. Then the two would dissolve into the one - at least momentarily.

"All right, Leah," he sighed. "Let's try it again."

"Are you sure?" she asked, reaching out to touch his arm.

"How can one be sure with love or magic, My Dear?" he replied, with the slightest smile. "All we can do is try again."

"Very well, lead the way," she said, rising to her feet. "Maybe if we master the room, we will find a place to wash up beyond it."

"I admire your practicality – no question about who's being tested here," he laughed as she pulled him up.

Arms entwined, they walked through the meditation room again, approaching the open doors of the magical bedroom. A sweet breeze was blowing the scent of roses through the open windows as they entered the violet room. Chris was acutely aware of his field, detecting a subtle vortex of energy as they passed through the doors. Slowly, they circled the bed and came to stand at its foot.

"So far, so good," he breathed, sensing the energies around them. He took her into his arms, lifting her chin to kiss her lips. He willed his field to maintain its sovereignty, kissing her from a place of greater consciousness than he thought possible, then he felt the pull on his field as the desire deepened, accompanied by the subtle fear of self-annihilation. He opened his eyes as Leah opened hers – and within her eyes he saw God.

Immediately, the fear vanished and he was thrust into his own feminine, which filled him with the need to devour. It was as if he were Mother Earth herself, ready to consume a jungle full of life – as she did every day. Leah felt her own field being sucked into Chris', just as he had felt his field being devoured by hers.

This is all about balance, she thought. It would do no good to try to overpower his feminine with her own. She could summon her masculine and separate herself from him or dominate him, but that would likely require that they be put to the test a third time. Additionally, she understood that Chris likely needed to experience the fullness of the feminine energy.

Leah asked for illumination – a gift of understanding. They were swimming in the ocean of the unknown. Having never experienced love so intense as to be destructive, they would necessarily have to move beyond knowledge and instinct into some soul awareness.

It hit her suddenly – a veritable lightening bolt of realization. Chris felt it move through her and was able to stabilize himself with the energy. Gently drawing away from her, he looked expectantly into her eyes.

"Chris, I know you! I mean I really know you – like inside your cells, inside your mind, inside your soul. It is amazing. I have known you forever. Why else would we have such a struggle holding our fields separate? We are not meant to be separate. We are one."

With Leah's realization they found the perfect balance. "On some level, I have always known that, Leah," he smiled. "I guess we needed you to have that recognition as well in order to come to this balance."

"It's so funny, Chris. After all that we have been through on this journey – all that I have failed to recognize – it comes down to something so simple. I have always known you. I have known myself in your dreams and you in mine. My mind didn't remember but what is an intellect if not an obstacle to true remembrance? We can do this, Darling," she concluded, beaming.

"Thank you for helping me find my balance there, Leah," he said, pushing the unruly hairs back from her face. "You prove yourself to be very perceptive and clever with the energies."

"I pray a lot, Chris," she said, smiling up at him. "Yet I expect we are a good enough match for each other, regardless."

"The question is whether or not we are a match for this room. We haven't tried the other doors, or the bed itself. I am hoping we get some rest."

Leah stood on the toes of her hiking boots and planted a great kiss on his lips. "It's time to do your thing, Darling. Conjure up a pool of steaming hot water for me. Surely, I am a sight for sore eyes," she laughed.

"Rest assured, you are not hurting my eyes," he replied. "But let's do a little more exploring. This room is most intriguing to me."

Together they poked around the room, smelling the roses and admiring the view over the village rooftops from the window.

"Look, Chris, beyond the village," she said pointing towards the mountains. Aren't those the golden doors on the side of the mountain that I spotted from the portal?"

"Quite right, Leah. I imagine we will see them close up before long."

"Oh, I hope so. I know there is something most remarkable behind them," she said, turning away from the window. "Let's leave the bed for now and try those doors on the far wall, Darling."

"I follow your intuition, Mate. Are we up against another puzzle?"

They approached the doors with caution, examining the latch. "No puzzles, Chris. Why don't you open it?" she suggested with a twinkle in her eye.

"I think you should open it," he teased. "You're the one looking for a hot tub."

"As if you wouldn't join me!" she exclaimed, taking the posture of a standoff.

"Well, if that's an invitation, I'd be happy to try the door," he replied, reaching for the latch.

Leah giggled and moved to stand behind him while he opened the door. After pushing down on the lock, Chris let out a low whistle as he peered within the room. "I wish I could take credit for conjuring this, Mate, but it is well beyond my imagination and skill."

"Oh quick, let me see," she cried, peering around his shoulder.

As he pushed the door open, they were bathed in a soft white light. Chris reached over to hold Leah around the waist as they moved into the source of the light. The floor, of pink-veined alabaster, was strewn with rose petals. Alabaster continued up the walls to meet high windows and a ceiling of glass. A small conservatory, the room held flowering vines, tropical trees and plants artfully arranged to create a natural setting. At one end of the room, water trickled down a rock wall into a carved alabaster pool of steaming hot water.

Leah moved beyond the rock wall at the end. "As odd as this sounds, this stone is soft, nurturing. My child feels totally embraced by this room."

Chris let out an appreciative sigh. "I wouldn't venture to guess where they got the alabaster," he said, stroking the velvety surface of the walls.

He watched her with pleasure as she inspected everything with a woman's eye and heart. Coming back to the other end of the room nearer the door, she circled a white table piled high with fruit, then spotted a wardrobe with clean clothing set out for them. "Someone must have called ahead reservations, Darling – and with the correct sizes. It must have been Don Eduardo – he is so good at manifesting," she laughed, touching her ruby ring.

"I wouldn't be a bit surprised," he smiled, plucking a passion fruit from the bowl on the table. Splitting it open, he offered half to Leah who buried her face in it, sucking the succulent seeds and pulp into her mouth. "You do get into it, don't you?" he remarked.

"That is why they named it passion fruit, isn't it?" she said, kissing him with her deliciously slimy lips. Playfully, they began licking each other around the mouth, sharing more passion fruit and laughter. Soon they were undressing each other, tossing their dusty hiking clothes in a basket near the door. Having come so far on the journey in impeccability, lovemaking did not even cross their minds.

They played as children in the hot water, and enjoyed every minute together in the glowing light of mid-afternoon. Feeling clean and renewed, they dried each other, wrapped their hair in the pure ivory towels stacked by the pool, and put on the bathrobes hanging in the wardrobe.

Fully expecting it to challenge them, they approached the bed in silence. Chris motioned for Leah to make the first move with the bed. She reached to remove a few pillows, but withdrew.

"Darling, why do I expect this bed to be full of snakes or little dragons or bugs?" she asked, looking for some assurance of safety.

"Too many movies, Mate. If anything, we will be confronted and tested with energy, but we already put an enormous piece in place. I say we deserve a rest, and let's go for it." Chris moved through the suite of rooms, shutting the doors. He returned to help Leah with the pillows and covers from the other side of the bed.

"Okay," she sighed, pulling a couple of pillows off the bed. "I know perfectly well that this is the work of the Masters and not any black magicians. This valley is about white magic after all."

"Exactly," he replied, pulling the covers back. They laid towels on their pillows to dry their hair, then dropped their robes on the tile floor and slipped beneath the silken linens.

Staring up at the canopy full of violet roses, Leah grasped Chris' hand and drew it to her lips. "I am sure we are in a hidden valley within the Cordellera Real, Darling – north of Titicaca Lake. In this stillness I feel near to the great Disc of the Sun."

"I have heard of such a place. Perhaps we will all be informed this evening. It seems a shame to shut our eyes to this wonder, but I am suddenly exhausted."

"So am I. Maybe the spell of the bed is deep and replenishing rest," she offered.

"I have no doubt," he whispered drifting off to sleep.

Listening to his steady breathing put Leah in a trancelike state that led her into dreams of deep remembrance. She awoke to the sound of bells – a clarion call to assemble. Finding herself wrapped in Chris' arms, warm, secure and deeply aroused, she willed the bells to be silent.

"It won't work," he whispered in her ear.

She chuckled. "It was worth a try, Darling. This is vastly more delicious than I had imagined."

"Is it now?" he teased, stroking her legs. "Well, I guess you are right. It is delicious." He nuzzled into her neck with kisses and drew her around to face him. On the verge of indulging their desire bodies, there was a gentle but persistent knock on the outer door. Groaning, Chris sat up on the edge of the bed. "Our Guardian Angels again," he sighed, throwing his robe on as he headed for the meditation room.

Leah was left trying to catch her breath – a few tears springing from her eyes. She tried to focus on the roses overhead while her breathing slowed. Chris had closed the bedroom door, making it impossible for her to hear him converse with whoever was at the door. He returned in a few moments with white garments draped over his arms.

"Party clothes!" he announced. He hung them in the bathroom wardrobe, and returned to sit on her side of the bed. Chris leaned over and kissed the tip of her very suntanned nose. "How long since you've had sex?" he asked, casually.

"Interesting question, Beloved," she replied, with a frown. "What if I can't remember?"

"Then you can't remember."

"And you?" she asked.

"I remember," he replied, looking absently out the window. "Though it was not memorable, it is still in my memory – like a ritual ending. I wonder what we will do to each other when we finally get the opportunity?"

"I would guess a complete meltdown or spontaneous combustion – at the very least," she laughed.

He was relieved to see her in good humor and vowed to watch himself for the duration of the Mission. He could not be certain that they would ever have that time together, but there was no harm in dreaming of it. "We have until the Sun sinks behind that mountain to ready ourselves for the festivities," he told her, glancing towards the window again.

"I adore this approach to time. Chris, I must tell you that I dreamed of being here before, many times. I am excited to see what they will show us tonight and tomorrow. Do you have a sense of what we will be doing?"

"Tonight, we begin a weaving with the people here," he replied. "They are our brothers and sisters as well as our hosts. Tomorrow is the alignment. Undoubtedly, we will be in the right place at the right time, with the right guidance. We would not be here if it were not part of the Mission."

"I agree. My dreaming suggests to me that there are many portals, which could be accessed here. Our hosts seemed to know we were coming. Perhaps they have received orders from a higher plane as well. If I am correct, this is the valley where Aramu Muru established his monasteries and scriptorium on the outer plane. That makes it a place of the Kumaras."

"Then we are in the right place, My Love. We await the great Dragon Lords!" he added in his wizard's voice.

"Geez, Chris!" she cried, drawing the covers up to her chin. "I feel like such a neophyte – no, a chicken - a wimp! Sometimes you give me the willies."

"That is the paradox, Mate. One minute it's the willies and the next it's carnal desire. You have touched on the core of the magus. Mark my word, Leah, before this Mission is over, you will know, love, and accept your dragon nature."

Shivering from the chills that ran up her spine, Leah let his words sink into her consciousness without resistance. "Am I Demetri's second dragon?" she asked, wide-eyed.

"He knows you are, Leah," he answered. Then leaning close to her face, his eyes popping, he whispered, "one day you will pluck out your own dragon's tooth. Mind you, their breath is dreadful!"

Leah screamed, hiding her face under the covers. His laughter followed him as he headed out towards the balcony again in search of hot tea. As he suspected, a renewed pot of coca tea sat on the table with clean cups. Pouring two cups, he returned to find Leah wrapped in her robe, inspecting the garments in the wardrobe.

"Thank you, My Lord," she said, with a slight bow while accepting the cup of tea.

"No trouble at all," he replied. "What have we here?"

"Well, I am not sure who is supposed to wear what, but one is a long linen dress and the other pants and a top," she said, laughing.

"I don't think I've worn white since my own christening," he said, laughing. "But, when in Rome.... I think mine is the dress. Look, it's too long for you."

"You're right, Chris," she giggled. "The pants and top would fit me. Look, here is a sash for your dress," she added, holding up a violet and purple band of woven fiber. "It is really quite handsome."

"This is a first - but no problem. Mukda and Ramandi dress like this all the time," he laughed. "I wonder if you're supposed to wear your jocks?" he added, sending Leah into peels of laughter.

Leah put on the slender pants and matching sleeveless top of white silk-like fabric. Simple woven sandals lay in the wardrobe for both of them. Chris' robe was also silk-like, simple, but quite striking with the sash. She slipped Inkari's breastplate over his head, then put on Qoyari's pendant of the Sun and Moon around her own neck. They brushed each other's hair while sipping tea, washed their faces and looked at each other in the mirror.

"We look much more like angels than dragons, Darling," she mused.

"It's not really me," he smiled, "but it will do for one night."

"How can you be sure it's for one night, Chris?" she challenged. "We could be here for ages."

"No we can't," he said, feigning shock. "We have a date in Bali, remember? And what about that hotel in Lima?" Then, holding the bathroom door for her he beckoned to her. "Come, My Angel, let's enjoy the night."

From their balcony, they could see brothers and sisters milling around the courtyard in their white garb. All of the men were in the long gowns with sashes while the women wore the pants. The Indians were permitted their native dress, as were the natives who lived in the valley. As the group checked in with each other,

Chris and Leah discovered that all the rooms were as beautiful as their own. They were all well rested and in a jovial mode.

Several of the welcoming committee came to lead them out of their complex back toward the central plaza. Sister Sarah joined them on the plaza and walked with the group to the second temple at the far end of the plaza. She explained that the temple adjoining their lodging was the Temple of Life. There, they would be returning in a short while to join the brothers and sisters in feast and dance. First, they would visit the Temple of Records, where she would introduce them to their community's purpose and ways.

After climbing the many stairs to the temple entrance, they were led inside to a meeting room where they could sit together in circle. When all were seated, Sister Sarah began her introductory talk. She spoke with authority from a place of passion. Clearly she was meant to live in this valley. Each person in their community was free to leave at any time, though bound to secrecy regarding the community and the hidden entrances to the valley.

"This is the Valley of the Blue Moon," she said. "We are an outer retreat of the Great Solar Brotherhood. We practice the Essene Way. We eat only organic, living food, do not partake of addictive substance and dedicate our lives to the service of the Truth. There are certain records that we transcribe and prepare to offer to the outside world as testimonies of Truth.

"The deepest-held Truths and ancient records are kept at the inner retreat. I do not know if your group will visit that retreat. It is the decision of the Masters. You are an honored group amongst the brotherhood, so it is quite likely that you will see it. There are a number of inner retreats around the Earth, and many outer retreats where men and women such as you can come to study, meditate and be of service.

"You are our guests. Do not hesitate to ask for anything within our means. The Masters have guided us in preparing your way. We do not know your Mission but do know that it is important. Our astronomers have been tracking the alignment and would eagerly share any and all information about it with you. They would also like to have input from those of you with that knowledge.

"I would like to take you on a tour of the scriptorium - the place where the records are continually rewritten to keep them alive and to educate those who are writing, and where the teachings are prepared for the outer world. We will not tour the Abbey, the place where those dedicated to meditation and enlightenment live, but we will walk by it as we end our tour. Aramu Muru, the last of the Elder Race to leave the Earth, founded the Abbey and this entire complex within the valley.

"The Valley of the Blue Moon is hidden within the Cordillera Real of the Andes north of Titicaca Lake. You have arrived through an interdimensional portal. Another of these exists beyond Puno, near the border of Bolivia. Believe me, yours was the easy way to get here." The group appreciated her humor; they hadn't thought it was quite as easy as she imagined.

"There is another entrance to the valley," she continued, "over many treacherous mountain passes. It is usually impassable, but the weather has been dry early this year and the way is not life threatening at this time. However, it is a long journey. Usually we can make this journey from June to August – a good time to travel the mountain passes of Peru.

"After our tour, we will go to the Temple of Life, where there will be a dinner buffet. Our people would like to share their arts with you through music, dance, light and sound. We ask that you make yourselves at home here. Ask us anything. Be curious. We love to share.

"In the morning, we will have a tour through the countryside to show you the way we grow our food, to introduce you to some of the Indian people here, and to visit some spectacular waterfalls. We will end at the Temple of the Sun, where you will be shown the temple room and the Disc of the Sun. This is not the original Disc of the Sun but an instrument of healing and vibrational attunement, like a magical gong.

"You will return to this temple late in the afternoon at the request of the Masters. I assume that your work will commence at that time, since the alignment begins around sundown. I am sure you are all aware that we are within the range of the alignment now, and will be for a day after the exact alignment also.

"I should think you will have three or four hours to rest after lunch and before your evening work. I invite any questions you might have – and hope that you will share with us a little information about who you are and why you are all together."

Jacques asked who, exactly, the Masters were who had given them their instructions regarding their group. She told them that Beloved Saint Germain, Lord Sananda Kumara and Lord Aramu Muru had contacted their oracles, thus far. She commended the group for drawing the attention of energies high and pure. Demetri elicited a good laugh from the group and their guide when he asked if they would be spending the next day in the white robes. She assured them that the clothes they arrived in were presently being cleaned and prepared for their day tomorrow. With a humorous flourish, he bestowed on Sister Sarah the blessing of Saint John.

She interrogated them about the Order of the Ruby, the women dreamers, the tribe of Don Eduardo and Doña Felicia, and life in the outside world. The group session went on several hours before she led them through the record and transcribing rooms. They were able to pull volumes off the shelves and read ancient words with true power. Their astronomers were waiting in another building to speak with them about the stars, the alignment and the signs read in the movement of the galaxies.

For those uninterested in the astronomy, their guide took them to a museum of artifacts from the Inca and pre-Inca people, the great civilizations of Mu and Paititi. Leah would not have missed it for the world. Golden images from the old lands activated cellular memory in many of them. Fortunately, the astronomically inclined members of the group caught up with them for a shorter version of the tour.

On their way back to the plaza, they passed the Abbey where monks dedicated to *The Way* practiced daily prayer and refinement of the physical form. It was a beautiful building with an air of serenity about it. The Temple of Life, on the plaza, was a great gathering place of the community. Apparently, celebrations were held there according to the cycles of the Moon and Sun.

This night, the entire community was present to welcome and entertain their guests. The community was ruled by a rotating Council of Elders that greeted the group at the front entrance. The food was healthy, tasty and very much appreciated by the group, who had had only fruit to eat since their big feast within the mountain. When all were satisfied, the food was taken away and the entertainment began. Truly inspiring, the music took them into transcendent places, which soothed the soul and relaxed the body. Leah found it difficult to stay conscious – as if she w⸢

being seduced into Dreamtime. She remembered having lived this way in many lifetimes, but felt strongly that her place was in the outer world now.

Crawling into bed exhausted for the second time in one day, Leah and Chris cuddled up to say good night. "Darling, isn't it strange that there are no children in the community here?" she asked.

"Apparently new members come from the outside," he replied. "One of the council brothers told me they were vowed celibates."

"Well, no wonder I fit in so well!" she teased.

"I wouldn't last two days in this place," he confided, with a smile. "I don't reckon I had any past lives here."

"Probably not," she agreed. "Can I ask you something, Darling?"

"Anything – though I can't promise an answer."

She propped herself up on her elbow to look in his eyes. "I am curious about my experience of Oneness with you. I feel it still and don't think it will ever leave me."

"It won't. Once we become conscious of such high vibrational realization, it cannot leave us."

"I'm so grateful, Chris. I know so many people searching for their Twin Ray - a deep desire to manifest the unmanifested I suppose - to feel complete. Yet, here we are in oneness and both manifested in form. It is a mystery to me."

Why don't we ask for help in our Dreamtime? If we find ourselves in the ashram of Lord Sananda tonight, we can ask about this simple but mysterious dilemma," he concluded, drawing her lips to his. They were careful to keep their affection on the surface and were soon soundly asleep in each other's arms.

Leah's dreams took her anywhere but the ashram of Lord Sananda. She found herself confronted by a sinister but invisible force. Furious that she could not materialize the nature of the aggression towards her, she awoke suddenly to the moonlit room.

Having released her to fight her nocturnal battle, Chris was sleeping on his side facing the window. Leah wandered into the bathroom. Then, wrapping herself up in her robe, she sat on the window seat to contemplate the night sky. As her racing heart stilled, she began to see strange lights in the sky. Red, green and blue, they were darting above the valley and beyond the peaks of the Royal Range. Though never one to see unidentified craft, she firmly believed that a space alliance existed as well as a force that opposed it.

"Perhaps this dimension is more open to the cosmic?" she pondered, as she watched the light.

Suddenly, the blue-lit craft darted right down into the village, beaming lights on the buildings of the plaza. "Chris!" she cried out, " Quick, come see this!"

He opened an eye to see her plastered against the window, wide-eyed and holding her heart. Alert to an alien energy, he bolted from the bed, grabbing his robe from the floor.

"What do you see, Mate?" he asked, kneeling on the pillows.

"Look, Chris. These ships have been darting all over the sky and now they are actually snooping around. You do see them, don't you?" She was out-of-breath excited.

"Absolutely, Mate. It does not feel friendly to me. Keep your eye on them and if they bring their searchlights over here, pull those drapes shut, you hear?" he said, on his way to the bathroom.

"Right. What are you doing?"

"I'm going to throw some clothes on and get down to Don Eduardo before they are discovered."

"Okay. Oh, Chris," she cried, "I was having a horrible dream about a conflict with a sinister force. Is this serious?"

"Likely – remember the warnings at the Round Table meeting?"

"How could I forget?" she replied, as he fled the room while zipping up his pants.

"How am I doing for time?" he called to her from the meditation room.

"Be quick, Darling. They are coming towards the Temple of Life."

She watched him run down the stairs, leaping over the last four feet of the banister, and circle around the kitchen to the outside fire where the Indians were sleeping. The ship hovered over the temple and started down their street. She prayed and drew the drapes together, keeping one eye on the lookout. Leah exercised caution without fear, and wrapped a cloak of invisibility around her field.

Chris was doing the same as he sped around the kitchen to the fire. He found Don Eduardo, Doña Felicia, Doña Lucia and Margarita in a huddle, leaning against the wall of the courtyard. He shook Eduardo's shoulders and the whole lot of them awoke at once.

"Visitors!" he said, in Quechua, pointing to the sky. By that time, the searchlight was beginning to cast itself into the courtyard. They roused themselves quickly, dragging their woven bundles with them as they followed Chris into the shadows between the kitchen and the wall of the complex. Other than the Indians, there was no outside evidence that their group was in the complex. The rooms of the rest of the group faced each other in a sheltered courtyard. It was likely that they had drawn their drapes for privacy, but the foliage and porch roofs protected them from the invasive light, anyway.

Don Eduardo and Chris threw a shield of protection over the complex, making it safe to speak. They were in agreement that the energies of the craft were invasive and sinister just as Leah had suspected. They watched the light flood the complex, illuminating the place where they had been sleeping. Don Eduardo placed his hand on Chris' arm in gratitude.

"You can thank Leah, *Wayki*," he whispered. "Dreams of sinister forces awakened her so that she sighted these ships. I was as sound asleep as you were."

Don Eduardo chuckled. "It is a good thing you have this woman protecting you, *Wayki*."

Chris laughed softly - wondering what Leah was up to at the moment.

When the light had hit her window, Leah removed herself from the window seat. The glass roof of the bathroom was flooded with light, as was the meditation room. Being a practical woman, she slid back into bed and pulled the covers over her head. This was exactly where Chris found her a half-hour later when he returned.

The Indians had reformed their huddle in the shadows and drifted back to sleep while Leah and Chris discussed the strange occurrence. In light of her dream, the ship's behavior and the warnings they had received, they agreed that the group should be informed first thing in the morning. A meeting with the community council would be suggested. The presence of the Ruby Order in this valley could easily bring an end to the community's peaceful way of life.

They fell back into an uneasy sleep after checking the skies again for alien craft. All was clear for the moment. The ashram of Lord Sananda was obviously not in the night's game plan. Both of them were in full warrior mode, holding on to each other as allies rather than lovers.

Not long after dawn, Chris gathered the men while Leah woke the women. The Indians were already speaking among themselves. While the group washed and dressed, some cooks arrived on the scene to start tea water and breakfast for the group. They were well into their discussion before breakfast was ready.

First and foremost in everyone's mind, was the Mission. Nothing was to stand in the way of the Mission – even the peaceful life of the valley residents who had received them with open hearts. The community elders were called into their circle, and they too agreed that if the Mission was important enough to draw out the sinister force, it was surely worth a good fight.

Extra guardians were posted at the entrance of the valley through the mountain passes and others would be sent to the two portals – three, actually if they included the Sun Temple. The morning's excursion was modified for the women dreamers, while the Order of the Ruby exercised their gifts to perceive the nature of the sinister force.

Meeting in the meditation room of Chris and Leah's apartment, the Order of the Ruby, seated on pillows in circle, went deep within themselves to search for the Truth and possibility of an impending conflict. For more than an hour, they were silent - meditating, dreaming or flying to search for answers. When all had returned their consciousness to the meditation room, Chris asked them to join him in an open discussion to resolve the situation.

Though dawn had come and gone without incident, Don Eduardo reported an imbalance in energies at the Tres Cruces portal and reentered Dreamtime to remain close to his warriors there. Brian and his warriors were alert but unaware of the energies detected by Don Eduardo.

Leah, drawing on her memories of the valley, had found the entrance of the land trail where the community guardians were gathering. Flying along the trail, to the snow-covered pass just before the valley entrance, she saw a group progressing towards the valley. Experienced mountain travelers, they had crampons strapped to their boots, but did not appear to have bulky weapons or baggage. She flew close to their faces, trying to identify members of the group. They were both Indian and Caucasian.

"I was astounded to see the face of Don Ricardo," she said. Then added, earnestly, "Chris, I am so sorry if the incident at Mistipukara has given us away. Their group energy was decidedly malevolent."

"Don't concern yourself, Leah. It may have helped them locate us, but this initiative is well beyond the capacity of Don Ricardo. How many were in the group?"

"Well, some were clearly porters, but we all know that the porters may be apprentices to the shamans with them. I'd say there were no more than twenty people total."

"All right," Chris said with a grimace. "What else have we got here?"

Demetri spoke up. "I went into the mythic energies and was confronted by reptilians. Obviously we are playing games of light and dark here. There are those who would keep humanity in its deep slumber – enslaved to their negativity. I am not completely sure of their alliances on or off-planet, but I have dealt with their energies previously. Of course, we don't know the nature of our Mission – and neither can they – but they will do what they can to block our efforts to complete this phase of that Mission. That I know."

"I know very well their alliances," Jacques declared. "They are those who seek to control the money in the world and who lust to control the nations of the world, as well. In financial realms, they do have much power. In world government, they have sought powerful alliances, but galactic intervention has kept them from succeeding at their quest by sabotaging those who agree to align with them.

"They have blackmailed many a magician to do their bidding, but they have never infiltrated the Brotherhood of Magi, let alone the Ruby Order. Without fail, they draw to their cause saboteurs, who turn on them as regularly as the Sun comes up. It is the Universal Law of Attraction applied to greed.

"My lineage has regarded them as bungling idiots, but they do have access to power through their alliances. If they somehow managed to coordinate an offensive, it might be a bit troublesome - especially with off-planet assistance. Was anyone able to find out the affiliation of the surveillance team?"

"110Xpl," Chris replied, casually. "It is an insignificant inhabited star on the Milky Way fringe. As a consciousness, the beings of this star are struggling with severely mutated DNA. To save themselves, they contracted with the power-hungry forces of the Taleks who have been banned from the Galactic Federation, and hang out in the Orion wasteland – the sea of in-authenticity. I suspect the Taleks promised them a rich pool of Earth genes."

Leah was looking at him, astounded. "Are you serious, Chris?" she asked in disbelief.

"Of course I am," he assured her. "The Taleks live and breathe separation. They are to separation what the Kumaras are to union. Fear and control are their modus operandi – the 110Xpls are very likely their slaves."

"What has the High Council to say about this?" Leah asked.

"I did pay them a visit," Master Mukda offered, his eyes twinkling. "Chris is correct about the alien ships. In and of themselves, they are harmless, but with Talek alliance – may be trouble. I think we can throw a strong shield over the valley.

"For the Ruby Order, it is most important to see this on the energetic level. I think we all do. However, the High Council pointed out that the alignment itself creates a portal. Earth and most of her solar system are aligning with the Sun and the Great Central Sun. For some it could be a ride out of the Milky Way galaxy – a similar opportunity to the phase shift departure of the Elder Race from the Earth. We can expect some opportunists to be hanging around this part of the galaxy now.

"Aside from that, they would like us to be very sure that we see the greater picture. Something has been set in motion. We have been relatively static, following slowly, but surely, the Divine Plan for this phase of our Mission. No one has provided us with a detailed agenda, road map - nothing. We have followed our hearts to this place.

"Be aware that energy is moving on a larger scale now. This means that the Ruby Order will be set into motion as well. The dark will force the light to move, and the light may become the dark – so what we might regard as opposition could very well be the force that catapults us into our intended Mission. To know that a force approaches us is but the breeze that precedes the eagle. How can we judge the breeze?"

"Are we to take a passive stance?" Peter asked.

"Only if you want to die!" Mukda boomed.

"Just checking," Peter whispered, with a shy smile.

Mukda laughed, his belly shaking uncontrollably. Leah, easily stimulated visually, began laughing at the sight of Master Mukda, and the circle fell into disorder for a few necessary moments. When the building energies were diffused, the meeting continued.

"Are we going to come up with a plan?" Ramandi asked.

"Perhaps we had better," Chris said, sobering up as best he could. "Let me ask Don Eduardo to join us again for the planning sessions." Closing his eyes, Chris slowed his breathing to project his consciousness to the portal at Tres Cruces. He found Don Eduardo's double at the outer portal, where his warriors were obviously preparing to deal with an invisible force of some magnitude. He asked Don Eduardo to return to the meeting for a short while to assist the decision-making process.

Soon Chris' eyes fluttered and opened to watch the return of Don Eduardo's double. The *ylloq'e* stretched his frame slightly as if looking for a good energetic fit then turned his attention to the group.

"*Waykis*, there is a menacing energy hovering around the portal. It does not yet make an advance, but we are mindful of it. I expect sundown to be an opportunity for this force to enter the mountain, but it is already out there. What have you concluded?"

After a short debriefing for Don Eduardo, the group moved into the planning stages of their resistance. It was decided that the rules of the warrior applied on all fronts, so the greatest effort would be made in assisting the self-defeat of the opposition. Beyond that, whatever happened would transpire impeccably, authentically and with a goodly amount of magic. They would need to provoke action before sundown, allowing them to be in the Temple of the Sun for the alignment. As a group, they acknowledged that this opposition could simply be a diversion to keep them from their appointed Mission. No time would be wasted resolving the issue.

The village council was asked to join them before the plan was finalized. It was decided that the most significant number of their group would assist the village guards and volunteers at the entry to the valley from the foot trail. Most of the women would go to that passage to help with placing obstructions in the path and to wall up the entry gate. Small groups would go to the portal entrances to assist the village guards there.

Master Mukda was, in a manner of speaking, to "hold space". With his staff, he would create an energetic bubble over the valley from a hilltop near the lake to ward off the ships from 110Xpl. If a greater challenge presented itself, he promised to think of something.

Don Eduardo, guarded by Doña Felicia, would project his double to the Tres Cruces portal and stay in telepathic communication with Chris. Accompanied by Leah, Demetri and Jacques, Chris would go back through the mountain portal to assist Brian.

Having felt a deep heart connection with Brian, Leah had refused to stay with the women at the passage. Chris had complete confidence in her martial abilities and felt her gifts of moving energy and telepathy would be more than useful to the team. Ramandi, who would be at the Temple of the Sun portal, recommended that Demetri take the Sword of the Master with them into the mountain, sensing the need for its power.

Susmo and Julio trekked up to the portal with Chris, Leah, Demetri and Jacques. They would guard the portal entrance to the valley and await their return. Chris had weighed the risk of being trapped within the mountain against the defense of the round table, the energies they had set there, Brian, and his guardians. In every way, it seemed worth it to take the risk. Leah gave Julio a tender hug and accepted Susmo's puma hold on her shoulders in good humor while they waited for Chris to open the golden doors of the portal on the face of the mountain. When the doors opened into a passageway in response to his magic, the four ruby warriors slipped within it to enter the amethyst room of the round table.

Chris asked Demetri and Jacques to take the places of Mukda and Don Eduardo at the table to stabilize the four directions. The Master's sword was set at an angle before the ruby eyes of the golden skull, and the scepter of Inkari was laid over it to form an X. A shimmering light surrounded them as the ruby rays of the activated skull bathed them.

The group willed themselves to return to Tres Cruces. While the space around them spun into the interdimensional shift, the four warriors closed their eyes and stilled their minds to make a smooth transition. The Valley of the Blue Moon was a Fourth-Dimensional reality accessible to those who were drawn there or, in the case of the opposition, those who knew how to access that reality. To all others, it was invisible. Shifting from Fourth to Third was not a difficult task for these four, but no one wanted to waste one second on technicalities when the true Mission was hours away. It had crossed Leah's mind that the Mission had already begun, for here they were in action. The wheel of yin and yang had been set in motion.

Not having tracked Earth time when they had moved through the reverse shift, the group had no clue when they arrived back at Tres Cruces. In actuality, a great deal had happened while they were making the shift. The group at the city gate had walled in the entrance and had dispersed themselves along the ridge to keep watch and prepare both an avalanche and a cascade of boulders as defense against intrusion. Peter cast a spell of invisibility around the gateway as added protection.

Perhaps sensing the impending arrival of the four ruby warriors, the sinister forces gathering at Tres Cruces had attacked Don Eduardo's men on the outside of the portal. Don Eduardo, as his etheric double, was undetected by the energy but was also unable to assist in the fighting. His men used every tactic they knew to resist the energy invasion, but were knocked out completely. They were still alive. The energy obviously could have killed them, but it had not.

Don Eduardo telepathically informed Chris and his men inside the mountain of the defeat, then used his double to track the source of the energy by flying out on the filaments that accompanied the energy. Meanwhile, the sinister energy prepared to enter the mountain. Brian and the other men were holding their positions with focused intent when the communication from the *ylloq'e* sent the five men at the portal into defensive posture. Brian did not need an explanation, and prepared to hold his position at the hidden passageway against the elusive force.

Leah thought the room would never stop spinning. Her intuition told her that time was of the essence. She communicated this to Chris in a glance, and rose as soon as the energies stabilized and the passageway appeared. Chris took up the Sword of the Master with no objection from Demetri, who preferred to have his hands free to strangle anything in his way. As they headed for the passageway, each warrior projected a bubble of protective light and invisibility around themselves.

The sinister energy entered the mountain as they entered the passageway. It bowled over the five *waykis* at the portal and headed straight for Brian. Brian could see the energy – a churning vortex of darkness – as it threw the men against the amethyst walls. Unaware that the passageway was materializing behind him, he fearlessly projected his bubble of light, trusting that he had enough life force to stop the dark vortex.

Brian's bubble blocked the passageway preventing the ruby warriors from emerging into the outer room of the Brotherhood's Temple. Chris did not want to distract Brian, who was projecting a tremendous light at the vortex. His shield looked flawless, but Chris wondered how long he could resist the energies and whether he or any of them were capable of destroying them.

Don Eduardo had not yet accessed the source of the sinister energy, which left them both vulnerable and without the information necessary to neutralize it with magic. He gave each of the warriors a turn at the head of the passage to see the valiant way Brian was fighting. Leah saw him as pure light – how she might have imagined Michael the Archangel in battle. Jacques had a similar reaction, but Demetri was worried.

Moving them all back into the passage out of earshot, he suggested that they pool their intent, silently asking Brian to physically move enough to let them through. All agreed that it was necessary. With that focused intent, they returned to the end of the passage behind Brian, and waited. Understandably, he was pretty well pinned against the doorway by the energy, but each time he felt a surge of their energy, he would inch along the wall towards the dark energy. Chris pulled his bubble in and popped out first, followed by Leah and the others.

When he saw the extent of the sinister energy, his heart started to pound. Energetically Brian was taking an awful beating, but he wasn't giving ground and he was still conscious. Chris couldn't even tap into his field to monitor his vital force, for fear it would weaken Brian's resistance to the attack.

All four of the ruby warriors were behind Brian, who was unaware of them physically. They jumped when the energy began using sound waves to intensify its attack - no more than a few minutes after they had emerged from the passageway. Brian visibly weakened, which prompted Chris to step forward where he could be seen. Shouting to Brian, he asked permission to enter his bubble. Brian nodded in reply. After he merged, he invited Leah, Demetri and Jacques within the merged bubble to strengthen the resistance. Brian felt the support immediately, but it was too late in coming. His body shook with fatigue and dissipated life force as the four warriors projected their combined field at the vortex.

Advancing on the energy, they were subjected to destabilizing sound waves so strong the amethyst wall behind them began to crack. Brian was on the floor, barely breathing when the energy shifted from a clockwise-attacking vortex to a counterclockwise vortex that sought to consume them. All four of them felt it coming and reversed their fields accordingly, but Brian could not manage the shift. They walked back over his lifeless body to put distance between themselves and the vortex.

Chris was well aware that the sword had no power within the bubble, but he was equally aware that the sword had no power against a nameless, faceless energy. He was not able to articulate his needs to Demetri or Jacques because the sound was so intense, but Leah picked up on it telepathically. She called out to Don Eduardo, asking where he was and what he knew. She let him know that the temple itself was in danger of collapsing – they within it.

Don Eduardo had become quite engrossed in what he was learning and observing – so much so that Leah's plea gave him a start. He'd followed one set of the filaments to a subterranean chamber, thinking it the easiest path to explore. He was certain that the other filaments were going to shoot out into the cosmos leading him to inaccessible or unintelligible information. He was watching a group of conspirators manipulate the energies from, or with, a great crystal. The scene in the temple was projected on the wall of their chamber. Dark ones they were, gleeful over Brian's defeat and ready to use whatever destructive force it took to take the others.

The great *ylloq'e* focused his intent on Leah, and sent her the following message: "I am in the lair of those who would continue to enslave the people of the Earth to their power-hungry governance. I am with the creators of religion, materialism, consumption and the infernal amnesia that keeps mankind powerless. Their affiliations are many, but the Taleks are surely behind the power they are accessing – and more. They are the enemies of freedom. How confident they are that those who would liberate mankind are now within their destructive reach. Leah, they are the enemies of the Master. You may destroy them."

Leah received the message and transmitted it to Chris as she received it. As soon as he received the last sentence, he commanded her to hold the bubble firm, while he withdrew with the sword. She did so without a thought to his safety or their own. Chris popped out of the bubble to their right, instantly retracting his own bubble as he raised the sword to the vortexing energy. Summoning his energetic body with his will, he was able to resist the force that instantly turned on him. However, time was of the essence because those manipulating the energy would be able to counter his force very quickly.

Pointing the sword at the center of the vortex, Chris spoke the mysterious language of the heart with such ferocity that Leah, Demetri and Jacques were put in suspended animation with their breath and hearts still. The vortex stopped and opened at the center, revealing the subterranean chamber, the crystal and those who would destroy the Order of the Ruby. Without the slightest shift of the sword's position, Chris bellowed into the chamber.

"In the name of the Master, I turn your energy upon you. Suffer the fate you would wish on others!" With that, he retracted the sword, then thrust it forward into the heart of the vortex. The sword poured a powerful sapphire light into the dark vortex. The light pierced the crystal in the chamber, and exploded it in a flash of yellow light. As the amethyst temple was cleared of the sinister energy and the warriors were released from their induced state of consciousness, they saw the walls of the subterranean chamber split and collapse, as if a great earthquake had occurred.

Leah looked first to Chris, who was watching the fading vision without allowing the sword to drop. Jacques and Demetri were attending to Brian – looking for a pulse or breath, for his body was lifeless. Kneeling to join the brothers on the floor, Leah sensed consciousness within Brian's field. Suddenly she rose and dashed through the passageway, returning in seconds with the Templar cross. As if the two of them had a single mind, Jacques held out his hand for it as she came to kneel beside Brian again.

The cross was laid upon Brian's chest, and Jacques began to chant the oaths of the Templars in Aramaic. Demetri removed Brian's boots and held his feet while Chris joined them, laying the sword at Brian's head. Chris knelt beside Leah, who was holding Brian's limp left hand. She began to breathe into the palm of his hand, calling his spirit by softly whispering his name.

Brian's eyelids fluttered as the etheric form of Don Eduardo came to hover above his head. His mouth turned up just enough to form a smile, which however weak, radiated light to all the warriors and the old *ylloq'e*. "You honor me in death," he whispered, causing tears to well up in Leah's eyes.

"Dear Brian," she wept, "we are all magicians. Let us bring you back, Beloved."

"I am fulfilled, Leah. I have completed my Mission," he said, in a voice barely audible.

Looking up at Don Eduardo, they all received an affirmation of Brian's statement. "Was it possible for an etheric double to cry?" Leah wondered, looking into the glistening eyes of the *ylloq'e*.

"I understand," she said, stroking Brian's cheek. "Brian, I have been so privileged to have known you and to have watched you come into your power on this journey."

Brian smiled at her then, meeting Chris' eyes, whispered. "What a master you are, My Brother. Did you destroy that evil energy?"

"It is destroyed, My Brother – with everyone's assistance, including yours."

"Can we do anything for you?" Leah asked.

"One thing only," he whispered - his life force waning. "Say good-bye to Natalie for me, Leah. Tell her I was not capable of the love she wanted or deserved in this life. It was not my calling. I have no regret – and neither should she."

"I will tell her, Brian. Natalie will understand. She is a compassionate woman. Can we do anything to make you more comfortable now?"

"Impossible, My Friends. I am held in the Light of God. It is time for me to go. I will ask Don Eduardo to help me on my way – one more time. Please?" he added, looking up at the form of the *ylloq'e*. Then he closed his eyes.

The warriors watched Don Eduardo guide Brian's etheric double through his crown chakra, freeing him from his body. With a trail of higher vibrational energies following them, the two men rose up through the ceiling of the amethyst temple towards the stars. Chris put his arm around Leah, who was caught between the joy and sadness of life and death. Sighing, Jacques withdrew the cross and went with Demetri to check on the condition of the Indians who had been knocked out by the dark energy.

"He's going home, Darling," Leah wept.

"Right you are, Mate," he whispered, "and it's our lot to stay."

When the Indians were revived, Chris materialized the outer portal, sending them out to help their *waykis* who had been hurt on the outside. He felt certain the portal would not be threatened again. The Indians provided him with weavings and wood staffs to fashion a stretcher for Brian's body. The ruby warriors carried the body into the room of the Round Table.

Sealing the passageway at both ends, they lay the body down upon the amethyst floor of the inner chamber. Jacques replaced the Templar cross on the table before his seat and took the Templar cloak to cover Brian. After taking their seats again, Chris united the scepter and the sword with their intent to return to the Valley of the Blue Moon. When the room stopped whirling around them, they rose to leave.

After they emerged onto the terrace, Susmo and Julio took the places of Leah and Chris carrying the stretcher. Susmo was freely weeping at the loss of his friend. Chris brought the Sword of the Master with him as well as the Scepter of Inkari. He and Leah stood for a long time on the edge of the terrace overlooking the valley, watching the Sun sink towards the west. There were no words worth speaking, but the feelings were intense. They offered them to the *Apus, Ñustas* and *Pachamama*. When the group carrying Brian's body neared the clearing at the edge of the village, Chris and Leah started down the path in silence.

Grief and triumph filled the courtyard as stories were recounted and Brian was honored amongst the group. Brian's body would be prepared for cremation by the community – an event that would, out of necessity, take place after the alignment. Don Ricardo and his companions had been turned back through the efforts of those at the city gate and Master Mukda's staff was being guarded by the community to keep the shield in place through the alignment. Don Eduardo was resting, but eager to join them for the evening.

Upon returning to their room, Chris and Leah removed their amulets, leaving them at the bedside. Chris laid the sword and scepter on the bed and joined Leah in a steady shower of hot water. They scrubbed each other vigorously to revive dissipated energy, as there would be no time for rest. She allowed herself a good cry while he held her in his arms then they ate the fruit and salad that had been brought to their room with coca tea.

In the wardrobe, they found fresh clothing. Chris had been left a pair of black pants, a finely woven black shirt, and matching ruby-lined, black cape. Soft black boots were a perfect fit. Leah cracked her first smile when he picked up the sword and slashed a Z in the air. Luckily it did not activate anything in the room.

She was given a floor-length dress of ruby-red velvet. Its plunging neckline was framed nicely with her long blonde hair. Delicate red sandals led her to believe that the rough part of the journey was over. For the second time, they stood before the mirror together, putting on the breastplate of Inkari and the pendant of Qoyari.

Chris stepped behind her, wrapping his arms around her waist and resting his chin on her crown. "Scared?" he asked.

"A little nervous," she admitted. "Chris, what am I doing in this dress? It doesn't seem exactly spiritual – and yet there is this familiarity. Do you sense it?"

"Let's close our eyes and see what we come up with," he suggested.

She leaned back against his chest, surrendering herself to vision. Moving backwards through her life, she searched for the source of the fragmented memory. Her consciousness expanded to a time eight years previous to the present moment. She was in that place between sleeping and waking one morning when she had seen a slender blonde woman wearing the exact ruby-red dress she had on. She strained to see Chris, but the background of her vision had been a blur.

The woman spoke to her in a soft voice, introducing herself as Sanara. There was intense love between them and a similarity that kept Leah wondering for years who Sanara really was. Now she understood.

When she opened her eyes, Chris was gazing at her through the mirror, his eyes ablaze with light. Reflecting back into her eyes, the light activated level of consciousness within her, and her White Heart pulsed a rub had not felt such intense Oneness with Chris, she might have feared l was an unfolding mystery to her, provoking chills and fascination.

"What did you see?" he asked, when the energies were stabilized.

"I journeyed back to a time when I was very different, Darling. I was given a vision of who I am becoming now – a woman named Sanara. Though I did not hold that vision in my consciousness, it guided my unconscious to this moment. Isn't that strange? You know, I think I knew her as a child as well."

"Of course you did, Love," he affirmed. "Tell me what you were like when that vision came to you."

Leah laughed. "A mess! Remember how you told me I would not have wanted to know you in your past - well, same here, Mate. I struggled a lot with my body - pain, food addiction, and menopause. It was a nightmare."

"It sounds like it was a healing crisis, Leah. Was that vision some kind of turning point?"

"It was, Chris. I have never thought of that piece. After that vision of Sanara, I began connecting with people who really could help me. My body was holding old injuries, past-life memory, even collective pain – you name it. Seriously, I wondered if I hadn't bit off more than I could chew in terms of clearing in this lifetime."

"I would argue that idea," he replied. "You seem to have digested it all very nicely." He ran his hands down her back and around to her hips, while grinning at her in the mirror.

"Thank you, Chris," she said, a little embarrassed.

Temple of the Sun

Clarion bells rang from the Temple of Life as Chris and Leah stepped out onto their balcony. Below them, gathered around Don Eduardo and Doña Felicia, were the Brothers of the Ruby, all dressed in black with ruby-lined capes. The Indians were in their native ceremonial dress – also black with red and black woven ponchos or shawls. Leah's dress was close fitting but not restrictive in the skirt, so she kept up nicely with Chris as they closed up their quarters and joined the group below. It was as if each step brought her more and more into her Sanara presence. She found herself capable of receiving the love and appreciation of the brothers in a profoundly more balanced way.

Leaving her to those adoring brothers, Chris took Don Eduardo aside to check on his energy levels. He was also interested in a firsthand appraisal of those misusing the power of the crystal within the subterranean chamber.

Don Eduardo had spent an enormous amount of personal energy projecting his double for an extended time and distance. However, he was the highest *ylloq'e* in the Andes, and knew how to replenish his energies quickly by tapping into Source.

Looking as well as ever to Chris, he spoke of the sinister group within the chamber as agents of the Taleks' Earth initiative. Steeped in separation, their group could not see themselves as part of something greater – a unified whole. Their shortsightedness was fear-based, so fear was what they marketed to those they controlled through their secret governments and banking alliances. Chris knew them well for he had made a study of their organizations, but he had never before been confronted by their ruthless misuse of power.

On a cheerier note, Don Eduardo reported that Brian had willingly become one with the light after moving flawlessly through the *bardos* (the afterlife dimensions in the Tibetan tradition). Chris raised his eyebrows in disbelief, certain that Don

Eduardo had facilitated some part of that scenario of ascension. Don Eduardo grinned sheepishly. "He deserved a conscious death, *Wayki*. Don't you agree?"

"Absolutely. I hope you'll come around to help me when it's my turn to transition," he replied, returning the grin.

"Rubbish!" - or some loose translation of that idea - was all that Don Eduardo had to say. He filled his cheeks with coca leaves indicating that the conversation had ended. Grinning, Chris met him, heart to heart, in sincere gratitude for his magic.

Just then, the women dreamers came as a group through the courtyard to join the others. Wearing the blue-violet robes of the initiated Sapphire Sisterhood, they were joined by the two native women, Doña Lucia and Margarita, in their ceremonial dress. Leah moved to embrace her beloved friends, aware that the loss of Brian would be grieved at the appropriate moment. These women were ready to dream.

The entire group was transported to the Temple of the Sun in a big farm wagon drawn by a team of horses. Colorful cloths had been spread on plank seats, making the cart look festive. In fact, amidst the atmosphere of victory and celebration, Leah was continually reminding herself that some serious work lay ahead. Chris maintained his focus through all manner of distraction, gradually pulling the group energy together into a place of focused power. By the time they entered the golden doors of the Temple of the Sun, the group was moving as one mind – their hearts beating as one heart.

Carved from a massive outcropping of mountain, the temple was warmly lit with sweet smelling beeswax candles. Hanging before a wall of hammered silver was a golden Disc of the Sun. In its center was the *ankh*, ancient symbol of universal life, and above the *ankh*, the all-seeing eye. Not the original Disc of the Sun, this disc was a vibratory instrument used to transcend disease or disorganization in the body. However, it also acted as a tool of dimensional shifting by bringing students of the community into contact with ascended teachers.

On the smooth stone floor, a double circle of cushions - ruby on the inside and sapphire on the outside – allowed them to sit exactly as they had in the Amethyst Temple of the Brotherhood. The temple doors closed as the group arranged themselves on the pillows.

Chris looked across at Leah and felt a chill run up his spine. Unable to take the time to trace the feeling, he was left wondering whether he had had a premonition, a remembrance, or an association. It was just as well to detach from it. Leah was a deep mystery to him – a woman who had denied her self - a queen who ran from her crown.

"May your path be strewn with roses this evening, Beloved Sanara," he said to her, telepathically. Her eyes sparkled in return as she sent her thoughts his way – "My Valiant Knight, may your way be as clear and calm as a mountain lake, your vision as penetrating as an eagle's, and your heart as radiant as the true Disc of the Sun. You, too, are a mystery to me."

Acknowledging her thoughts with the slightest grin, he bowed his head to draw the energies of the group together. When they became still, a small native man came from behind the Disc of the Sun with an array of gong hammers in his hands. He laid them out on a golden table to the side of the Disc, then took a seat on a white cushion beside them. Clad only in loose, white pants that came to his knees, the man wore a white cloth band around his head similar to a dojo headband. Obviously lubricated with special oils, his body was incredibly muscular, yet supple. He sat in complete tranquility, awaiting a signal to bring the disc to life.

"Beloved Brothers and Sisters, " Chris began, opening the circle. "At last we are at the moment of our Mission. Earth is entering the planetary alignment with the Great Central Sun and will remain within that geometry for several hours. We can expect an enormous magnetic pull towards the Central Sun. Our Mission is to utilize that force field to access higher dimensions, but return to complete our Mission on Earth. I wish it were as simple as it sounds.

"Dreamers, Sisters, your time has come. I am not certain how far into the force field you will be able to stretch yourselves, but it is imperative that you stay anchored to the Earth holding the dream of the future – the Golden Cities – in the Earth field. If one of you shatters the dream, we will not be able to access the energies necessary to manifest it.

"The Sun Disc will take you to that frequency, opening the dream to you. Then it is your responsibility to hold that frequency as vision - without wavering. You will know when that frequency arrives because you will be in the Golden Cities.

"The Ruby Order will move within the portal of alignment to our appointment with destiny. Even as we do this we are not separate from the dreamers – we are an extension of their dream. We must co-create the magic of this auspicious time together. Are we clear?"

The women were obviously ready to do their work, and the Ruby Order felt confident in their dreaming power. Doña Felicia announced that her guidance was to stay with the dreamers, a request honored by all of the Ruby Order. If anyone knew her place, it was Doña Felicia. She would strengthen the power of the dreamers with her presence. The Divine Plan would work out the rest.

Chris asked Sheik Fakoum to begin their journey with an invocation of some sort. He chose a poem of Rumi, simple yet profound, and followed with a song of Divine sweetness. As the song ended, the circle drew the shimmering light of his angelic voice around them in a cloak of protection.

One look from Chris to the man who would charm the Disc of the Sun brought him to his feet. He chose a gong hammer with a large, soft sheepskin head and began a subtle calling of the energies. Everyone felt the vibrations moving through their physical and etheric bodies – balancing and clearing energies. When all blockages to that frequency were removed, the Disc player chose a different hammer and began to send vibration through the emotional field. On it went, until their fields were cleared through the Eighth Frequency – their link to the Cosmic.

Finally, he chose an odd spiral-handled hammer and began to dance with the disc, creating an indescribable sound. Those watching him could not tolerate the intense contrast between the physical strain on his body and the transcendent nature of the sound, so they closed their eyes to go within. The dreamers captured the Golden Cities, anchoring the frequency and vision of Fifth Dimension, while the Ruby Order transited through that frequency to a place where the music ceased. Held in a palpable silence until Chris asked them to open their eyes, the group had little awareness of their bodies or the space they had entered.

To their great surprise, they found themselves seated at a round table of translucent gold in soft cushioned chairs of the same opaque metal. Doña Felicia's seat, to Leah's right, was empty and the women dreamers were not present. The floor, high walls and domed ceiling of the windowless temple room appeared to be liquid mother of pearl, with inlaid gold geometry.

Where the Disc of the Sun had been, there now appeared two golden doors framed by an elaborately carved doorway. The golden skull sat in the center of the table, its ruby eyes watching the doors. Don Eduardo knew it was the skull his lineage had safeguarded for so long – safely transported to the higher dimensions.

Chris laid the sword and scepter on the table in front of him, glad to be able to loosen his grip on them for at least a moment. Spared the task of deciding what action to take, he visibly relaxed when the two great golden doors opened. Dressed in a deep blue robe with an emerald cape, a fair-skinned man of incredible stature stood in the doorway. Serpents of solid gold circled his waist as well as his neck and wrists. Wavy blonde hair fell past his shoulders and framed intense but soft eyes of clear blue. Bringing with him a wave of peace and wisdom, he stepped into the room and bowed.

"Brothers and Sister of the Ruby Order, welcome to the inner retreat of the Solar Brotherhood. I am Lord Aramu Muru, your humble servant." He bowed once more and, walking around the table, came to sit between Susmo and Leah in the seat of Doña Felicia. The tall master towered above them all.

"I do not often journey back to this dimension, but have gladly come to assist all of you in your quest. The Ruby Order has been present in the Andes since our migration from Lemuria and, as you know, the lineage of Don Eduardo has safeguarded this golden skull for a very long time. We are happy to receive it into the higher dimensions as Don Eduardo's lineage completes its Mission on the Earth."

Lord Muru bowed to Don Eduardo, who seemed pleased to give up his charge. The skull looked right at home in the center of the table. Then Lord Muru looked to Chris with an enchanting smile. "Lord of the Ruby, I see you have brought your beloved, wearing the red gown of Resurrection. You have chosen an opportune moment in time to attempt a leap of consciousness. I hope all fares well for both of you."

Chris nodded to Lord Muru, then glanced at Leah, who obviously had not understood the meaning of Lord Muru's words. She held her attention remarkably well for one thus challenged. Lord Muru took note of her strength as well as her beauty and laid his hand upon hers in blessing. Leah felt her body levitate from the energies he was gifting her, and grasped the chair with her left hand to stay at the table. Again, the visual effects of her own experience tickled her humor, until Lord Muru, pleased and amused, let go. All of the brothers joined in the laughter, creating a warm and amiable atmosphere for their work.

"Lord of the Ruby," he resumed, "tell me what you know of the Mission at hand."

Chris weighed his words carefully, speaking on behalf of the group. "Lord Muru, we have followed an invisible star looking for the way in which we might serve. Ours is a widespread, elusive brotherhood, not given to organization at any level. For the most part, we are content when left to our individual Missions, meeting each other occasionally in Dreamtime but never really knowing who is embodied and where.

"Here and now, we find ourselves drawn from around the Earth to access the higher dimensions as a group. We conclude that a Mission greater than our individual Missions exists and that we are here to be activated to that greater Mission. As always, we are at the service of the Kumaras, the Solar Brotherhood, the Siriun High Council, the Crystal Council and the Galactic Federation."

"Excellent!" Lord Muru replied. "The Ruby Order has been called upon many times in the long history of the Earth's conscious evolution. It is fitting that the incarnate order be present as she ascends into a place of autonomy.

"I cannot guarantee that your Mission will be without danger or risk. It will likely cause you to access power previously unknown to you. Each of you must become conscious of yourself in all dimensions – at all levels of awareness within God. For as the Earth's people awaken and seek their liberation, that liberation will be opposed by those who would control and enslave – who have done so for too long a time. You have already had an encounter with some of their agents. You were wise to turn their energy back on them. In that way you aligned yourselves with Universal Law and nonaggression.

"A portal is opening between Earth and the Great Central Sun – the Heart of God - at this moment. Time and space will fall away as the force of this attraction dissolves the dimensions that separate us. Many on Earth will feel a quickening in their hearts. You who have conscious hearts will find them ablaze with the Ruby Flame of the Sacred Heart. It will be your teacher, your companion, and your greatest ally at this time of awakening, for as the hearts of liberation quicken, the fearful fist of the opposition will naturally tighten its grasp – how else would this vast an energy move?"

The group was solemn as Lord Muru continued to speak. "You will learn about the roots of this polarity you have just experienced, which clearly exists in the human culture, as we proceed with this meeting. I am here to welcome you and open a few doors on your behalf."

As Lord Muru finished speaking, the liquid mother of pearl wall behind Chris began to melt, revealing an enormous golden Disc of the Sun. Many of the group recognized this disc's similarity to the replicas made of the Disc that had hung in the Qorikancha, the Temple of the Sun, in Cusco when the Incas ruled. The face of the Sun was circled with a band of twelve symbols important in the Inca cosmology. It was, like their table and chairs, an opaque fluid-looking gold – unlike gold they had seen in the outer world.

"Witness the original Disc of the Sun, Brothers and Sister of the Ruby," Lord Muru said. "It is made of transmuted gold, as is this table and your chairs. Its powers were never fully understood by the Incas, for they were under the influence of the same human cultural limitations that still exist today. However, the Elder Race understood the true power of this Disc of the Sun and how to use it, for we were never affected by the great amnesia that swept over the human race. It was through this Disc of the Sun that we, the Elder Race, left the Earth. It cannot be used by those of low frequency or intent to do the same, but know that it is a portal for phase-shifting - moving outside time. That is why we are called the Lords of Time."

Lord Muru rose and walked towards the Sun Disc. "We will use the magic of this disc at this moment of conjunction with the Great Central Sun to bring the higher dimensions to this retreat. Students of the inner retreat are often taught by the masters who use holographic projection to visit here. This auspicious time of alignment affords us the opportunity to expand the range of the disc's portal to the center of the Universe."

Tucking his hands within the folds of his robe, Lord Muru casually circled the table while continuing his discourse to the group. "Beloveds, my contribution to this occasion is the telling of a story. It will help you understand your Mission, which will be given to you by others.

"What I will share with you is knowledge kept within the Brotherhood of the Red Hand, a brotherhood active in the preservation of Truth. I work very closely with this branch of the Solar Brotherhood, whereas your branch works more intimately with Beloved Chohan - Saint Germain, and the Amethystine Order. Now, let me begin my story."

The group shifted their positions slightly as Lord Muru moved about the room. His body posture, facial expressions and gestures brought the story alive for the group. "Perhaps you are aware that there was a time on the Earth when the present madness did not exist," he began. "Legends of Mu abound with descriptions of a peaceful society that lived by Universal Law in a true paradise. That is a Truth. However, that was a long time ago, prior to the immigration of peoples to Mu from beyond the sea.

"In that long-ago time, the people of Mu lived at a much higher frequency than mankind presently lives. They took pleasure in shared experience, the success of another, and the advancement of their society. When I say "took pleasure", I mean exactly that. For example, when they shared experience with one another they actually felt pleasure – a blissful, heartfelt feeling of fulfillment. When one member received an insight, he immediately shared it with others, who experienced it as well. You can see a shadow of this philosophy in the group-oriented eastern religions, but only a shadow for hierarchy replace equality in the east.

"What happened? Who were these people who came to the shores of Mu and destroyed paradise? We must go back further in time. There have been, as you know, many starseedings upon the Earth. The Elder Race, more closely associated with Venus, made an agreement with the Galactic Federation and the Siriun High Council, to prepare Earth for a number of advanced life-form starseedings. The Siriuns had already been experimenting with less complex life forms on Earth.

"We came to Earth traveling through the dimensions without being born or giving birth. In fact, our way of procreating would be inconceivable to those on the Earth. We were not constrained by genetics and the need to mutate to evolve. However, we were aware of that necessity in the human genetic makeup.

"Take note that we were not the only ones aware of it. By the time the Siriuns seeded Mu, they had developed genetics aligned with ascension. In other starseedings, new genetics had to be introduced to realign those lineages with the ascension coding. To upgrade the genetics, the Siriuns and other Starseeders have either used the methods of incarnating new genetics or sending specific mutation-oriented DNA.

"Those other starseedings were exceedingly susceptible to genetic manipulation. Understand that the Lemurians lived every day aligned with Truth and Love. This was not the case elsewhere on the Earth, though the Lemurians established many colonies with that intent.

"Within the Earth sphere, genetics are shifted through mating patterns and mutation. Today, most mutations are accidental - though DNA in the early lineages was not so easily flawed by the environment. The environment supported authenticity of DNA, whereas now it is difficult to withstand the distortions of an environment destroyed by the culture itself. As anyone can see, present human culture is self-destructive at all levels of consciousness including the molecular.

"There are those in the galaxy who saw an opportunity to use humans as slaves to their urges – their addiction to power. Deeply invested in separation, they sought only personal power and control.

"Initially, the population of our galaxy was co-creative, living within the Orion star system, where the initial stargate was located. When the great war of An took place, most of the beings of An took sides.

"Because each human carries a soul memory of this conflict, there is a constant sense of loss, separation and longing that accompanies each incarnating soul on Earth. Obviously this happens to all souls who experienced that war of separation, but on Earth it is particularly powerful because there is loss of memory with embodiment. Each Earth body contains within its physical and etheric form the remnants of prewar identity, the reptilian brain and the wings of the birds – the Dracos and the Akhus. To integrate the two is to move to a place comparable to the Kumara lineage, which never saw the separation of the two tribes.

"The Kumaras declined participation in that conflict – retreating to the planet Venus. When the war was over, many colonies representing both sides migrated to Sirius, Arcturus, the Pleiades, and other stars within the Orion system. The Taleks populated a dark star within the Orion nebula and have, over the cosmic clock of time, aligned themselves with many of reptilian lineages. It is important to understand that neither the reptilians nor the bird tribes, both invested in separation, recognize themselves in the other, but any scientifically informed human knows that the essence of both exist within the human body.

The Kumaras honored the separation which occurred because it has provided lessons of cosmic proportion to all those in the galaxy. Energy moved dramatically, as those souls took one further step of separation from God. Since that time, the Galactic Federation has been formed to unify all members of the galaxy. Of the many populations now present in the Siriun system, the strongest is aligned with the Solar Brotherhood, represented by the Siriun High Council. The Siriuns opened a second stargate within their system that links other Suns in the galaxy, like your Sun, with the Great Central Sun. It is through that stargate that our guests will be with us this day.

"But let me continue my story, as it is relevant to your Mission. The beings of Talek evolved into one of many sinister forces within the galaxy. Luring away some of the most brilliant Siriun genetic engineers, they developed a series of viruses capable of mutating the DNA of all the human starseeds – Siriun and otherwise. These viruses were introduced on Earth through an interdimensional portal in the Middle East. This area has been plagued by invasive energies since that time, because the Taleks have tried to control that portal.

"What did this viral DNA create when it intercalated into the human genome? It created fear and hatred. How could one mutation of the genome create such devastation – and why?

"These viruses, which caused flu-like symptoms, found their way into every cell of the various human life forms. It took a number of cycles of cellular renewal to become completely integrated, but after that event it was passed on to all generations. The mutation soon became part of the human collective experience. It started in the Middle East but eventually penetrated every sector of the Earth, including beloved Mu.

"The mutated gene was critical to the regulation of the human pleasure center. In the space of several generations, humans lost the ability to feel pleasure – true pleasure, as it was known in Mu. Within the collective consciousness, pleasure became like God, a dim memory. Trying to regain the feelings of pleasure lost to this ruthless sabotage of evolution, humans have grown profound desire bodies resulting in addiction to pseudo-pleasurable things, which have momentary gratification. In fact, their appetite for such gratification has clearly become insatiable. Profound frustration has led to hatred. This collective amnesia – the loss of Truth and Love - was the result of intergalactic sabotage. Unfortunately, you have heard only part of my story."

Lord Muru came to sit next to Leah again, fixing his eyes on the golden skull. "Why would any beings do this? What was there to gain? The answer is energy. The sinister forces do not know how to generate their own life force. That ability was lost to them because they abused it. These are the workings of Universal Law. Because of this, they became scavengers of energy throughout the galaxy, exploiting the many ways energy can be obtained.

"To the sinister forces, Earth looked like the answer to all of their energy needs. Humans were not very intelligent creatures, but they were designed to be able to tap into the vast energies of Earth to renew their own life force. Genetic mutation of the pleasure center – the loss of Truth and Love - disempowered humans and left them open to control through fear and hatred.

"The sinister forces feed off the energies generated by fear, drama, killing, manipulation, and hatred – all negative energies. The more they can generate, the more life force they obtain. Often they create holographic inserts of such drama to generate human emotion for their personal use. Illusion or not, these dramatic events in human history have kept the sinister force nourished and increased the depth of amnesia. As you can see, it is an ugly affair.

"Many of you are aware that there are agents of this sinister force on Earth. Four of you recently encountered some of their power. These agents believe they have personal power because the Taleks promised them power. They have a considerable ability to feed off others and create drama with fear and hatred.

"In truth, they are the puppets of those intergalactic forces that would control Earth. These agents created fear-based religion to deepen the amnesia. They infiltrated world governments and have control of world financial systems and produce addictive substances for the human slaves – drugs, casinos, alcohol, cigarettes, pornography, to name but a few. All fear-based systems are agent-directed feeding sources for the negative forces. They wish to control the world.

"In addition to these agents, there are a multitude of human beings who have been further mutated towards certain addictions – one of them being the sucking of energy from others, subtly or otherwise. Being pure slaves of the sinister forces, they are not conscious of their power.

"Those of you at this table were born into Truth, so were not sought after as energy slaves, but you have been born with the basic mutation and the collective hold it has on all cultures. Through discipline, impeccability and alignment with Truth and Love, most of you have overcome the collective control, but the mutation remains. It will be removed during our time together.

"Understand that these forces have no love for Earth. However, her destruction is not their aim either, for that would eliminate a great source of energy feeding for them. If the human population were to awaken from their amnesia and feel once again the beauty of sharing, creating and being together, their source of energy for the sinister force would be cut off. I hope I have accurately depicted the opposition for you."

"All too vividly," Chris thought as a few essential pieces of the puzzle fell into place.

As the group nodded their understanding, Muru leaned forward to complete his discourse. "You might ask what it was like to watch this plague of fear and hatred overtake humanity. Because our race was not dependent on DNA, we were untouched by the viruses. We chose to broaden our Mission to keep the Truth alive on Earth by repeatedly teaching it to the mutated ones and by documenting the Truth for the future. The Siriuns tried to counter the mutation, but it had been designed to be a dominant feature of the human genome and had spread steadily over the planet.

"Most of my race elected a ninety-degree phase shift, and left the Earth through this Disc of the Sun. Feeling that they could be of greater service from the higher dimensions, my fellow Kumaras – consciousness within the Elohim - have ceaselessly worked on behalf of humanity and the Earth. A small group of our race was left on Lemuria. The Motherland of Mu had already broken up - most of it having been swallowed by the sea. I had agreed to stay until the dawn of this new age when so many humans would become spiritually ready to remove their shackles. Countless times, the Kumaras have sent group aspects of themselves to show humanity the way. Individual aspects are incarnate at this time to help humanity prepare for Earth's ascension.

"Those Kumaras who had agreed to stay on Earth worked with the Order of the Red Hand to spirit away the Truth in a multitude of places around the Earth. Some of those records have been destroyed, but many survive to this day and will be revealed when humanity is capable of understanding their true history.

"A small team of Lemurian priest-scientists worked with us to make two great crystals. In those crystals we programmed Truth and Love. A gift for the future, these crystals could open the hearts of those who had, through diligent work, attained an evolved frequency of light. The combination of light and love would create a Master Frequency capable of supporting the excision of the viral DNA from the original mutation.

"Before the final destruction of Lemuria and our migration to the Andes, we flew in our ships to a distant land where one of the crystals was sealed within an enormous freestanding rock. We took the other crystal to the Andes - where it was used within the monasteries of the Solar Brotherhood.

"Regrettably, when my attention was diverted during the establishment of the Inner Retreat, the monastery was infiltrated by the agents of the sinister force and the crystal was stolen. We know that it has been reprogrammed with *false* truth and love to seduce those who acquire light. The crystal has been cloned to create five additional crystals. Lord of the Ruby, we are grateful that one of these was destroyed earlier this day."

Lord Muru bowed towards Chris, eyeing the Sword of the Master, then slowly met the eyes of each member of the Ruby Order. "Those seeking enlightenment had best know the importance of discernment," he said with a sigh. "Take some moments to integrate these truths, discussing them amongst your group. I will return shortly," he added, rising abruptly to leave through the golden doors.

The Ruby Order watched the glistening border of his green cape disappear through the golden doors, then sat looking at each other, a bit bewildered. Leah drummed her fingers on the table absently to break the silence. "We all know he is absolutely right," she said. "I, for one, have been extremely frustrated in my work because even those of tremendous light cannot seem to separate themselves from addictive patterns. Pleasure is a dubious word. It does not belong in any human language."

"Do you believe that a virus could have been constructed to cause such an amnesia, Leah?" Jacques asked.

"I have thought for a long time that certain flu viruses were designed DNA – whether from aliens or our own governments. What a fabulous way to control people. Then you can give them flu shots loaded with whatever you like. Is it possible, scientifically? Indeed. I am a reformed molecular geneticist – a Siriun at heart - and yes, it is possible, Jacques."

She had taken Chris by surprise. "You never told me you were a scientist, Leah," he said.

"An M.D., actually," she said without apology.

"Why didn't you tell me?"

"You never asked, Chris," she offered, then added, with a smile, "technically, I am an M.D. but I was drawn to genetic research. We all have our pasts, Darling."

Master Mukda laughed, tickled to see Chris in a mild state of shock. "You two will have to get to know each other when this part of the Mission is complete. I like your energy together."

"Glad to have your blessing, Immortal Teacher," Chris said, winking at Leah. "You are right, Leah. I never would have thought to ask. Please forgive my reaction."

"It's not important, Chris," she replied. "Tell us, do you know the location of the intact original crystal? What big rock is he talking about?"

"Ayer's Rock - Uluru, of course," he replied. "It wouldn't hurt any of us to show up there for activation. What does anyone know about the four remaining cloned crystals and stolen original?"

Don Eduardo cleared his throat before speaking. "I have had some association with the Order of the Red Hand who have been secretly tracking the copied crystals. Lord Muru must have the latest information about them. The original is deep within the Earth at an enclave of the secret government. Do you think it is part of our Mission to find them?"

"I do," Chris replied. "I think it is no mistake that we have already destroyed one of them. I expect that the cloning is difficult, but it could be done again to create more. The lost original must be found."

The group entered an extended discussion about the secret government and their off-planet alliances. Earth was clearly vulnerable at this time of her ascension into the Fourth Dimension and beyond. Strategies for discovering the whereabouts of the original crystals were bandied about until Chris asked if some of the order would be willing to form an active global team for this part of the Mission. He realized that their time together was drawing to a close, and wished to initiate the energetic commitment to the Mission.

"Count me in, whatever that means," Demetri interjected. "This sounds like my kind of treasure hunt."

Flu Viruses

"Noted," Chris replied, glancing around the circle. "Obviously some of us will be more physically active than others on this aspect of the Mission. If Don Eduardo had not stretched his etheric double about as far as a double could be stretched, we would not all be sitting at this table now."

"True enough," Jacques, offered. "I would be willing to join you. Beloved Saint Germain has been fighting this sinister force for a long time from the ascended state. I am sure he could give us valuable information about the original crystals. There is so much we don't know."

"Let's not dwell on that," Peter said. "I feel it is so important to recognize this genetic flaw in ourselves and truly understand it– especially if it is to be corrected. That way, we will have more compassion for others when the sleeping state becomes a dim memory for us. I will do what I can as an active member."

"I, too, would like to see this change, so count on me," Susmo added. "I see my own patterns and those of my culture. We are emotionally connected, but it evokes drama instead of giving us pleasure."

"On the other hand, my culture is very mental," Peter replied. "Our pattern is to accumulate more knowledge, missing the feelings altogether."

"I see something here," Leah spoke up. "Because of this genetic flaw, we have established a nasty group of filaments in the collective assemblage point. They appear to be connected to our own luminous eggs through the mental and emotional fields. I would instinctively suspect that a neuropeptide gene has been altered. The work of ascension may allow us to sever these collectively driven urges and those personal core beliefs about getting our needs met. Still the defect remains.

"Sorry to be rambling - and, by the way, count me in - but my purpose drives me to help people overcome the amnesia. Our addictions cost us our freedom in every way. That is the whole idea behind drug trafficking, gambling, drinking alcohol, even religion – to use addiction as a means of controlling populations. It is such an enormous waste of life force. I see ways to improve the soul's journey, but I don't see how to remove the flaw in the everyday world." She had spoken passionately with a healthy flush blooming on her cheeks.

"Hopefully we will find the answers you seek as this day unfolds," Lord Muru replied, silently entering the room, his eyes on Leah. "Now, Beloveds, I invite you to step into an adjoining room to take refreshment while we rearrange the seating in this room. We will call you very soon, for the time of alignment is upon us."

Easing themselves out of their golden chairs, the Order of the Ruby followed Lord Muru to a doorway that had been undetectable in the pearl wall. They were ushered into a large room of pink-toned pearl where a banquet table held bowls and plates filled with living food. It felt very grounding to have the opportunity to walk around, chat and enjoy light, vital food and drink. Leah sought out Don Eduardo, eager to give him a hug and share heart space with him. Asking Julio to interpret, Leah asked if he was in communication with Doña Felicia and the dreamers.

"She has witnessed our meeting with Lord Muru, *Wayki*," he replied. "I am not sure how much of our encounter the other women have been able to vision, but they are holding the space for us with amazing intent."

"That is good to hear, Don Eduardo," she said, relieved. Leah could not dissociate herself from the women's Mission. "Regrettably I have not yet learned to be in two places at once," she laughed.

"Soon, *Wayki*, soon," Don Eduardo said using a serious tone. Then he laughed heartily amused at the way in which he had shocked her.

Leah laughed. "At this point, I am willing to believe anything. Julio, you have been very quiet. Are you understanding all that is being said?" she asked.

"Most everything," he replied. "I am wanting very much to be an active part of the Mission, *Madrina* Leah, but I am not sure I will be able to leave Peru."

"If you are supposed to be with us, Julio, it will be so," she answered. "For now, it will be good to finish school and decide what you will do next. If you are needed, the Divine Plan will make a way for you to be there. What do you think about that?"

"You are always right," he replied, a little disappointed. "What will you be doing, *Madrina*?"

"My calendar is very full, *Wayki*. After this journey, I return to my home for a little rest and work at home, then I travel around my country, teaching. When that is finished, I will go home again, then travel to Australia next year."

"Will *Wayki* Chris come with you?" he asked, his eyes filled with love for her.

"Oh no, Julio. Chris has his own life. When I go to Australia next year I will see him there."

"Will it hurt your heart to leave him?"

"I don't think it will, Julio. Just like you, Don Eduardo and Doña Felicia, he will always be in my heart. We will have a wonderful time when we are together and when we are not, we will still have a wonderful time. It is detachment, Beloved One."

Don Eduardo wanted to know what they were discussing, so Julio took the time to tell him. He nodded his head in agreement; understanding what Leah was trying to teach Julio. "We do not know the outcome of this meeting, Julio," the *ylloq'e* said. "We are detached from that as well - even the idea that it will have a happy message for *Pachamama*."

Julio's eyes brightened as Chris joined their group. Chris touched the shoulder of the *ylloq'e* while putting his arm around Leah. He had been speaking with Jacques, Demetri, Susmo and Peter who were all excited about the possibilities of active duty. Moreover, they and the rest of the group were most curious about Lord Muru's plan for the exact alignment.

While they were returning their plates to the table, one of Lord Muru's assistants from the Inner Retreat came into the room bearing eleven crystal glasses of sparkling water on a golden tray. He asked that each member of the group drink fully of the water. It was intended to help them tolerate a very high frequency.

Shining with the radiant energy of the Sun, the water felt tingly as they drank it down. A very pleasant humming energy filled their bodies as well as their fields. The assistant explained that they were now in a unified field of solar energy – an energy that connected all the Suns in the Universe with the Great Central Sun. The assistant excused himself, telling them that Lord Muru would be with them shortly.

No sooner had the assistant disappeared than Lord Muru entered the room - his emerald cape flapping in the breeze he created behind him. Gathering the group together, He announced that the table and seating had been changed in the temple room. Members of the group were to enter the room silently, find their seats and settle themselves quickly. Time was of the essence since the planets, the Sun, and the Great Central Sun were soon to be at their exact conjunction.

Hurrying into the room, the Ruby Order found two semicircular tables of the transmuted gold. Facing each other to form an open circle, the tables were equipped with microphones and headsets at each place. Vases of gold and ruby roses were placed between every other space at the tables. The group found their assigned places at the table facing the Disc of the Sun. Sword and scepter marked the center chair as Chris' seat. Leah was to his right and Master Mukda to his left.

While everyone was getting seated, Lord Muru strode to the entrance door and stood before it. As the room came into attentive silence, he opened the door to a field of radiant violet light. With a brilliant smile on his face, he bowed to the group and announced, "Order of the Ruby, I present to you the Lord of the Amethystine Order, your beloved ascended leader, the Count de Saint Germain."

Leah wondered if everyone's heart was pounding as loudly as her own when Saint Germain emerged from the violet light. She glanced to her right to see the ecstatic face of Jacques as he beheld his teacher.

The Count appeared in full military dress – a deep indigo blue uniform with gold trim and a dashing indigo cape. Of average height, the Master looked to be in his mid-forties - in perfect shape and radiant health. His close-trimmed golden brown beard and mustache framed a narrow face with an aquiline nose and doe-like deep violet eyes.

When the group spontaneously sent forth heart energy, his charismatic response was almost overwhelming. Saint Germain strode over to the table opposite the group and took the seat across from Chris. Towering over him, Aramu Muru sat to the left of Saint Germain. Lord Muru announced that Saint Germain would open the meeting with a discourse after the remainder of the guests had arrived. Presently, all energies were to be focused on the Disc of the Sun as the portal to the Great Central Sun opened.

Fixing their eyes, as well as their intent, on the Solar Disc, the Order of the Ruby witnessed something akin to an ignition of the central face of the Sun. It flamed out yellow-orange then the energy retracted into a swirling mass of light within the disc.

The swirling mass of light suddenly became still, and like clouds at sunset, hung within the disc's center. Four figures appeared to be walking towards them as if emerging from a tunnel filled with yellow-orange clouds. As these figures came towards the disc itself, a golden stream of light emerged from the disc connecting it with the floor.

Single file, the four beings came down the ramp of golden light into the room. Aramu Muru and Saint Germain stood to greet them, while the Order of the Ruby rose out of respect. Clearly alien beings, the four were neither male nor female in their appearance or characteristics. Robed in shimmering silvery blue caped body suits the beings were slight in form, graceful and silent in their movement. Familiar to many in the Ruby Order, their disproportionately large heads had enormous silver eyes that were both kind and luminous. Their leader motioned for all to be seated while they took their places, filling in the chairs to the left of Aramu Muru. Lord Muru introduced them as a delegation from the Siriun High Council.

Attention was, once again, drawn to the Solar Disc, where two more beings approached the room through the portal. Human in appearance, two average-sized men in red robes walked down the golden beam, to be greeted by Saint Germain and Lord Muru. As before, the rest of the table stood in greeting until the two, delegates from the Arcturian Crystal Council, took their seats far to the right of Saint Germain - one of them sitting next to Julio at the left end of the Ruby Order.

With three empty seats remaining, the group turned their attention back to the Sun Disc, where three figures could be seen within the portal. Though entirely different from one another in form, the three aliens were dressed in identical robes of radiant gold-trimmed ivory. Lord Muru introduced them as a delegation from the Galactic Federation, and signaled for all to be seated.

As the group took their seats again, Lord Muru asked each member of the circle to wear the headphones on the table before them. He began speaking into his microphone. Lord Muru explained that the microphone system would allow each contributor's words to be simultaneously deciphered and interpreted into each member's language. Some would be speaking the language of the stars, with references unknown in some cultures. The best possible choice of words would be used to describe such references. He asked each individual at the table to speak into the microphone when using their vocal systems. When all were appropriately equipped, the system was successfully tested and the meeting officially called to order.

Before another word was spoken, a circular piece of the floor opened at the center of their circle. Rising from the cavity within the floor was an elaborate monument of carved amethyst gemstone. At the monument's apex burned the Maxine Flame within a golden, thousand-petaled lotus. Similar to a Masonic stone marker, the monument came to rest with the Maxine Flame at the level of most everyone's heart. Simultaneously, the amorphous center of the Sun Disc stilled itself in the form of a magnificent, winged dragon.

Those of the Ruby Order were grateful to have drunk of the light elixir before moving into the frequency now present in the room. They were alert, completely in the moment, and connected to their Higher Selves.

Not wasting a moment, Saint Germain began his discourse as soon as the monument was in place. Speaking in an authoritative yet soft voice, he was able to pull the filaments of the group together with his first words. "In the presence of the Great Central Sun, there is no separation. Let this spirit of brotherhood, which now unites us; guide the Mission of the Order of the Ruby. You are the Earth-embodied representatives of the highest warrior-magicians within the Brotherhood of the Magi. Your Mission is at hand. You will be hearing from our galactic alliance shortly, but first, let me say a few words about the individual and the Mission.

"You will be called upon to use the full extent of your magic. Circumstances will present themselves to deepen your present magic, thus increasing your power. As you know, any misuse of this power will result in termination of your lifestream, causing physical death. This is standard procedure within the Ruby Order. Each of you agreed to this prior to your present incarnation. Should your Mission be terminated in this way, you will rejoin us on the higher octaves without judgment or recourse. There is no other place in the Universe with greater limitations of consciousness than Earth – and that is a kind way to put it!"

The Ruby Order smiled as he continued. "Lord Muru has briefed you about the nature of human amnesia. When that veil is lifted for you, you will be in the full power of your Mission. I would ask that you have no fear in using your personality on behalf of the Mission. Each of you has embodied with exceedingly charismatic personalities. Use them – do not abuse them. As you know, it is possible to use the ego without attachment to it."

"You are here to help activate, assist, and defend humanity's ascension. This culminates millions of years of work bringing the consciousness of Earth to this threshold. Conscious human evolution has had its ups and downs, and is now a critical factor in Her ascension process. The magi have served this process at the request of and with the direction of the Kumaras, who have guided that evolution of consciousness on Earth since the first starseedings.

"With respect to Lord Muru's discourse previous to this meeting, I reiterated the importance of reversing the viral mutation which has separated humans from their higher bodies. I assure you that I will work closely with each of you as the cloned crystals and the mutated original crystal are retrieved – or destroyed. Clearly an important part of your Mission this crystal retrieval will put you within range of the enemy.

"I say enemy in the human sense, for they are merely God-beings living the most profound separation. Know throughout this Mission that you are a hair's breadth away from being them. Know that at this level of play, light and dark cannot be understood in human terms, and that human conditions can mask friend and foe until betrayal shakes its vicious head in your direction. Be guided by your ruby hearts and the profound intuitive gifts that each of you carries. See through the illusion. There are those who do not comprehend the difference between a reptile and a dragon – do not fall prey to this distortion." Leah and Chris shot quick glances at each other – both had expressions of wonder on their faces.

"Beware the promise of a New World Order and hidden agendas within nations and political alliances. Contemplate often the true nature of freedom. Obviously there is a precise timing to your Mission – certain parts of it need to be in place before you will be able to assist humanity's ascension. When that time comes, all those around the Earth who have been working towards ascension in myriad spiritual practices will have the opportunity to participate in an octave shift to the higher dimensions. If their numbers are great, all of humanity will have the opportunity to join them. This is service in its truest sense. If you do not complete your Mission prior to that time, the opportunity will not materialize.

"Some of you will be working closely with me in America and other democratic countries where foundational concepts of freedom have been implanted and nurtured. Do not be discouraged when you find ignorance, resistance, restriction and corruption in these lands, their peoples and governments. Remember that the phoenix rises from the ashes of destruction to herald a new day. Be surprised at nothing. Separate yourself from drama of any kind. It will poison the Mission. Continue on your personal paths of self-correction. Above all, remember that you have unlimited assistance from the higher realms."

Bowing slightly to the circle, Saint Germain deftly touched the arm of Aramu Muru, signaling the end of his short discourse. The Ruby Order transmuted their disappointment in the brevity of their leader's speech and turned their attention to Lord Muru, who introduced Lord Abatan head of the Siriun High Council. Seated at Lord Muru's left side, Lord Abatan acknowledged his three associates from the council before speaking to the circle.

"I speak on behalf of the entire Siriun High Council," he began, "including Emissaries Kymit, Lhaje and Bakaras, who have accompanied me. We are a council of six - all androgynous leaders of Sirius B. Like all of you, we are members of the Great White Brotherhood – the Brotherhood of the Sun.

"Sirius is the closest Sun to Earth other than her own Sun, and we have had a long-term interest in Earth's well-being. She is unique in her level of darkness as well as her visual splendor and potential. She has been a fertile field for genetic research. I am certain that the delegates of the Galactic Federation will tell you more of Earth's history within the galaxy. I am here to share with you the Siriuns' role in the genetic-based evolution of consciousness on the Earth as it pertains to your Mission."

Lord Abatan's luminous eyes scanned the Ruby Order in a way that activated energy within their bodies. He asked that they tolerate a tingling sensation at the cellular level while the group's DNA was being prepared for a reversal of the mutation. He also asked if anyone in the group would prefer to remain mutated. "It is always your choice," he commented, scanning them once again.

No one declined his offer of freedom from unconscious urges and the awakening of true pleasure within, so he continued. "Before the Kumaras established bases on Earth to hold a life-sustaining polarity, we were called upon to create species to inhabit the planet. It took a long time in Earth years to learn what would and wouldn't thrive on Earth – our goal being a balance between all species and a stabilization of species with their environment.

"For ages, the rest of the galaxy paid little heed to our research because Earth did not hold a very high frequency. Of course, the object of our work with the Kumaras was to elevate that frequency. As part of this collaboration, the human species was developed.

"As you may know, the Siriun Mission is to heal separation. We began our Mission of Union after the Orion War of An. We saw Earth as a child of the Great Central Sun - Source. When the Universe last exhaled, Earth was created and flung out to the edge of the Universe. Few would have the courage, let alone the resources, to elevate her frequency and bring her back to the Heart of the Universe, the Great Central Sun.

"But, for every exhale, there is an inhale. We knew that a day would come when the Great Central Sun would call us all back to the Heart of the Universe. Earth could not be forgotten, lest she compromise our own ability to return. Do you understand that the actions of the smallest aspect affect the whole? One cell in your body refusing to hold higher frequency can deny you ascension. It is true.

"That is how we felt about Earth. We feel that way about the enemies of Earth as well, and all those who would delay or deny the union that exists between the exhalation and the inhalation of the Universe.

"See yourselves in those who would harm the Earth – both those on the Earth and those off the Earth. You have played all of the roles so that you might love the enemy during this Mission. Let love guide your magic. You will activate both sides of this conflict on behalf of the Mission, for all must return to the Heart of the Great Central Sun.

"Encourage humans to understand that their lives, though microscopic, affect Earth's and humanity's ascension. It does matter – every thought, every word and every action - more than they could possibly comprehend.

"After we established a number of human lineages capable of accessing and increasing their own energetic fields – meaning that they had the capacity for self-contained ascension and union with the Source - Earth suddenly was of interest to many in the galaxy. The Pleiadians, the Arcturians and others who saw an opportunity to broaden their experiences in the Universe carried out good-intentioned starseedings.

"At this point you might be wondering where the souls came from for these incarnations in humanoid bodies. For millions of years, the souls of the humanoids we created were individuated forms of the Earth's own soul. They were of the Earth.

"With the new starseedings, souls came to incarnate in new designs of human bodies from other planets, stars – including Sirius, and other solar systems, for the express reason of experiencing life on Earth. These souls of higher frequency were able to incarnate and experience Earth without losing consciousness. The Galactic Federation - the governing body of the galaxy, approved these experiences.

"You can imagine our dismay – our disbelief of the Divine Plan - when beings like the Taleks seduced several of our geneticists to assist in their devious plan. With their viral mutations, the humanoid souls of Earth lost their connection to her – lost their remembrance of pleasure, a natural gift of the Earth. Those who incarnated from the stars and other planets lost consciousness of their origins and became trapped in the cycles of karma as they were forced, like the Earth souls, to concentrate their energies in their desire bodies.

"You might reference this as "the Loss of Paradise", because consciousness and pleasure, Truth and Love, were lost. This was the advent of the misuse of power on Earth to which all incarnate beings are susceptible. It is nothing more than a reflection of the Taleks' own misuse of power. I make an example of the Taleks, but know that there were others who came before and after them with similar intent.

"This enormous cycle is coming to completion, but with considerable resistance. Those invested in separation fear the loss of identity that must come with Divine Union. They cannot see themselves as Source becoming Source. As a result, they have systems in place throughout the Universe which hold a strong field of separation – individuation.

"You have all incarnated in these systems to experience this separation. You, of the Ruby Order, come from mixed lineages dedicated, on soul level, to healing separation. We are asking you to use your magic and love to move energy on Earth for her ascension into autonomy.

"I know it looks bleak when the activities of humanity are assessed, but an underlying commitment of Earth souls towards autonomy is being guided and respected by the Federation and the High Council. If she successfully takes her first step towards Union, our work, that of the Kumaras and many others, will be finished. In doing so, she will shake off the negativity and move into the light.

"I cannot impress you enough with the importance of your Mission. The mutation must be reversed through the collective attainment of Christ Consciousness, and the harmful crystals must be destroyed or deactivated. Further clones cannot be made without the original, making its confiscation of the utmost importance.

"You will each be guided by specific Masters who willingly cross through the veil to assist this Mission. We would ask that you find a way, through your technology, to remain in contact with each other. Four years hence, we will meet with your group again at a location made known to you at that time.

"When the present meeting is concluded, Emissary Lhaje, our senior geneticist, will release a new viral preparation, which contains a gene encoding an enzyme capable of specifically excising the mutation from your DNA. You will experience a mild set of flu symptoms.

"This virus will spread around the planet as you carry it forth mutating all those of a specific frequency. Those who are living in density will appear to be immune to the virus, but it will wait within them for the appropriate frequency of activation.

"You have, in all, twelve strands of DNA carrying genes of varying frequencies. This mutation occurred on the fourth DNA strand, which encodes universal love. It exists at the Fifth-dimensional harmonic – Christ Consciousness. Our new virus with the excision enzyme gene will also intercalate into that strand of DNA. Over time, as people come into their Christ bodies, you will see more and more individuals activate to this consciousness as the DNA mutation reverses. Some of you will play an active role in this activation."

Looking directly at Leah, he said. "Lady of the Ruby, you are quite right to believe that a high-frequency neuropeptide gene was mutated. Having invested many life streams in our laboratories, I appreciate your level of disappointment with those on Earth."

Leah could not resist laughing. "Thank you, Lord Abatan," she spoke into the microphone. "That part of my Earth experience has always been a puzzle to me."

Lord Abatan rose and walked around the table to stand between Chris and Leah. From beneath his cape, he withdrew a golden scepter identical to Inkari's but with the opposite torque in the staff. He laid it in front of Leah, brushing his hand against her cheek as he returned to his seat. Chris reached over to take her hand for a minute, grounding the charge of energy that Lord Abatan had given her. Everyone at the table stared at the scepter, remembering Jacques' remarks about Inkari's scepter. When Lord Abatan reengaged his microphone, he spoke to Leah softly, without his more military style. "Lady of the Ruby, secure this scepter in the Earth where the dragon lines cross - at the place of the Mother Temple."

"Dragons, again," she thought, squeezing Chris' hand. Lord Abatan turned to look at Chris. "Lord of the Ruby, the scepter you hold shall be secured in the Earth at Titicaca Lake, where the dragon lines also cross. Attend to this before leaving the Andes. You will be guided to the spot. With the planting of these scepters, you herald the return of the *wiracochas*, the Shining Beings, to Earth.

"My gratitude to all of you for following the guidance of Don Eduardo, our most revered representative in the Andes, to be at this meeting. Lord Muru, Saint Germain, members of the Galactic Federation and the Crystal Council, that completes our presentation. Thank you for this opportunity to communicate our aspect of the Mission directly to the Ruby Order."

The entire Siriun delegation arose and bowed to the circle. As they took their seats again, the Order of the Ruby arose and bowed to them. Seated once again, Chris took the microphone and thanked them for their timely counsel, then turned the floor over to Lord Muru once again.

"We will now hear from the Arcturian delegation. We have with us two members of the Crystal Council, which forms an arm of the Galactic Federation. Please take the floor, council members."

The council member nearest to Julio turned on his microphone and spoke in a gentle manner. "Thank you, Lord Muru. We are grateful to be included in this momentous meeting. I am Lenpasa and my associate is Abud. We were asked to represent the many intelligences in the galaxy who have had an interest in Earth.

"Like others, we starseeded Earth using DNA engineered from human samplings, and incarnated in human form for a long time. When the mutation occurred, we became trapped in cycles of karma and were forced to earn our ascension just as any Earth-born human.

"Many of us continued to incarnate in hopes of rescuing those who had been trapped and their offspring, but the resulting loss of consciousness caused us to complete our cycles of karma and cease Earth incarnations. Now we are incarnating again to help with the ascension. At this time, those with higher soul consciousness will remember who they are and be of some service to this great Mission.

"We have many regrets from that ancient time of incarnation. Vested with power, we were led to misuse it. Given authority, we learned to control. With wealth, we developed materialism. We became hopelessly self-absorbed.

"It seemed that the mutation amplified in our incarnates but in fact it was the amplitude of our true frequency which intensified all we did or tried to do. You might say we were more intense than most," he offered with a chuckle. "It is easy to see these patterns in your world today, because our genes and the genes of others remained in your gene pools and have distributed themselves in all the cultures.

"We had a very large incarnate population on Atlantis which, originally a Pleiadian project, had become a melting pot of starseedings prior to its demise. Great reptilian forces came to play there with the misuse of power. We have all taken our turns incarnating into those experiences to help us integrate our own light and dark.

"We must not think of the reptilians as something foreign to us. They are a metaphor for our own destructive and indulgent self – the desire-driven incarnate - but also for that group soul longing which inspires us to live for the community. We find them a source of humor too, which is a good thing.

"We are here to warn you of the misuse of power – though your Order truly does not tolerate deviations from impeccability. Control is an obstruction of the Divine Plan and will seriously hinder your Mission, Earth's ascension, and the eventual liberation of all those who have ever had an unconscious incarnation on Earth.

"You have the support of the Galactic Federation because most members represent soul consciousness which has left pieces of itself in the Earth realm. When Earth liberates herself, we all ascend.

"Do you see this paradox? Humans think of us as Divine ascended star beings, and we are waiting around for human consciousness to release us from our past."

Every member of the Ruby Order was astounded. As starseed themselves, they were subject to the same limitation. Countless lifetimes had been spent trying to elevate human consciousness, while clearly being party to it.

"All those who have incarnated unconsciously on Earth, be they starseed or Earth-born, are connected," Lenpasa continued, "by the very nature of DNA. Yet we feel so separate, so distinct. That too is the nature of DNA. I don't pretend to know what our Siriun friends know about DNA, but I do see how it has and still does inform us – even though we shed those bodies tens of thousands of Earth years ago.

"I trust that you can see your Mission as integral to the liberation of all Earth-connected souls. When those nucleotides of bondage are liberated from density, some of us will immediately merge with Source. We have waited a long time for this opportunity.

"In this way, you might see Earth as a portal of liberation. That is why so many of us are interested in her present progress. Then too, those who value power more than Oneness will do all that they can to try to block her ascension.

"We would ask that you think in terms of soul rather than race or star systems. Some of you are clearly associated with certain starseedings, but believe us when we tell you that you have experienced most of the intelligences in the galaxy and beyond. All of you have the good sense to see beyond race consciousness, color and culture.

"Know yourselves as souls – consciousness that exists eternally. You are Source incarnate on a Mission conceived by Source itself. Should you forget that, we ask that you not hesitate to contact us through journey or meditation. The Crystal Council is at your service. Thank you, Order of the Ruby, Lord Muru, Saint Germain, representatives of the Federation, and the Siriun High Council for hearing our humble plea for liberation."

Lenpasa involved the entire table in the bowing procedure once again then asked Lord Muru to continue the meeting. Lord Muru asked the delegation from the Galactic Federation to speak.

The Federation spokesman was sitting to the right of beloved Saint Germain, whom he touched lightly on the arm before beginning. Humanoid in appearance, he stroked a long beard before leaning forward to the microphone. His two colleagues were obviously of different galactic races than he. They were representatives of the many interdimensional civilizations in the Milky Way galaxy.

"I bring you greetings from the entire Galactic Federation, an organization which strives to keep balance and harmony in the galaxy. We are here to fill in the gaps of information relevant to your Mission. I am Senior Representative Var-An from a fairly advanced Orion civilization. My colleagues are Representative Omsathar, whose home is in The Pleiades and Representative Nu, who comes from the region of Draco. We are three of over a thousand representatives from as many civilizations, committed to peace and ascension.

"It is our task to open deeper memory within each of you regarding the history of Earth in this galaxy. Not all habitable planets, stars and planetoids are represented in the Federation. Certainly the behavior of the Taleks and those like them led to their dismissal from the organization.

"We are here to remind you that Earth has been banished for many millions of years. This had nothing to do with any of the life forms or genetic experiments carried out on Earth. If anything, those have been attempts to pull her back into the frequencies of the Federation. It really has to do with the choices made by the Earth soul itself.

"Just like the humans who have come to develop upon her, Earth made a choice long ago to be in density. She consciously chose density –and she was not alone, for many other planets have gone her way as well. Humans had not yet been developed at that time, but remnants of Earth's soul-struggle with the darkness remain and influence the collective mind of humanity.

"Through the compassionate heart of the Elohim, the Kumaras – the mighty planet tamers from Venus - agreed to work with Earth through the millions of years of her evolution into light. Bodhisattvas by nature, the Kumaras are still with Earth from the ascended realms.

"Six times it was necessary for Earth to shift axis, water, ice and land to come into closer alignment with the Great Central Sun. With each shift, a golden age of conscious evolution was born. The Kumaras were messengers of the Truth, whether in their cyclopean bodies or as incarnate way-showers like *Wiracocha,* Jesus, Krishna and Buddha. In collaboration with the Siriuns, they manifested new genetics on Earth at appropriate moments of conscious evolution.

"Now Earth is on the brink of the Fourth Dimension. This evolutionary step will allow her to access higher and higher dimensions, will reinstate her in the Federation, and will bring her into alignment with the Great Central Sun permanently. Currently, she is surrounded by a corona of light – the first stage of becoming a star. This corona is anchored in the Christ Consciousness grid, which was put in place around the Earth by the consciousness of Jesus and the Magdalen – both Kumara aspects. It continues to grow, emanating more light, as Earth is able to contain more light. Fifth Dimension will give Earth her autonomy in the galaxy, and the work of the Kumaras will be finished. We are grateful that they, who could be within the Heart of the Source, chose instead to shepherd the wayward.

"All that holds Earth back now is humanity. Remember you cannot separate the two, for the collective consciousness of humanity is spread like a blanket upon her surface. Humanity has Earth in its unconscious grip.

"Your Mission is designed as part of her seventh evolutionary leap. Whether it is necessary for Earth to shift her poles and cleanse her surface is immaterial. She will do what is necessary, and it is important to be fearlessly detached from her decision. If it were possible for humanity to elevate the collective consciousness to Fourth Dimension and actually support her quest – who can predict the outcome?

"Humanity is self destructive – that is clear. If this cannot be reversed, humankind may be mirroring its own demise. It would be a pity, since a sizable investment has been made to elevate consciousness genetically, but the souls would incarnate elsewhere with less challenge and more support.

"The misuse of power is, once again, a critical issue on Earth, especially with those who are self-destructive. You have heard from many on this panel regarding the opposition. Be watchful that self-opposition is not a factor. Stay centered, removed from drama and connected to all your resources. Do not succumb to temptation or doubt.

"Let us reiterate the major aspects of your Mission to clarify the Federation's support of the same. You are to find and destroy the cloned crystals, which are helping to keep humanity in a state of insatiable desire through fear and hatred. Seize the stolen original crystal, which is currently in the hands of the opposition, and return it to Lord Muru for reprogramming. Bring Light and Truth together to create a master frequency of ascension – first in your own hearts, then in the hearts of others.

"As you help others, monitor the feelings of pleasure received from such work and communicate that to us telepathically. Protect freedom, Truth, and love, both as a measurable capacity and a potential. Dispel fear, hatred, betrayal, false love and that which has no resonance with Truth. Do this with open hearts that emanate the power of love.

"As humanity accept its divinity and turns away from desire-driven, lower-body, behavior, its capacity for light will increase. The latent virus, which will have spread throughout the Earth, will become active and intercalate into humanity's fourth-level DNA, producing the 'enzyme' capable of excising the energetic mutation.

"From that point on, hearts will open, Earth and all those who have embodied there will be liberated, and your Mission will be complete. A new Golden Age will commence. We are grateful for your commitment to this Mission. Rest assured – the Federation is with you."

With much official bowing, the Senior Representative Var-An closed his short discourse for the Galactic Federation. Lord Muru asked the members of the Ruby Order if they had any questions.

Jacques leaned forward to his microphone, directing his question to Saint Germain. "Beloved Teacher, Father of the Magi, I can conceive of a way to link all of us together on Earth, but what of the channels to the other realms? While we are here as a group, would you indicate levels and pathways of assistance in finding the crystals, and with the remainder of our Mission?"

"Beloved Jacques," he replied, in a lighthearted tone, "we are ever at your service. You can communicate with us telepathically or in Dreamtime." Then to the group, he said, "I am in communication with Jacques on a regular basis and I think it would be best if Chris and I established that link as well. All of you should regularly visit the ascended advisors with whom you are affiliated, whether the Siriun High Council, Crystal Council, the Kumaras or myself – or all of us.

"With a Mission this weighty, we would not want any of you to feel abandoned. Yet you will have to accomplish the physical aspects of this Mission without our help. I have been guiding this Mission for thousands of years. The best of the Order of the Ruby were sent to complete it. Partly we must let the Divine Plan unfold, and at the same time, we need to move some energy. I will not be far away."

"Thank you, Beloved Master," he said, bowing his head.

Ramandi turned his microphone on, indicating that he had a question. Lord Muru motioned for him to go ahead. "It seems that the sinister force is already in control of government, finance, religion and so forth. What hope have the twelve of us against such opposition?"

Lord Abatan chose to answer the Maharajah's question. "We are aware of the heavy infiltration, but ask that you give the virus a chance to open doors for you. Many of you will be actively engaged in lifting the consciousness of humanity. We expect that a wave of enlightenment will result from all of your work. Be hopeful."

"Thank you, Lord Abatan," he replied. "We are a hopeful group."

Chris leaned forward to speak next. "I would direct my question to the Galactic Federation, but any of you are free to answer it," he began. "What of the Taleks? Obviously they still have access to Earth and humanity. Will we be confronting the Taleks?"

Var-An responded to Chris' question. "Lord of the Ruby, I understand your concern. The Taleks have had their way with Earth, but that will be ceasing. Our forces will be working to bring their agents and the Taleks back into harmony with the Federation. If we fail at that Mission, we may have to eliminate their form."

Lord Abatan added a Siriun perspective. "We are launching an effort to close the Middle East portal, Lord of the Ruby. We will keep you informed."

"Thank you both," Chris said, not entirely happy with their replies.

Leah put forth another question as Chris settled back in his seat. He was a bit overwhelmed by the magnitude of the Mission for so small a group, but greatly relieved that interdimensional channels could be accessed and that the Federation ʰᵃᵈ some plans to assist with the Taleks. When Chris' thought pattern became Leah asked Lord Abatan, "Is this virus which is capable of excising high-level DNA, the first virus? No, let me rephrase my question. Have the Siriuns been starseeding with viruses for some time now?"

"Clever, you are, My Dear," he replied. "Many of the viruses humans are experiencing are akin to starseed. Humans are an ongoing experiment, though their egos would have them believe that they are the experimenters. Our present experiments are less risky, far quicker and simpler than constructing an entire genome. There were times in the evolution of human consciousness when that was necessary, but now that the energies of ascension have accelerated, those seedings are useless. The average human cannot distinguish between our viruses and those of the opposition. I would ask you where humans think viruses originate?"

"Anywhere but the stars, Lord Abatan. Of that, I can assure you!" she replied, with sparkling eyes.

Lord Abatan laughed with the rest of the council. "Your humor is missed on Sirius, Sanara," he said, his eyes shining at her. "I would remind you of infectious viral or germ warfare as well – sometimes at the hands of one's own government. Look for infiltration by the opposition when such things occur. Those viruses are meant to depopulate or debilitate humans and are constructed in Earth laboratories."

"These experiments are gradually coming to the attention of some humans," she replied. Leah's eyes met Lord Abatan's in remembrance and communion before he fielded the next question from the group. The time of questioning quickly ran out.

Lord Muru indicated that the returning rays for their star brothers were close at hand. Lord Abatan's associate, Lhaje, was asked to pass the virus to the group. He rose and removed a small vial from his robes. Standing next to Demetri, he unscrewed the lid on the vial as Lord Abatan asked Demetri and the rest of the Order to breathe deeply just once above the vial. Lhaje stood next to each member as they took the airborne virus into their respiratory systems. If nothing else, it tested their complete surrender to the Mission.

When Lhaje had finished with Julio, he came back behind the Order of the Ruby and returned to his seat with the High Council. The dragon within the Sun Disc hissed then emitted a blue ray of light from its mouth that gradually took over the portal. Retracting into the mists, the dragon disappeared. Chris detected a subtle sigh of relief from Leah, who had put a remarkable strength forward during the intense encounter. Looking around at the rest of his group, Chris assessed a high level of understanding and commitment to the Mission.

Members of the High Council were the first to rise, bow and take their leave of the group through the Solar Disc. They were followed by the delegation from the Galactic Federation and the two members of the Crystal Council. When all of the star beings had walked out of sight, the dragon returned to guard the portal.

"Brothers and Sister of the Ruby," Lord Muru spoke, indicating that all headphones could be removed and microphones turned off, "I would impose on you one more time to leave the room while it undergoes transformation. We have time yet, within the alignment, for one additional prearranged contact. If you could return to the banquet room and remain in silence for a short while, we will recall you."

The Order of the Ruby rose and bowed to Saint Germain and Lord Muru. Chris left the Master's sword on the table before him with both scepters laid over one another in a cross. Integrating immense activation, both he and Leah were grateful for a time-out in silence. In the banquet room, the brothers sat or stood in meditation while Leah leaned back into Chris' arms, calling forth strength and protection. She sensed the movement of a dangerous, yet magnificent, energy.

The Siege Perilous

Lord Muru sent an assistant to invite the Order of the Ruby back into the room. Indicating that Leah and Chris should stay a while longer in the banquet room, the assistant ushered the other members of the order into the temple room. They took their seats around the original round table of transmuted gold, where Aramu Muru and Saint Germain were already seated.

Leah and Chris were in Oneness with the powerful energies surging around them. Both of their hearts were beating fast in anticipation of the unknown. Surrender was reinforced as they searched within for answers.

Chris realized that he had been tested very little on this journey. Coupling that with Lord Muru's statement about a dimensional leap and Leah's red dress of Resurrection gave him the uncomfortable feeling that his time had come. He hoped that Leah would not have to undergo any serious testing, aware that she had been stretched a number of times on this unpredictable journey.

Reading his thoughts, she squeezed the hands that had been holding her around the waist and looked up into his eyes. "Don't worry about me, Darling," she thought, sending the message telepathically to him. "Remember, we are going to know God in this lifetime. I am not attached to form, though my heart, in this body of mystery, will always be yours."

"Oh Leah," he thought, "I am so deeply in love with you. What if I had to choose between you and the Mission?" Chris leaned over to kiss her sweet neck.

His kiss felt like the brush of a hummingbird's wing against her skin. Heart aching, she turned to be held against his strong body. "We'll be okay, Chris," she thought. "I just have a sense about it. But if you are asked to let me go, *do it*. The Mission is above our humanity."

"Leah, you are so strong – and insightful," he sighed, silently.

"And scared," she thought, looking into his eyes.

Just then the temple door opened and Lord Muru's assistant asked that they come with him. Holding his hand lightly at the back of Leah's waist, Chris prayed for strength as they entered the room, for that terrible, yet magnificent, energy was upon them.

The Order of the Ruby sat in a circle around the table, with Lord Muru and Saint Germain sitting opposite the one remaining empty seat. Simple mathematics told Chris and Leah that they were looking at the thirteenth seat of the Round Table. It was a King's chair of elaborately ornate gold. Broad armrests of gold framed the ruby-red velvet seat and chair back. Rubies and diamonds were inlaid in carvings of the upper chair back and armrests.

Chris walked up to the back of the chair while Leah fell behind him on his right side. On the table in front of the chair were the two scepters crossed as an X. Placed over the X, its point towards the Masters, was the sword of Jesus.

As soon as he came into position behind the chair, the Disc of the Sun launched itself into the space above the table, taking up the expanse of the entire domed ceiling. Leah and many of the brothers jumped as the dragon appeared, hissing and breathing fire.

"Steady your heart," she repeated in silent mantra. Her thoughts seemed to help both of them focus their energies. Chris was using all of the powers at his disposal to remain calm, centered and alert. Leah's mantra helped him enormously to find that place of peace within, where the magician was in mastery. When that moment of stillness occurred, Saint Germain began to speak.

"Lord of the Ruby, do you know this seat before you?"

"I do, Master Chohan, it is the Siege Perilous."

"Indeed it is," Saint Germain replied. "Who might sit in this seat?"

"He who has fought a well-armed knight, My Lord."

"How do you interpret that, Lord of the Ruby?"

"He who has conquered his humanity, my Lord. He who is the master of his ego and one with his Divine Self."

"Quite right, again. It is also the seat of impeccable intent. How do you define that, Dear Brother?" Saint Germain said, with a smile.

"Intent from a pure heart not influenced by the promises of personal power or Earthly possession. Again, it is beyond the human experience, aligned with the Mission."

"Is it beyond Earthly love?" he asked, seriously.

"It is," Chris replied, feeling his heart ache ever so briefly.

"Yet you have brought your Beloved with you to this seat, the position of Jeshua at the Last Supper, the position of the Grail Knight at Arthur's table. What is more, she is wearing the red dress of Resurrection. Explain yourself, if you will, Christian?"

Chris took a deep breath, drawing from his center of power. "Beloved Master," he spoke, measuring his words carefully, "if one were seeking to live beyond the illusion of the human condition, experiencing death might be necessary. It might also be necessary to experience separation from all that you love to completely resurrect – to be birthed into light. I do not pretend to understand this fully, but the Divine Plan has brought me here with all that I love in this Earthly realm standing

[handwritten in left margin: Steady your heart Mantra]

behind me, dressed for resurrection. I trust the Divine Plan of my soul, and as you know, I am at the service of the Kumaras and the Solar Brotherhood."

"And your Beloved?" he asked, looking at Leah.

"I am here to serve, Beloved Master," she replied, bowing slightly. The dragon hissed at her reply causing Leah to immerse herself in the mantra once more.

Saint Germain smiled at the two of them. "How perfectly beautiful their souls looked together," he mused. He was not certain of the outcome of the daring feat, which their souls were calling in. It would be a pity if they were lost to the Mission. However, his assignment was not to question, but to facilitate.

"Very well," he replied, after his brief reverie. "Our time is running short. Christian Kramer, if you choose to sit in this Seat of Peril, you may experience physical death or vanish from the Earth plane in some other way. Your soul, of course, will not be lost, for indeed, you are impeccable. At the very least, you will have the experience of separation and death on every other level. Frankly, I never did this myself, but a few brothers have survived to find the Grail.

"If you do return, understand that you will no longer be what is considered human. More than this, I cannot tell you. Naturally, you have the support of myself, Lord Muru and your brothers and beloved. The choice is entirely yours."

"Thank you, Beloved Master Chohan," he breathed. Chris took precious moments to connect fully with each of the Order of the Ruby. All of the Order seemed very serious except Master Mukda, who looked delighted. Chris could not resist sharing a quick smile with his Dreamtime teacher.

Then he turned within to check the resiliency of his field, the flow of his energy and the strong and vital link to his Divine Presence. When his consciousness moved around his heart, he felt Leah's presence. Listening carefully, he heard her whisper. "Let me go, Darling. We will never really be apart."

"Wise Leah," he thought. "You know I have not broken this attachment. Thank you, My Beloved, for being so strong. I will break it as I am taken from you."

"Beloved," she whispered back in thought, "please do not sacrifice one second of your perilous flight to me."

Saint Germain and Lord Muru, who were monitoring their telepathic conversation, were more than a little amazed at Leah's detachment. She urged Chris to take his opportunity for liberation.

Chris remembered her from his childhood dreams and all those Dreamtime encounters throughout his life. It has all been about this moment, he concluded. She was meant to give me the strength to sit in the Siege Perilous with courage and impeccability.

He bowed to the two Masters and moved to the left side of the chair. Leah moved to stand behind the chair's back, creating and holding a space of liberation for Chris. As he pulled the chair out, the dragon hissed once more. "Liberation, liberation," Leah chanted within.

Chris pulled the chair beneath him before easing himself onto the seat. As soon as his body made contact with the seat, the room began to shake with the magnitude of a serious earthquake. The brothers held tight to chairs and the table as they swayed every which way. Accompanying the quake was a sound more frightening than an oncoming tornado. The Sun Disc flared dramatically. Its flames licked the space above the round table as the dragon, obviously agitated, reeled about within the disc, hissing fire.

Above the monstrous sound and violent shaking, Saint Germain's voice rode forth with absolute power. "Lord of the Ruby, take up the sword!" he boomed.

Chris grasped the gem-studded handle of the Master's sword and immediately the Point of Power fell to the tabletop. The dragon lowered his head towards the table, letting go a blast of sapphire light that engulfed Chris. Raising the sword to the dragon's mouth, Chris let the powerful sound of love speak from his heart. In that moment, the dragon swooped down to funnel Chris up into the blue light, while the room became as quiescent as the mother puma had at Brian's side.

Sinking slightly, Leah grasped the chair as the sound tore the cords of attachment from her heart. Her mind lost all telepathic connection with Chris. He was gone from her life. She caught her breath and stood tall behind the chair once again, trying to hold the elusive space of liberation for her Beloved. Blue smoke, smelling of ozone, hung in the space around the chair.

Saint Germain drew her to his gaze and addressed her. "Lady of the Ruby, you have an admirable amount of personal strength and dedication to the Mission." She bowed her head slightly, and acknowledged his words. He continued, speaking to her in a tender voice. "I understand that your spirit enjoys setting precedent, Beloved Sanara. It is extraordinary for a woman to be tested in such a way, but I am asked to offer you the opportunity to sit in the Siege Perilous as well."

Leah was stunned. The flame of fear rose up within her, but she was able to smother it with love. How could she pass up an opportunity to die and resurrect into the light? As great as her commitment to the Mission was, her commitment to Source was greater. If the Divine Plan wanted her on Earth, she would return. She surrendered completely to the greater reality.

"I accept this offer, Master Chohan," she replied, breathlessly.

"Then take your seat, My Child. Reach out to hold the Point of Power within your hands as you sit down. May the force of your own God-Presence be with you."

"Thank you, Beloved Master Chohan," she replied bowing, then moving to the right of the chair. With her heart keeping a deafening beat, she reached forward to pick up the Point of Power. All of the brotherhood held her in a space of love and protection. Each had loved her in his unique way – this Goddess of their Dreamtime.

With pounding heart, free spirit and complete surrender, Leah lowered herself onto the seat. The Earth did not quake, the wind did not howl, but the dragon lowered his head to swallow her up in the blue light. Letting her heart speak its powerful language, she held the Point of Power towards the dragon's mouth and Heart-Spoke, "Truth!"

As Leah vanished into the Sun Disc, the room was filled with dragonflies. The insects, symbols of voracious transformation, swarmed around the space above the table before being sucked up into the blue light as well. The room was left in stillness.

•

With the sword in his grasp, Chris soared into the blue light. He continued on through the membranes of successively higher dimensions. The sword did not allow him to explore those dimensions, but drew him steadily towards a light far brighter than the Sun. He felt a stressful convolution within the cells of his body as all human limitations were being shattered.

With objective clarity, all the events of his life were reviewed. He witnessed them with a ruthless kind of understanding, which left no room for remorse. In doing so, he was liberated from the memories, conscious and unconscious, that bound him to that life. The filaments of his luminous field – the beliefs that had shaped his reality – fell away, leaving him without a reality – without a reference point.

Had he not been soaring towards the Great Central Sun, Chris would have experienced this as a complete psychotic event. Instead, he felt the exhilaration of liberation from that life. As his journey continued, he passed through the stream of consciousness that was his soul; experiencing the countless lifetimes he'd spent on Earth in service to the Mission. He witnessed his soul as lifestreams in other galaxies as well as on Venus, Sirius, Arcturus and many of the star systems of the Milky Way.

The weaving of his soul's journey came to completion as he touched the light – a light so intense he lost consciousness or, more precisely, his consciousness shifted from the orientation of the human mind to that of his Divine Presence. As Earth interpreted consciousness, he was dead.

A soft blue light helped to bring his consciousness back into form. He became aware of Beings around him who were speaking in whispers as they worked in the blue light. He had no awareness of his body – no feelings of pain or joy - but he knew that his luminous body was lying face-up on an elevated platform.

Allowing his consciousness to float above form, he bore witness to his Divine Presence. Like the Beings hovering around him, he was a blonde-haired, blue-eyed giant of androgynous character. His body was being activated to the full power of his own God-Presence.

When he fully embodied his greater consciousness, the Beings completed their work on his body, returning it to its Earth-embodiment form. One of the Beings helped him to a sitting position on the table speaking to him gently, while the others quietly left the room. "Welcome to the Temple of the Kumaras within the Great Central Sun, Mana Sanar. We are your brothers."

Head swirling, Chris grasped the table to steady himself. "Thank you, Brother. You are Basha, are you not?"

"It is wonderful that you remember. Earth life is such a deep sleep; we wondered how you would make your transition. However, it has been very simple – glorious in fact. You can see the benefits of the enlightened path on Earth."

Chris nodded his spinning head. "Have I transitioned off the Earth plane, then?" he asked.

"This is so, Brother. I cannot say what is in store for you next. We were asked to stabilize you in your higher body. That is all."

"This is not my Earth body? It looks just like it." Chris said.

"You can look any way you choose now, Mana Sanar. Usually after transition, our brothers and sisters want to stay in their Earth form for a short time. It is quite comfortable after we heal its wounds and fully activate the higher body. If you would prefer to be a tiger, just intend it." Basha stood back, folding his arms before him.

"That's all right," Chris laughed. "I don't mind feeling comfortable at this moment."

"Very well," Basha replied. "Do you think you can walk now?"

"Let me try," Chris said, sliding off the table. Quite unsteady on his feet, he grasped the table and walked around it several times, trying to get his balance. "I feel tremendous energy in my body," Chris remarked. "I am sure you would not appreciate the metaphor, but it's as if my internal motor has been cranked into high gear."

Basha smiled. "I understand the metaphor. We are completely aware of the Earth experience – down to its most insignificant-significant detail."

"Does it make any sense to you – the human experience?"

"Cycles of darkness move into cycles of light on Earth. The cycles used to last for ages. Now they are more rapid. You could visualize an upward spiral shaped like a cone. Experience is moving towards the tip of the cone – very accelerated. All of this, and more, will enter your consciousness now that you are in higher body," he said. Then reaching below the table, he pulled the broken sword from a shelf beneath the table. Chris reached out to grasp it as Basha offered it to him. The sword's true power surged from handle to blade as it connected with the energy in Chris' body.

"Come with me, Brother," Basha announced. "There is work to be done."

Chris followed behind the flowing blue robes of Basha as they left the healing room. Entering a hallway of polished sapphire, the two brothers walked passed a number of doorways to the left and right before arriving at a golden arched door at the end of the hall. He asked Chris to wait in the hallway for a moment while he slipped inside the room.

Chris welcomed the opportunity to check in with his internal energy systems. He felt none of the limitations of Earth reality where energy channels could easily congest and become blocked. Balanced, calm and receptive, he leaned into the sapphire wall, waiting for Basha to return.

Before long, the door opened wide and Basha ushered him into a small, yet ornate, temple room. From the vaulted sapphire ceiling, golden fixtures of diffuse blue light offered magical illumination. At the far end of the room, a graceful arch of carved gold framed the entrance to an altar, which was filled with little lights similar to butter lamps. Behind the altar there was a golden replica of the Sun Disc.

The beauty and power of the room was nearly lost to Chris the moment he set eyes on the Master awaiting him. Seated expectantly, in a throne-like chair of gold and sapphire, was Lord Sananda Kumara. Appearing to Chris in his Earth-form of Jeshua, Lord Sananda raised his hand in greeting, a benevolent smile upon his face. Dressed in the simple linen robes of an Essene with long wavy hair of burnished gold and great blue eyes, Lord Sananda sat in the magical light of his Divine Essence.

Sword in hand, Chris walked steadily towards him to kneel at his feet. With two hands, he raised the sword before Lord Sananda, then laid it on the sapphire floor at his feet. Looking into Lord Sananda's eyes, he said, "Beloved Master, all authority rests at your feet. I am the servant of your every wish." Balanced on his hands, Chris lowered his body to lay prostrate before the Master.

"Rise, My Son," Lord Sananda spoke in a voice melodic and gentle. "Truly you have returned to your Father's house with a pearl of great price." Chris rose to one knee, and watched Lord Sananda's soft eyes scan the sword. "The sword is as beautiful as ever, but it is your own light that warms the heart, My Son."

"Thank you, My Lord. I trust that I have been of some service to the Mission on Earth," Chris said, rising to one knee.

Lord Sananda motioned for Chris to sit in an empty chair next to him. He eased himself into that chair while Lord Sananda rotated slightly to face him. "Following a path to enlightenment is service in itself, Mana Sanar. However, as you know the

Mission of the Ruby Order has not been brought to completion. You will have to return to Earth, Beloved Son."

Chris' heart sank at the thought of leaving the high state of consciousness present in the Great Central Sun. "As you wish, Lord Sananda," he responded.

Lord Sananda smiled, reading his thoughts and feelings. "You will not lose this consciousness, My Son. You have passed the test of death, as I have many times on Earth. When you return, it will be in fully enlightened service. Your personal work is complete.

"I would commission you to continue your work of transcending the human body. I would like you to fully ascend in this embodiment. That is the pearl of the greatest value, Mana. Now, I would like to detail the Mission."

Lord Sananda talked at length about the Mission, the sinister force, possible locations of the crystals and those on Earth whom Chris could and could not trust. Chris' willingness to detach completely from life had brought him to a new level of initiation on the Earth plane. He could expect further initiation as his ascension process continued.

Occasionally, Lord Sananda would project a hologram of a time in Earth's past, present or future, clarifying a point he was making. Chris felt himself taking all that Lord Sananda said into some vast field of awareness now open to him. Lord Sananda reassured Chris that he would not lose that awareness when he was back in embodiment.

At length, Lord Sananda asked Chris about his feelings for Sanara. It was then that he realized he'd forgotten about her completely. "My Lord," he replied, "Leah – Sanara - is a woman of mystery – an enigma. Somehow I have managed to detach from her in this experience and no longer feel the urges of human bondage. I love her in a way that shatters my sense of self."

"She is a mystery," He smiled. "I would agree. She is also vital to the Mission. Mana Sanar, you are to fully activate her codes of light as the Mission progresses. When she is fully activated, she will activate others and awaken many people from their slumber.

"Guard her with your life, My Son. You are her warrior guardian, and she must survive the Mission. As you might imagine, the opposition will try to stop her. You are free to use her Mission to draw them out."

"What is the timing, My Lord?" he asked, trying to frame all that Lord Sananda was saying in the context of the Mission.

"She will come into her power within four years – and within seven, she will transcend her body."

"Whew!" he breathed. "I will have my hands full."

"You already do," Sananda replied, smiling.

Chris smiled as well. "How does the Mission regard the consummation of our relationship?" he asked, frankly.

"We are not asking you to deny your humanity, My Son. I did not. Sometimes activation in human form is sexual. You will learn much from each other's love. However, a day will soon come when energies would best be conserved for ascension. Until that time, she would benefit from the grounding and you could experience the Divine Feminine. In most cases, sexuality is addiction that increases the amnesia, but in those who are fully awakened, it can open a mysterious door to God."

"Thank you, My Lord," he replied, wondering how he could have forgotten her until Sananda brought her name forward.

•

Leah moved quickly through the blue light, transiting the same dimensions as Chris had. She felt the final healing of her life issues and saw the journey of her soul through time. Allowing the Point of Power to connect with the immense light before her, she burst through the last membrane into that unconscious space of death.

She found herself floating in the softest pink light, her consciousness gradually focusing itself on form, and she saw her Divine Body of Light lying beneath her on soft cushions. Having no way to measure, she did not realize how gigantic her form was, but gazed, in wonder, at the wave in her long hair and the light around her body. Tended by a blonde-haired woman, her body's energy was being activated then balanced in a series of magical passes. When the woman was finished, her consciousness was allowed to drift down into the form and awaken.

"I AM Nada," the woman whispered. "Welcome to the Temple of the Kumaras, Sanara. You are within the Great Central Sun."

"Beloved Lady Nada," Leah said, trying to sit up. "I have petitioned you so many times. Were you healing me?"

"In a way, Sanara," she replied, while helping Leah to sit. "I was balancing the energies of your transition. Sometimes a great amount of time must pass before consciousness resumes on the higher planes. We do not have the luxury of time with you, Beloved."

"Have I died?" she asked.

"Indeed, Dear One," she replied, gently. "It is a beautiful experience, is it not?"

"Incredible, Lady Nada. I felt so supported by the Universe."

"That is because you were without fear and attachment, Sanara. Death is a birth into the Divine - liberation from the unconscious Earth plane."

"Does everyone come here in death?" she asked, looking around the beautiful room.

Lady Nada laughed softly. "No, My Dear. Consciousness returns to the highest level of its attainment, but few from Earth come to our temples. You are one of our children returning home."

"I did not attain that level of enlightenment, Dear Nada," she admitted. "Why would I be here?"

"It doesn't matter, Sanara. You are Kumara."

"Did I even complete my Mission?" she asked.

"It is not for me to say, Beloved. You are guided by another, Sanara - even though I have been in your field for some time bringing you Divine Feminine energies. I was asked to balance and activate you here. Do you feel ready to move to another part of the temple?"

"Let me try to walk, Beloved Nada," Leah replied, easing herself off the table. As she slid off the cushioned table, Leah came back into her Earth form - less than half the height of Lady Nada. "I feel like Alice in Wonderland," she laughed, smoothing her red dress back into place.

"Try walking with me, Sanara," Lady Nada said, smiling. "I promise you – no rabbit holes."

"Or Mad Hatters and strange queens?" Leah asked, wobbly on her feet.

Lady Nada placed the Point of Power in Leah's hand. "Only love, Darling One," she breathed, as Leah staggered a bit. "Only love."

"I feel so dizzy," Leah admitted, holding on tighter.

"I know. You were quite expanded. Now you are integrating all of that into your Earth body."

"But I don't need this body, do I?" she asked.

"Sanara, focus your consciousness on walking right now. You will have all of your questions answered. We just need to walk a short distance."

Leah took a deep breath. "I am so sorry, Lady Nada. Death seems not to have interrupted my need to inquire." She steadied herself on Nada's arm and made good progress to the door of the room. They left the room of soft pink to enter a corridor of sapphire stone.

When they arrived at the end of the corridor, Lady Nada asked Leah to wait there for her while she went ahead to prepare the space. Leah held the tip of the sword to her heart, aware of the power it held – and aware of her beating heart. She realized she had not felt anything in the body of the Kumara. Guessing that human feelings and emotions were quite foreign to this plane, she leaned against the wall, trying to silence her questioning mind.

The woman who opened the door to her was not Lady Nada. She was Leah's height with an oval face, blue eyes of extraordinary light and long, golden-red hair. "Please come in, Sanara," she said, her voice very much like Lady Nada's. As the door opened she saw the woman's black robes and knew that she was a High Priestess of Annu, a member of the ancient Sisterhood of the Sun.

Leah was led into a sapphire temple identical to the one Chris had entered. Tears filled her eyes as she saw the Disc of the Sun and the many little lights beneath it. The woman, who stood at her left side, moved back a step to reveal Lord Sananda, as Jeshua, seated upon his throne. The tears spilled forth as she practically ran to his feet. Leah knelt before him and bent to kiss his sandaled feet. Placing the Point of Power in his awaiting hands, she looked up into the eyes of the Master.

The woman who had brought her circled behind Leah and came to sit on a second throne chair next to Sananda. Leah knew her then as Nada and as Mary Magdalen, Jeshua's queen. She turned on her knees to kiss her feet as well then the sapphire ring of the sisterhood, which had been extended to her. Mary was still the high priestess of the Order, guiding the sisterhood from her ascended state even as Saint Germain guided the magi.

"You are Mary, are you not?" she asked the woman.

"I am choosing the body of that embodiment to be with you now, yes," she replied to Leah.

"I have seen you once before, Beloved Mary - in a vision. Your hair was darker, streaked with gray and your eyes were dark as well. You told the story of your life to your granddaughter in that vision."

"You see me now as I was when Jeshua and I married - barely out of my childhood, Beloved. The Mission changed my body, but not my soul."

She drew Leah over to sit at her feet. Leah leaned against the corner of Mary's chair, as Lord Sananda began to speak to her. Mary rested her hand on Leah's shoulder.

"Sanara, daughter of my heart," Lord Sananda began. "How beautiful you have grown in every way."

"Oh, My Father and Lord," she cried. "I cannot tell you how good it is to be in your presence again – both of you. How can I be of service to you and your Mission?"

"*Our* Mission, Beloved," Lord Sananda replied. "Think of this as a family Mission."

"Gladly, My Father. What would you have me do?"

"You must return to Earth, My Child."

Leah's heart sank. "I have come home to hear that I must leave. But why, Father?"

"Your Mission has not even begun, Beloved Sanara. It was necessary for you to pass through the illusion of death to come into your full power. You are one of my many gifts to the Earth. You must return."

A big tear rolled down her cheek as she looked into his tender eyes. "Very well, Father. What would you have me do?"

"Thank you, Sanara. I know it is a trial for you to return. You detached completely. However, you have much to do on Earth. You will return in a state of complete awareness - your Divine Presence. Your DNA has been activated to all twelve strands.

"Use the gifts that begin appearing in your life. One of these gifts is to activate others to their Missions. First you will activate the many Priestesses of Annu who have incarnated to assist this ascension process. Then you will activate the Brotherhood of Magi, who will be needed to manifest the Golden Cities. Closely guided by Saint Germain, you will assist in the awakening of America to its destiny. Your work will take you around the world on a Mission of awakening humanity.

"With your full DNA capacity available to you, you will be capable of raising the frequency of those around you, much as I did as Jeshua. In time, many will come to be in your presence. Activate with words, My Sanara, but also with your heart. Use your talents and our guidance to open codes within others offering them an autonomous path to God and release from suffering. You will be guided and taken care of in all that you do for the Mission. You will be led to powerful places on the Earth where many of your own codes will open. Do not worry – not for one single day of your life. We will take care of all your needs."

"How do I begin, Father?" she asked. "This Mission seems vast and so unlike me."

"It is unlike Leah. It is not unlike Sanara. Begin at the great rock where the Lemurians' crystal is hidden. There you will gain the power to activate the hearts of others. The virus you are carrying will take care of the rest."

"Will there be danger, Father?" she asked.

"That cannot be avoided, Beloved," he said kindly. "You will have protection from my most trusted warrior and the entire brotherhood. Walk upon the dragon lines, Sanara. Let the dragon activate your power."

Suddenly, she remembered Chris. "Father, am I to pluck a tooth from the dragon's mouth?" she asked, her eyes wide.

Sananda laughed. "Only if you want to, Sanara. If you wanted to, I am sure no one could stop you."

All three of them laughed, enjoying his reference to her courage. "I am remembering a certain man, Beloved Master. He is Kumara - Mana Sanar. Could he be this warrior you reference?"

"He has died as well, Beloved," he said.

"He feels a part of me. I do not understand it but feel that he has somehow survived the death," she offered. "He was so strong and high in his magic."

Mary stroked Leah's hair as she was speaking, conscious of her many struggles in love. "Even if he has," Sananda said, "like you, he could be very different after the experience."

"You are right, Master. I will accept your greatest warrior with complete gratitude. Have you more for me?"

"I do. It is for our lineage, Sanara."

"Yes?"

"You were born into our bloodline," he said, resting his right hand on Mary's arm. "Keep in mind, as you travel the world, that you are fulfilling certain prophecies of the bloodline. Few know what they are, do you?"

"I am not a religious person, Master," she replied.

"Good. You will not find them remembered there. They are hidden within certain Gnostic writings. Do you remember how I have been quoted as saying 'this you will do, and more,' My Daughter?" he asked.

"Of course. I use that quote all of the time when I am teaching," she replied.

"Then practice it," he challenged.

"Oh my," was all she could think to say.

"You are good at disconnecting people from the crutch of religion. You give them ways to connect directly to Source. You help them find God in the natural world and in all people. Is that true?"

"Yes, Father," Leah replied, "that is my joy."

"Then do something for me, Beloved."

"Anything, Beloved Master."

Lord Sananda was authoritative without being harsh. "*Be God*. Sanara, do greater things than I did. Show people that they are the Messiah – then false prophets or agents of the sinister forces will not fool them. Then they will see God in every human being, in every flower, blade of grass and butterfly.

"Make them aware of their power – just as I tried to do. Stay pure. Do not waver in your Truth. You are not on Earth to sacrifice your life for mankind – none of you are. This is not about suffering. It is about love."

Leah gulped hard. "Is there anything else, Father?" she asked, humbly.

"Yes," he said, lowering his voice from waterfall to flowing brook. "It is part of your purpose to transcend the human body, Sanara. I think you will find this a pleasant challenge."

"I admit that is more to my liking than the rest of this Mission, Beloved Master. I have fewer problems with personal discipline."

"Your human problems have vanished, Beloved. You will get timely advice from Saint Germain and his lineage. Have you any questions, Beloved Sanara?" he asked.

"Millions!" she exclaimed sitting upright. "I could stay right here asking them for several millennia."

Lord Sananda and Lady Nada laughed with her. "Just ask them in your meditation, Beloved. I will be happy to answer them. Now we would like to hold a short ceremony to complete your initiation into Kumara consciousness. Would you allow Lady Nada to prepare you?"

"How beautiful," she sighed, grasping Mary's hand.

"Go with my beloved Twin Ray, Sanara," he said, looking into Mary's eyes with a mystic's love. "We will meet in the great Temple of Initiation."

She arose, bowed before Lord Sananda then followed Mary through the main entrance doors of the small temple into a large atrium. Mary pointed out the huge golden doors of the Temple of Initiation on the left, but took Leah down a corridor past those doors.

Turning left into another corridor, they walked parallel to the temple for some time before entering a room to the right. There, Mary turned Leah over to two women who were to assist her in preparing for the ceremony. Mary slipped out of the room to ready herself, promising to return for Leah in a short while.

After removing her red dress, the women ushered Leah into an adjoining room that contained the sacred baths. She was bathed in a tub filled with roses, then dried and rubbed with sacred oil of rose. Bliss filled her consciousness.

Leah sat still for a long time while they wove tiny rosebuds into fine braids dispersed throughout her thick blonde hair. When they reentered the dressing room, her eyes came to rest upon an exquisite Arthurian dress of luminous brocaded ivory fabric. Embroidered pink roses cascaded down the bodice to a dropped waist and floated along the hem of the skirt.

Like the red dress, the neckline was cut to a low curve and trimmed with roses. Embroidered around the wrist of the long sleeves were pink roses, with light green stems and leaves, which climbed up the wrists. Diamonds were scattered over the circumference of the clinging skirt, like the stars of the Milky Way. Helping her into the dress, the women made her feel like a bride preparing to meet her heart's love.

They replaced the pendant of Qoyari on Leah's chest. As a finishing touch, they placed a high collar of sparkling diamonds around her neck to match those in her ears. All of this preparation was carried out in silence, much like a ceremony itself. When Mary reentered the room, as her full Kumara presence, Lady Nada, she came to stand behind Leah, who stood before a full-length mirror. Lady Nada, twice Leah's height, was resplendent in simple but luminous white and pink robes.

"What do you feel, Sanara?" she asked.

"Warm and tingling, Lady Nada - like the Christ Bride," she said in wonder.

"You are a queen of light in Christ," she said, smiling. "Shall we go?"

"As you wish, My Lady," Leah answered.

As they walked from the room, one of the women handed Leah a single luminous ruby-red rose. She thanked both of the women and followed Lady Nada into the corridor. Walking a short way, they stopped before a pair of golden double doors. Leah supposed these were doors into the Temple of Initiation. Amazingly, she felt relaxed, joyful and not the least bit nervous. In fact, she noticed that no negativity existed in this state. There was nothing to rob her energy or distract her from purpose.

Suddenly, Leah could hear a chorus of voices that sounded like angels coming through the temple doors. She was lost in the beauty of the music when Lady Nada knelt to kiss her softly on the cheek.

"My blessings to you, Sanara, for all that you are," she whispered.

Her smile was as vast as her heart space. Leah turned to Nada and returned the kiss. "Beloved Nada, please be with me. I am drawn to you as one who completes me in some way. Would you help to guide me on this Mission?"

"Always, My Darling Child," she replied, rising. "When you feel touched by the depth and mystery of the feminine, there I AM."

The door cracked open in a flood of sound, indicating that the time of ceremony was at hand. Lady Nada asked Leah to enter the room with her head bowed in humility. Led into the angelic frequency as an innocent child of light, Leah watched the sapphire floor beneath her feet. She stepped over gold inlay to stand within the corner of a triangle. In a whisper, Lady Nada asked her to raise her eyes slowly to the acceptance of her Mission.

As her head began to rise, she found herself in the corner of a Star of David. Across from her, in an opposite corner, she followed her eyes up the length of a being wrapped in a cloak of ruby red. When she saw the breastplate of Inkari, a brilliant smile crept across her face. He reciprocated as he saw the pendant of Qoyari - a crooked grin sweeping over his handsome face. When their eyes met, vortexes of ruby light reached out over the space between them to join their White Hearts.

Behind Chris stood Lord Sananda in his full Kumara presence - his brilliant Christ light like a beacon of hope for the Earth. The sword rested in a gem-studded sheath hung at his side. They had entered through identical double doors on the opposite side of the temple.

Lord Sananda and Lady Nada urged Chris and Leah forward into the center of the star, where Chris wrapped her up in his arms like a reclaimed treasure. The temple was filled with cheering voices as he kissed her fully on the mouth.

"I had to die to my humanity to be able to love you as you deserve to be loved, Sanara," he whispered.

"I had to die to my humanity to be able to receive your love appropriately and love you in kind, Mana Sanar. It would not have worked as we were, and the Mission would have been jeopardized."

"We cannot fail the Mission, Darling," he replied, holding her at arm's length to see the beauty of her light.

Her smile was radiant. "Failure is a human creation, Beloved. We are Divine."

Lady Nada and Lord Sananda came to lead them up towards the temple altar. A Solar Disc of transmuted gold filled the wall behind the low altar where the Maxine Flame burned vigorously. Glancing towards the rear of the temple, they saw a multitude of Kumaras, the source of the cheering as well as the singing.

The Temple of Initiation was a large vaulted room much like a cathedral of sapphire, ruby and gold. The sapphire floor held a chain of inlaid gold Stars of David from the main entrance doors to the altar. Within the large alcove containing the altar and the Disc of the Sun, the walls and rounded ceiling were ruby. Representing the primary rays of red, blue and yellow, the ruby, sapphire and gold created a space of union. Suspended above the altar was a great golden dragon with ruby eyes. The dragon's wings were fully spread, demonstrating the balance between the *Akhu* and *Draco* self embodied by the Kumaras.

As they neared the altar, temple assistants brought forward two enormous golden throne chairs. Placed before the Maxine Flame with their backs to the Solar Disc, the chairs were identical in structure but different in seat and back coverings.

Lady Nada took the chair on the right, which was covered in deep rose velvet, while Lord Sananda seated himself in the left chair, to Lady Nada's right, which was covered in royal blue velvet. Chris stood before Nada and Leah stood before Lord Sananda. Seated, the Kumaras were still towering above them, but were far less distant. Those in attendance brought their singing to a close – a silence falling over the vast temple space.

Lord Sananda, who looked nothing like Jeshua in his Kumara body, prepared to speak. Somehow, his robes of light blue and white held light – as if they had been made of diamonds. Chris and Leah were swept up in the immensity of love that flowed from both of the Masters' fields. The four of them were held in a luminous egg of light made of love filaments.

Lord Sananda's brilliant, yet soft, eyes were penetrating and expansive – able to see into each of them at once. He looked far more a warrior than Jeshua, Buddha or his many other embodiments. He looked the part of a planet tamer, Leah thought.

He began speaking the language of activation.

"Beloved Children, there are a few words that I wish to speak to you. What I have to share with you is your own story. You already know the greater Mission and your parts within it. Now I would take you into deep remembrance.

"In your resurrection, you will return with truths that few would understand. For this reason, and more, you have each other. You are Kumara. You have always been Kumara. When we choose to embody on the Earth, we usually remain conscious of our lineage. For this Mission, it has been necessary for both of you to experience the human condition before returning to complete consciousness. A great healing is happening on Earth now. To guide others in their healing, it was wise to have you experience that healing yourselves.

"There is a mystery in our lineage, the Messianic lineage, which we share with other lineages, for example, the Avatar lineages. In fact it is a quality of the Divine Presence of every ascended being.

"We, of this lineage, are way-showers, teachers of consciousness within the Universe. A group of us have been working with Earth but, as you can see, there are many Kumara aspects gathered here to honor you who are working on Earth as well and elsewhere in the Universe.

"What I must share with you is quite simple to understand, but enormous in its scope. It is essential to your resurrection, for it will change your lives immeasurably.

"You have felt a profound attraction to one another on the Earth, which remains in this ascended state. You might have cause to think that you are Twin Rays. Lady Nada is, to me, the completion of myself. We came as one from the Heart of God. All aspects of God were sent out to increase the greatness of the Source of all light. On our journey, we saw that we contained both masculine and feminine aspects within our whole – the play of light and dark within Oneness.

"Like all other aspects of God, we separated to experience far greater challenge and opportunity. I traveled on the Masculine Ray, while Lady Nada traveled on the Feminine Ray. Now we are bringing those two opposites back together as we journey back to the Heart of God.

"That is not a mystery to humanity, but it has been misunderstood. Experience with your Twin Ray within the unconscious realms of Earth is usually not pleasant. The reflection is very intense – I would say intolerable – in the unconscious state. It is far better for one of the rays to remain unmanifested while the other embodies. When I have Earth-embodied with Lady Nada, at least one of us has done so consciously. The two of you are not Twin Rays."

Both Leah and Chris understood what Lord Sananda was saying. Many humans interpreting fragmented truth had romanticized the notion of Twin Rays. Neither of them felt that kind of intolerable reflection of each other. Chris grasped Leah's hand as Lord Sananda continued.

"Here is the mystery. You are both aspects of the same consciousness." They glanced in each other's eyes and knew that Sananda had spoken Truth. Chris squeezed her hand as the Master continued. "You are Oneness, not opposition reflecting. I will use my life as Jeshua to clarify this Truth, because both of you were present there – in Oneness.

"When I embodied as Jeshua, it was but an aspect of my Kumara presence, Lord Sananda. Humanity was not ready to experience my full presence. There was no need. Lady Nada embodied an aspect of herself, as Mary Magdalen. In those aspects, we were Twin Rays together, playing out roles in a greater Mission.

"Because that Mission was so important to the future of Earth and humanity, each of us sent additional aspects of our Kumara presences to assist us. For example, Lady Nada sent aspects of herself to embody Mary Salome, Simon Magus, and our granddaughter Angelica. She saw to the preservation and protection of the Sisterhood of Annu, which carried the codes of consciousness for the future.

"I sent aspects of myself to embody my brothers, James and Thomas, John the Beloved, and my son, Josephes, who would be the Fisher King. The lineages preserved by these aspects of myself hold the Truth upon the Earth to this day.

"All of these were powerful embodiments for that Mission. The pity of humanity is the way in which they have, with each of our Missions, fabricated religion around a distorted understanding of the Truth we have spoken. However, from a greater perspective, this is how consciousness is developed.

"In that embodiment as Jeshua, my brother James the Just, who became Joseph of Arimathea, held fast to the Truth in Jerusalem until he was forced to leave. He founded the only true Christian Church, which he took to England to merge with the Celtic teachings. His ready assimilation of the existing Truths is a demonstration of the meaning of the Grail Codes.

"As young men, he and my Jeshua aspect had gone together, with Simon Magus, to England to activate the land for James' future work there. Soon, the Golden City will fully anchor in that land because of the Camelot Initiative – another embodiment project of the Ascended Masters. Both of you know the importance of James to the Mission, then and now, for both of you were part of his life stream. That is why you feel Oneness together. You may find others upon the Earth for whom you feel this same resonance for James was a full twelve-fold aspect of my Sananda presence.

"Each twelve-fold aspect has the opportunity to send forth twelve aspects as well. In this way, I can be active in one hundred forty-four embodiments throughout the Universe at once.

"Mana Sanar and Sanara, you are part of me. You travel on the Sapphire Ray of Love and Wisdom. Here is what you must remember. I AM an aspect of something greater as well - so is Nada and every Kumara. We are Elohim, and the Elohim is part of something greater – on and on until we are in the Oneness of Source.

"As James, you might consider yourself a Group Soul. As Chris and Leah, you might consider yourself individual souls – though do not be so rigid, for you, too, have aspects of yourself working hard in other galaxies and star systems.

"In your travels upon the Earth, you will be drawn to others who are aspects of my Kumara presence. You will experience aspects of Lady Nada that mirror you completely.

"I would ask that you be fully conscious of the fact that Lady Nada and I, in our desire to return to Oneness, cannot take that ascension step until each aspect of our self supports it. Now, you see the immensity of the Mission of return.

"When we are ready, when our Earth Mission is complete, we will gather all aspects of ourselves together for that ascension step. Until that time, we ask that those who represent us do so at a level of consciousness that assists us as well as the Mission."

Somewhere during the discourse, Chris put his arm around Leah to steady her. It was as if the whole of the Universe suddenly made sense to her. Lord Sananda asked if either of them had any questions about what he had just disclosed to them.

"I do, Lord Sananda," Leah said, a bit shakily. "Is this why you would like me, and likely Chris, to transcend the human form in this lifetime?"

"Indeed," he smiled. "I would like all aspects of myself to fully ascend. The key codes exist within your templates. We will not leave the Earth realm until the last Golden Age is fully in place and the sinister force cannot survive there, but I would send you out again as Bodhisattvas."

"As you wish, My Lord," she replied, bowing slightly.

"I am curious about the sinister force, My Lord," Chris said. "Does this force reflect to Earth and humanity the nature of their own darkness as well as their own sinister nature?"

"It does, My Son."

"Might it have been part of the Divine Plan for Earth that this force present such a mirror to her?"

"I see where you are taking me, magus," Lord Sananda laughed. "You are quite right. There is no movement if light does not chase the dark and the dark does not chase the light. I believe you would like to know our role in Earth's drama."

"It is true, my Lord," Chris replied.

"Very well, I will speak Truth to you. We, the Kumaras, embodied as the traitorous geneticists who created the viruses for the Taleks." Leah gasped, sure that she must have been a part of that. Lord Sananda read her mind.

"Those embodiments were not aspects of myself – though your many lives as Siriun geneticists naturally were part of me, Sanara. There are Kumaras traveling on all Seven Rays. Yet we were all part of that seemingly villainous act. The Mission is vast - cosmic in nature.

"You must cease to think of this sinister force as an evil creation. It is not inherently evil, though humans and others, like the Taleks, through their density, have spawned evil from it. Had we not created this darkness to contrast our light, Earth would never have moved from her place of stagnation. That was when energy started moving for Earth.

"What has happened, due to the unconscious nature of the viral mutation, is that fear and hatred have, through the human mind, created evil on the Earth, and the sinister force are those aligned with this evil.

"It is time to bring balance to Earth by giving humanity the power to feel God again. Humans, creations of the star beings, have been in service to Earth's ascension through that amnesia. Isn't it interesting how children instigate their parents' work? Soon the shackles will be removed from Earth and humanity as all ascend together."

"Thank you, My Lord," Chris replied, bowing to Sananda.

Sacred marriage

"As this Mission progresses, you can expect that I will come into form occasionally to support you. I am there for you always as part of your own consciousness. Be, for me, the Shining Beings, the new *wiracochas*, Inkari and Qoyari, who will activate and awaken humanity to their Divinity. We have played those roles together many times."

Together, Chris and Leah bowed before Lord Sananda and Lady Nada. Two assistants approached them from each side of the alcove to place a deep blue pillow before them at the feet of the two Masters. Lord Sananda asked them to kneel upon the pillows; their hands joined in union.

"This is a Divine Marriage, a Sacred marriage, My Children – like nothing that exists on Earth. Even if you choose to live apart as humans, you are bound in consciousness to your origins. As all humans, you will return with free will, but you will return with the consciousness of your mastery as well. Thus will you be beyond human. Be joyful in your work and play. Find God in everyone and everything.

"I send you back to Earth to snatch the pearl from the mouth of the dragon for humanity and the planet. Return it to your Father's house with your full ascension."

Lord Sananda stood, drawing the sword from its sheath. Light burst forth from the healed blade as he laid it on Chris' right shoulder. "Guardian of the Light, Lord of the Ruby, Mana Sanar, My Beloved Son, go forth into the world as the master you have always been. Be blessed in the light."

Lifting the sword, he placed it lightly on Leah's right shoulder and spoke. "Daughter of the Stars, Lady of the Ruby, Sanara of my own heart, Beloved Child, fulfill the prophecies of our bloodline, awaken humanity to their own mastery, their own Divinity. Open your heart to the world." Light from the sword charged Leah like a lightening bolt. Chris held tight to her hand, helping to ground the charge. Then Sananda placed the sword above their joined hands.

"No human can separate that which has been joined in the light of God. You are the bride and bridegroom of your own Christ Presence. You are blessed."

Tears rolled down Leah's cheeks as the beauty of the Sacred Marriage revealed itself to her. To be autonomous, about one's own Mission and ascension, worked hand in hand with supporting the other from a place of non-judgment, as well as honoring the Christ Presence within the partner and devotion to the Mission. It would be a living paradox – relationship without enmeshment.

She wished with all her heart to stay with the Kumaras, but knew that her Mission was unfulfilled on Earth. Chris seemed comfortable with anything. Right there was a rich field of learning for her, she thought.

Lady Nada read her thoughts and, touching Lord Sananda's arm lightly, asked if she could speak to Leah. Lord Sananda was radiant as he took his seat once again to listen.

Lady Nada spoke in her soft, fluid voice. "Sanara, you are a woman this time. Allow that you have a greater connection to feelings than Mana Sanar. It is natural and you can use it as a resource for the Mission, for yourself, and for him. Your place, right now, is on Earth, but you can create this reality wherever your Mission takes you. Allow your passion for learning to be replaced by the simple act of being and feeling."

"Thank you, Beloved Nada. I so needed to hear that," she replied.

"Very well," Lord Sananda boomed. "Go forth as the Gods you are!"

Everyone in the assemblage stood to bring forth their androgenous angelic song of Oneness. Chris took Leah fully into his arms, aware that he would lose his identity to her – and that that was the Divine Plan. She felt that same loss of self as they kissed again. What had created fear and separation in their room in the Valley of the Blue Moon now generated bliss in liberation. When they drew apart, Lord Sananda and Lady Nada indicated that one step remained in the Resurrection of life in light. Asking Chris and Leah to follow behind them, the cosmic couple circled the altar and walked directly into the translucent center of the Solar Disc.

Held in the warmth of the love frequency through a tunnel of golden light, Chris and Leah emerged behind Lord Sananda and Nada into a luminous meshwork of Sacred Geometry. Awaiting them in that space of light was another Kumara of tremendous light. Lord Sananda introduced his brother, Sanat Kumara, Lord of the Worlds, as one who stood there, in the Heart of God, as Twin Rays in Union. He was able to hold the union for long periods of time before experiencing separation again. Though at an advanced stage of ascension for a Kumara, Sanat Kumara was still bound to the Mission on Earth.

"We are in the Heart of God, Beloveds," Sanat Kumara said. "Gather around me and be still while we expand our awareness of the God Presence - Source of all life."

The five of them formed a circle within the sphere of geometric light, each looking outwards into an ever-expanding complex of light. Within seconds, light geometry folded within itself, forming a more complex structure – a process that continued infinitely.

Sanat Kumara called out, "We are the Light," and their combined consciousness shot out through the Light Matrix to the Infinite. In this expanded consciousness there could be no separation. All was Light.

The experience, which may have lasted a fraction of a second, encompassed all ages and aspects of the present Universe. It healed all difference and opened the Universal Mind within Leah and Chris. When they were fully contracted again into the circle of five, Sananda pulled them back to gaze upon Sanat Kumara once again.

The great Master spoke for a second and last time. "Now each of you knows yourself as God and together you know yourself as God. Find a way to gift this Oneness to humanity through the beauty of your lives on Earth. It is time."

Chris and Leah bowed to Sanat Kumara, who then turned his attention within to his quest for Oneness. Sananda and Lady Nada led Chris and Leah back through the tunnel of golden light and through the Solar Disc into the Temple of Initiation. They paused before the altar to bestow a final blessing on Chris and Leah with the light of the Maxine Flame. Sananda touched the tip of his sword in the flame and then to each of their hearts.

"Remember," he said, "that we have come into Earth's galaxy on the Sapphire Ray of light, yet another manifestation of separation. In the reality of Oneness, we are Light complete. That is the true meaning of Union.

"You must journey back now to the Earth as Divine humans, for the final moment of the conjunction is at hand. If you would turn and leave through the main doors of the temple, you will find yourself traveling through the blue light to the Inner Retreat, where your brothers and sisters have held this space for you with our dear Muru and Beloved Chohan. Go with our blessings and all of our love."

Lord Sananda and Lady Nada turned them around to the voices of the Kumaras and their many aspects raised in glorious song. "Do not look back, children," he cautioned. "Yours is the future."

Amidst the singing and trumpet calls of the Kumaras, Chris and Leah walked, hands joined, down the aisle of golden stars and through the temple doors. The blue light swirled around them in a cocoon of Oneness as they sped through the wormholes of the Universe. At journey's end, they were turned upright and released to walk through the dragon's open mouth, as the star beings had before them.

The Solar Disc was positioned, once again, behind Lord Muru and Saint Germain, who rose to greet them. Radiant with Divine light, Chris walked the golden bridge to the temple floor taking Leah's hand as she followed him. They were embraced first by Lord Muru and Saint Germain before being circled in celebration by their ruby brothers.

As the group took their seats again, the dragon sent out its last breath of fire before disappearing into the orange clouds of the Solar Disc. The clouds swirled into transmuted gold, bringing back the original Inca face of the Sun.

Chris stood behind Leah, who sat in the Siege Perilous without peril. Spread before her on the table were the six blue diamonds with their silk pouch that Master Mukda had used in the grid work back in the Amethyst Temple of the Brotherhood. She looked at them in wonder.

Master Mukda leaned over to whisper in her ear. "I won't be returning home the long way, Beloved. All this hiking around is hard on an old immortal."

Leah squeezed his hand while turning a bit to give him a kiss on the cheek. "I will see you in my dreams, Beloved Teacher."

Lord Muru brought the brothers to order with one strong thought form. "Beloveds Sanara and Mana Sanar, no words describe the feelings we all have about your safe return to Earth. Few initiates attempt death and Resurrection – and even fewer survive it. You have showered us all with the light of the Great Central Sun. Thank you."

Leah and Chris bowed their heads to Lord Muru, who asked Saint Germain if he wished to add any closing remarks. "Thank you, Lord Muru," he began. "I believe the Mission is in good hands," he said, drawing back to study the group. "I merely wanted to warn you that I will precipitate before you now and then to offer assistance. There are times when direct contact is absolutely imperative. In time you will cease to be startled by my sudden appearance. Pay attention to the feelings that precede my presence, a mild electrical charge, and you will know of my arrival from the higher octave."

"Can we call you if we need you, beloved Master Chohan?" Leah asked.

"I will be monitoring the Mission every moment. If I see that you need me, I will appear. Otherwise, call to me in your meditations, morning and night. I will come into your awareness."

"Thank you, Master Chohan," Chris replied. "Is there anything else we should be aware of on the more subtle energetic level?"

Saint Germain smiled brilliantly. "When an Ascended Master is about to touch your life, the air will be filled with the scent of roses."

•

Lord Muru and Saint Germain said their formal good-byes to the group as they all rose from the table. Leah slid the diamonds into the six sections of their pouch and set them at her place while saying her good-byes. Saint Germain left first, walking through the door of his arrival into the violet light. Lord Muru reminded the group of the women dreamers who had been holding this space for them throughout the alignment, asking the group to focus their intent on the women in order to travel back to them.

After Lord Muru's departure, they rearranged the seating to take their original places leaving empty the seat next to Leah and eliminating the thirteenth chair. The group entered the meditative state. With golden scepters in hand, Chris and Leah sat opposite each other drawing the women dreamers to them. Before long they heard the strange sound of the gong player, who was still dancing in front of the Disc of the Sun. His music intensified as they reentered that reality, then quieted as he used the different hammers to come down the frequencies, grounding them in their bodies. When he was sure they were fully present in the Outer Retreat, he silenced the gong, laid down the hammers and disappeared behind the Solar Disc.

Chris opened his eyes to gaze upon the women dreamers. Sitting in silence on their cushions, they looked truly serene. The members of the Order of the Ruby began to open their eyes as their luminous fields anchored back on the Earth plane. Chris nodded to Leah, indicating that she should be the one to pull back the dreamers.

"Beloved Sisters," she called, softly. "We have returned to the Earth plane, grateful for the impeccable way in which you have held the space for us. Gently allow your filaments to travel back to your bodies, anchoring the Golden Cities within your expanded luminous fields." The Ruby Order watched the women's filaments contract from a very expanded state, becoming more visible to them as they returned to the Earth plane awareness. "Slowly open your eyes, Beloveds. Receive our love and profound gratitude for a successfully completed Mission."

As the women opened their eyes, they were drawn to notice the magnitude of light surrounding both Leah and Chris. Obviously something profound had taken place in dimensions beyond the Earth plane. When all were back in their bodies, stretching legs and torsos, Chris spoke to the entire group.

"Brothers and Sisters, I suggest that we share what we can with each other back at the hostel. After a good night's sleep, we can organize a fitting farewell for Brian as well as our own departures. We will celebrate endings and beginnings."

Everyone arose to share hugs, tears and laughter. The women circled Leah, examining her dress and the flowers in her hair. Kissing each of them as true sisters of her heart, Leah let them know the depth of her feelings about them – how true to their calling they had been. She wanted to hear all of their stories as they gathered under the stars for dinner. Soon they had piled into the horse-drawn wagon and were hanging onto each other, singing and laughing like youths on a hayride, as they bumped along the dirt road back to the village. Sirius, Orion and the Pleiades stood out amongst the canopy of stars above them, while Venus hung over the mountains to the west.

A feast awaited them in the courtyard of the hostel where stories were shared along with cooked sprouted grains, raw and steamed vegetables and hot herbal teas. Big baskets of fruit had been placed near the fire for the Indians and in each room of the hostel.

Leah and Chris spoke to no one of their experience in the Great Central Sun, but the others spoke amongst themselves of the pair's loss and return through the mouth of the dragon - Resurrection.

When spirits began to wane, the brothers and sisters took their leave of each other, looking for a solid night's sleep before their last day in the Valley of the Blue Moon. Chris followed Leah up the stairs to their apartment, aware for the first time that the diamonds in her dress were like twinkling stars. She stopped on the balcony to gaze up at Sirius, Chris stepping behind her to hold her against himself.

"I have always had such an affinity for that twinkling blue star, Chris. Now I understand. I felt a powerful Oneness with those little Siriun Beings."

"They were quite a contrast to Lord Muru," he mused.

"Astonishing beings," she sighed, "all of them."

"Do you remember our pact – to know ourselves as God in this lifetime?" he asked.

She laughed. "Nearly instant manifestation, My Magus. What will we do next?"

"I would like to feel true pleasure," he said, bending to kiss her neck.

Leah turned around to face him, receiving his kisses and returning them. "Darling, it pains me to remind you that we are going to be experiencing Lord Abatan's flu before we know true pleasure."

He laughed. "That whole hypothesis needs to be tested, don't you think?" he said, lifting her up in his arms.

She cradled her head against his chest, feeling the strong pull of Oneness within her heart. He opened the door of the outer room and locked it behind them. Her heart began to pound as he took her through the inner doorway to the bedroom. Setting her on her feet at the foot of the magical bed, Chris lifted her chin to look into her eyes.

"My Beloved Leah, tonight I will allow myself to be lost to your compelling power – without fear, without regret, and without the passion that had driven me to you previously. I wish to honor myself within you. I wish to honor the God within you."

"Chris, I feel this way as well. Everything has changed. My insatiable desire for you has transformed into a deep respect and love. Let's journey out together to that central point in the heart of God. Do you think we can do that?"

"I would not put anything past you, My Love," he laughed, lifting the pendant of Qoyari over her blooming hair.

She unhooked his ruby cape, letting it fall on the floor behind him, then drew Inkari's Sun Disc over his head as he bowed before her.

Together they hung the Inca gold from the posts at the foot of the bed. Each of them walked to the side of the bed where they had slept before. Turning to face the bed, they extended their arms towards each other - palms open to receive. Like shimmering stars, the Priestess and the Magus beheld each other in the light of their Kumara souls.

"My Beloved Sanara, Lady of the Ruby, Daughter of the Stars, High Priestess and Goddess of the temple within my heart, I offer myself to you; as protector, friend, and Divine consort. I ask nothing in return – but humbly accept all of the riches you might offer me."

"Mana Sanar, My Beloved, Lord of the Ruby, Dragon Master, Son of the Sun, Magus of the temple within my heart, I accept you as my holy guardian, friend and

Divine consort. I offer you my unwavering love, friendship, and support in all that you do, as well as what we must do together. I ask nothing in return, yet I gratefully accept the riches you might offer me. You have truly won my heart."

Epilogue

By late afternoon the following day, the brothers and sisters, with the help of the community, had built a funerary pyre of dry timbers and brush out on the open hill where Master Mukda had planted his staff. Brian's body had been washed, rubbed with oils, and re-clothed in white with the Templar cloak.

The pallet carrying the body was placed on the wagon. Dressed in the ceremonial robes they had worn the previous day, the men and women walked behind the wagon as it wound its way to the pyre. The setting Sun was about to touch the mountains when the men of the Ruby Order lifted the pallet from the wagon to place it on the pyre.

It was the Hour of Power. Brian's body was surrounded with flowers brought by the women. Pulling his staff from the Earth, Master Mukda released the shield over the valley and caused a great flame to ignite on the staff's end. He touched it to the brush, lighting the blaze to begin the ceremony.

As the flames rose up to consume Brian's body, the brothers and sisters spoke their memories, their feelings and thoughts about his heroic contribution to the Mission. Natalie spoke of the tiny flame she had carried for Brian and her willingness to let it go. Each was releasing filaments of attachment that might have held Brian back or in any way colored his next embodiment.

Tears rolled down the faces of all the men and women who had come such a great distance on the strength of a dream. Each would play out their lives on behalf of the Mission.

On this night, long into the darkness, they bore witness to the transitory nature of life. As the embers glowed before them, the Southern Cross rose overhead, a tribute to a Templar Brother – a warrior of the Truth and Light.

About Jessie Ayani Ph.D.

Jessie received her shamanic training in the Andes. She is an international workshop facilitator and leads groups on transformational journeys to the Andes, Provence, Egypt and Mount Shasta. Jessie resides on Mount Shasta, the Holy Mountain of North America, which is also an Ascended Master retreat.

For up-to-date information about travel and training programs, a more complete biography, books, audio products, and healing sessions, please visit our website. For information about a particular trip or workshop, call, write or email Heart of the Sun.

**HEART OF THE SUN
P.O. BOX 495
MOUNT SHASTA, CA 96067
heartofthesun@snowcrest.net
www.shastaspirit.com/heartofthesun**

GLOSSARY

Ak-an the star Sirius in the ancient language of the star beings
Akhu a star being, one who comes from the stars
Alto mesayoq (all-toe mes-eye-ak) high priest or priestess on the shamanic path
  of initiation
Altiplano the high planes of Bolivia around Titicaca Lake
Annu the Sun, coming from the golden age of pre-Egypt
Apu (ah-poo) masculine spirit of the mountain – highest attainment of the
  masculine
Apus (ah-poos) plural, masculine spirits of the mountains
Assemblage point the point of integration of the luminous (filamentous) field –
  provides the individual's view of reality
Ayahuasca (eye-yah-wash-ka) the vine of death, vision vine of the Amazonian
  jungle
Ayahuascero (eye-yah-wash-care-oh) the pampa mesayoq, medicine man who
  prepares the ayahuasca
Aymara (eye-mar-a) an old culture (language of) centered around Titicaca lake
Bruja (brew-ha) a witch, herbalist
Chaska Quechua word for star, references Venus and Sirius
Cordellera Real The Royal Range of the Andes
Curandera a woman healer
Despacho an offering – literally to send off
Elder Race the Great White Gods, Kumaras, Masters from Venus
Elohim Consciousness of which the Kumaras are part
Filament a thread of the luminous field and Universal Light Matrix
Hanaqpacha the world of Higher Consciousness, Fifth Dimension and
  beyond
Huascar Inca (Wash-car) gate guardian of the Ukhupacha
Inkari the son of the Sun, legendary man of prophecies
Inti the Sun
Jeshua biblical name for Jesus
Karpay (car-pie) Andean priesthood initiation
Kaypacha (kie-pacha) this reality, Third Dimension
Kint'u (kin-two) three coca leaves gathered with specific intent
Kint'ui (kin-two-ee) the offering of the Kint'u
Kumara the Lords of Light, Masters from Venus who prepare planets for
  consciousness, the winged serpents, dragon lineage
Kuraq Akulleq (coo-rak ah-coo-lek) Elder chewer of the coca leaves, the master
  shaman
Kuya Hampeq (coo-yah ham-pay) healer who uses stones, a level of the
  priesthood
Lemuria the last part of Mu to submerge
Limpia a cleansing
Llankay (yan-kai) lowest of the three Incan chakras (near the navel) governs will
  and manifestation
Madrina Godmother
Mamacocha Mother Water

Mamaq'illa (mama-kee-yah) Mother Moon
Maxine Flame a representation of the Source, all light within light
Merkaba the star tetrahedron, three-dimensional star of David, the
    vehicle of light travel
Mesa (may-sah) a woven bundle of powerful stones and objects, an altar, literally
    - a table
Mestizo (meh-stee-zo) one of mixed blood, half Indian – half Hispanic
Mu The Motherland, now submerged continent in the Pacific
Munay (moo-nigh) the power of love, the middle of three Andean chakras at the
    heart
Ñaupa (ñow-pah) ancient and primordial beings of the darkness
Ñusta (ñoos-ta) feminine spirit of the mountains – highest attainment of the
    feminine
Pachacuti (pacha-cootie) mythic guardian of the Hanaqpacha, a winged serpent
Pachamama Mother Earth
Pachakamak Heavenly Father
Pampa Mesayoq expert healers, level of the priesthood
Pampas grassy plains, flat areas
Paqo (pa-ko) shaman
Prana life force, Chi
Quechua (cetch-wa) language of the Incas and present Indians of Peru
Qorikancha Inca temple of the Sun in Cusco, now the site of Dominican
    Church
Qoyari daughter of the stars, sister-bride of Inkari, first Inca woman
Quetzalcoatl (ket-zahl-kwatle) guardian of the Kaypacha, a winged serpent,
    great White God
Quinoa (keen-wah) high protein grain/grass seed of the Andes
Ranchero a horseman or cowboy
Salk'a wild, undomesticated
Sananda Kumara the I AM presence of Jesus/Jeshua, Master from Venus
Siriun High Council governing body of Sirius, overseers of genetic
    experiments on Earth
Sirius Chaska, the closest star to Earth, the dog star, sister Sun to our Sun
Tayta Inti (tie-ta In-tee)Father Sun
Taleks fictional star beings of ill-intent, linked to the sinister force
Tejidos (te-he-dose) weavings
Tiwanaku ancient city of Titicaca lake, now raised up and distant from
    the lake
Ukhupacha (u-who-pacha) the dark, interior world of shadows, Fourth
    Dimension, unconscious
Wayki (why-kee) spiritual brother or sister in the Andes
Wiracocha (we-dah-cocha) Foam of the Sea, Shining Being, a great God, our
    luminous body
Vicuña (vee-cune-yah) the smallest of the llama family, the finest, most costly
    wool
Yachay (ya-chai) the highest of the three Inca chakras, Third Eye, represents
    wisdom and vision
Ylloq'e (yolk-eh) the highest magician in the Andes – plural **Ylloq'e cuna**

About Our Other Books and Audio CDs

The Lineage of the Codes of Light

A powerful truth-in-myth about the women of the Sisterhood of the Sun who have carried the light codes of consciousness for this present time of transcendence. Walk in the footsteps of the priestesses of Annu from the first times, Zep Tepi, as the mission of the current starseeding unfolds. Learn of their relationship with the kings of the House of David, the Incas, and the Brotherhood of the Magi who have been the guardians of the unbroken Lineage of Light. Learn of the roles of Mary Magdalen, Isis, Lilith, Morgaine and others in this planetary ascension initiative.

Like The Brotherhood of the Magi, the Lineage of the Codes of Light is highly activational for the reader. It has brought women together around the world to renew the bonds of sisterhood as the Mission comes more fully upon us. Not just a woman's book, the Lineage compresses a long history of planetary ascension to bring us to this moment. ISBN 0-9648763-1-0

Kintui, Vision of the Inca's; The Shaman's Journey to Enlightenment

From the Empire of the Sun, Kintui brings into our lives the timeless journey to enlightenment. Anchored between Earth and Sun and supported by the four sacred directions, the shaman's path to higher consciousness unfolds as one of the fully realized human being. Here is a powerful call to the future, a spirituality which asks us to shed dysfunctional belief systems and everything else that stands in the way of our personal power.

Kintui was written as a non-fiction introduction to the three worlds of the Incas, the cosmovision of the Andes that supports this path to God, and the ecletic synthesis of metaphysical knowledge that resonates with Jessie Ayani's Truth. Though often recommended by spiritually oriented tour leaders as background reading for Peru, Kintui will help you walk any spiritual path. ISBN 0-9648763-0-2

Deep Trance Shamanic Journey; Volume One: Pachamama's Child

Jessie's magical trance voice combined with Richard Shulman's music takes you to the higher dimensions for healing and enlightenment. Not simply a guided meditation, these journeys actually move you into higher frequencies, excercising your hidden gifts of interdimensional travel.

Journey One takes you to the Fourth Dimensional center of your assemblage point where you have complete power to change your reality. Supplied with a six-page booklet of background information and instructions, this journey is one of the most powerful you will every take. Journey two is a delightful romp through the fairy kingdom while in the warm embrace of Pachamama. Chase away negativity, the blues, stress and exhaustion with this treasure of dimensional magic. ISBN 0-9648763-6-1

A Few Words from Jessie about her forthcoming work....

While writing The Brotherhood of the Magi, I saw clearly the next story in this series - obviously the crystals must be found and destroyed. The quest is on! Chris and Leah will meet again in Australia, move on to Bali for Dragon Activation, then complete this portion of their Mission in the Himalayas. They will be joined by Demitri and Jacques and will visit Ramandi and Master Mukda. Maybe 2003, so stay tuned! The second CD in our series will help you heal addiction. It is a journey that works with high magic. We will also explore the energies of our unmanifest Twin Ray. As Magi goes to press, I am inspired to write a cookbook and wellness guide for those interested in rejuvenation, ascension and immortality. Now, this could be fun!

Workshops, Retreats and Journeys with Jessie Ayani

Miracles, Magic and Mastery

Explore the landscapes of higher consciousness in a light-activating weekend training. Each of us has the capacity for miracles, magic and mastery encoded in our luminous body. These codes of light are activated by truth and the deep remembrance accompanying one's own truth. Jessie has defined a path to God that is autonomous, simple and fun. This path of liberation puts you in direct connection with Source. It is for those who are willing and ready to take full responsibility for their own enlightenment.

Note: Advanced training groups meet regularly at certain locations for continued work.

Vision Quest on Mount Shasta

Each August, Jessie leads a week-long camping retreat on the Holy Mountain of North America. This includes hiking to pristine lakes, high mountain meadows, waterfalls and sacred sites conducive to meetings with Spirit and the Masters. After an optional soak in the hot springs, the group heads to the wilderness in a hidden valley of fairies and gnomes to vision quest under the stars. Expect magic since this beloved mountain holds the Christ Consciousness frequency. It is where Heaven and Earth meet.

The Magdalen Pilgrimage – Provence/Languedoc

Every September, Jessie spends two weeks in Southern France with a group of 12. From St. Maximin la Ste. Baume, the center of Mary's experience in Provence, the group journeys out to visit sacred sites related to Mary's ministry, meditation and death. In addition, the Templar, Cathar and Cistercian legacies are explored. Provence holds the Gnostic mysteries, the Black Madonna and embraces us in every way with cordiality, simply delicious food, renowned art, and magical light. A visit to Montsegur, Carcassone, and Rennes-le-Chateau in the Languedoc is included.

Peru/Bolivia

In April each year, Jessie leads a group of pilgrims to the sites of the Incas and land of the feminine light ray. All journeys include the sacred sites of Machu Picchu, Ollantaytambo, and Pisac in Peru as well as Tiwanaku and the Islands of the Sun and Moon in Bolivia. In Peru, the group works with the Q'ero Elders, the last of the Incas, and in Bolivia with the Yatiri shamans of the Aymara people. Additionally the trip may include sites on the Peruvian side of Titcaca Lake (Sullustani, Uros - the floating Island, Taqile Island and the interdimensional portal of Aramu Muru) or a more rugged trip to the Kallawaya medicine people, the white magicians of Bolivia.

Trekking jouneys are also offered on the Inca Trail with Javier Casapia Salas and Jessie leads expeditions to Mount Ausangate (the Christ Mountain of Peru) for veterans of her Peru/Bolivia trips.

Egypt

This is a powerful trip of activation of the ancient Starseed memories, the initiatory journey of Jesus, his family's flight when he was a babe, and the legacy of the Pharaohs. The trip includes a five-day cruise down the Nile visiting temples, 3 days in Luxor at the Valley of the Kings and other temples, the pyramids, Sphinx, and Heliopolis. We stay in 5-star hotels, have excellent tour guides and secure transportation. This journey is taken only during politically stable periods in Egypt.

All this and more on our website www.shastaspirit.com/heartofthesun

ORDER FORM

Please send:

_____ copies of Kintui, Vision of the Incas

_____ copies of The Lineage of the Codes of Light

_____ copies of The Brotherhood of the Magi

_____ CDs, Deep Trance Shamanic Journey, Volume I
Pachamama's Child

Name: _____

Address: _____

City: _____ State:____ Zip: _____

e-mail _____

I ENCLOSE THE FOLLOWING PAYMENT:

Kintui $15.95 X _____ (# of copies) = $_____

Lineage $18.00 X _____ (# of copies) = $_____

Magi $18.00 X _____ (# of copies) = $_____

CD $16.00 X _____ (# of copies) = $_____

CA residents add sales tax of 7.25% $_____

Shipping and handling (1st item $3, add'l items $1 each) $_____

Total enclosed $_____

MAKE CHECKS PAYABLE TO:

Heart of the Sun, P.O. Box 495, Mount Shasta, CA 96067

Orders will be shipped within 10 days of receipt of payment.
You may copy this form.